WATER PRODUCTION AND WASTEWATER TREATMENT

WATER RESOURCE PLANNING, DEVELOPMENT AND MANAGEMENT

Additional books in this series can be found on Nova's website under the Series tab.

Additional E-books in this series can be found on Nova's website under the E-books tab.

WASTE AND WASTE MANAGEMENT

Additional books in this series can be found on Nova's website under the Series tab.

Additional E-books in this series can be found on Nova's website under the E-books tab.

WATER RESOURCE PLANNING, DEVELOPMENT AND MANAGEMENT

WATER PRODUCTION AND WASTEWATER TREATMENT

B. ANTIZAR-LADISLAO
AND
R. SHEIKHOLESLAMI
EDITORS

Nova Science Publishers, Inc.
New York

NOTICE TO THE READER

The Publisher has taken reasonable care in the preparation of this book, but makes no expressed or implied warranty of any kind and assumes no responsibility for any errors or omissions. No liability is assumed for incidental or consequential damages in connection with or arising out of information contained in this book. The Publisher shall not be liable for any special, consequential, or exemplary damages resulting, in whole or in part, from the readers' use of, or reliance upon, this material. Any parts of this book based on government reports are so indicated and copyright is claimed for those parts to the extent applicable to compilations of such works.

Independent verification should be sought for any data, advice or recommendations contained in this book. In addition, no responsibility is assumed by the publisher for any injury and/or damage to persons or property arising from any methods, products, instructions, ideas or otherwise contained in this publication.

This publication is designed to provide accurate and authoritative information with regard to the subject matter covered herein. It is sold with the clear understanding that the Publisher is not engaged in rendering legal or any other professional services. If legal or any other expert assistance is required, the services of a competent person should be sought. FROM A DECLARATION OF PARTICIPANTS JOINTLY ADOPTED BY A COMMITTEE OF THE AMERICAN BAR ASSOCIATION AND A COMMITTEE OF PUBLISHERS.

Additional color graphics may be available in the e-book version of this book.

LIBRARY OF CONGRESS CATALOGING-IN-PUBLICATION DATA
Water production and wastewater treatment / editors, B. Antizar-Ladislao and R. Sheikholeslami.
p. cm.
Includes bibliographical references and index.
ISBN 978-1-61728-503-5 (hardcover)
1. Water--Purification. 2. Water-supply. I. Antizar-Ladislao, B. II. Sheikholeslami, R.
TD430.W3634 2010
628--dc22
2010025803

Published by Nova Science Publishers, Inc. † New York

CONTENTS

PREFACE

This book includes selected paper and is the result of a very successful 3-day symposium on *Water Production and Wastewater Treatment – Technologies, Advances and Issues* as part of the *8th World Congress of Chemical Engineering* in Montreal in August 2009 which my colleague, Dr. Blanca Antizar-Ladislao, and I organized and convened.

The importance of the topic showed the interest, almost 100 paper and poster presentations, and number of people participated and contributed to the symposium. There were excellent talks covering various aspects and topical issues related to water production and wastewater treatment in industrial and municipal sectors.

Some talks were focused on removal of a specific contaminant, specific technology for the process, experimental findings, or process modeling. Others had wider perspective and were covering the importance of water production and wastewater treatment in the context of our current industrial society and the energy and climate change. The papers covered a unique mix of issues related to both water production and wastewater treatment.

Success of such events always depends on many people and factors. I would like to gratefully acknowledge the financial contributions of Royal Academy of Engineering for travel and attendance at the Congress. I would also like to thank all the participants and presenters at the Symposium for their contribution enriching the Symposium, my colleagues at the technical committee and reviewers for assisting in selection and review of papers, and Dr. Antizar-Ladislao for her significant contributions in co-organizing the Symposium with me.

Professor Roya Sheikholeslami, Ph.D., P.Eng., C.Eng., F.I.ChemE
Chair of the Organizing Committee
Symposium on Water Production and Waste Water Treatment
8th World Congress of Chemical Engineering

In: Water Production and Wastewater Treatment
Editor: B. Antizar-Ladislao et al.

ISBN 978-1-61728-503-5
© 2011 Nova Science Publishers, Inc.

Chapter 1

TREATMENT AND REUSE OF WASTEWATER FROM A PETROCHEMICAL COMPLEX

Noah I. Galil[1] and Yael Levinsky

Faculty of Civil and Environmental Engineering
Laboratory for Industrial Wastewater Treatment and Reuse
Technion – Israel Institute of Technology
Haifa 32000, Israel

ABSTRACT

Wastewater from petrochemical complexes is characterized by a diversity of pollutants, including free and emulsified hydrocarbons, phenols, cresols, xylenols, sulfides, ammonia and cyanides. The treatment of this wastewater is usually based on a multiple stage approach, consisting of physical, chemical and biological treatment processes. Wastewater treatment and reuse has been developed and applied at a petrochemical complex in Haifa, Israel. The solution was based on: (a) multiple stage treatment, creating several technological barriers, in order to avoid uncontrolled emissions into the neighboring marine environment; (b) maximal reuse of treated effluent and oil, for minimizing the disposal of pollutants outside the industrial zone; (c) step-by-step development, design and implementation of the treatment process enabled to establish the best operation and efficiency at the existing units and these could be used as starting conditions in the development of the next treatment stages; (d) flexibility and complete independent operation of the treatment units significantly increased the reliability of achieving a final effluent of high quality. The biological treatment process has been efficiently protected by preliminary flow regulation, to control hydraulic and pollutant loading. Additional protection of the biotreatment was achieved by the removal of free and emulsified oil by gravitational oily-water separators (API) followed by dissolved nitrogen flotation (DGF). Biotreatment is achieved by aerated ponds followed by a submerged biological contactor (SBC) for the removal of dissolved organics and for nitrification. Effluent polishing treatment is operated by chemically-enhanced sedimentation and by sand filtration. The treatment-recycle system in the petrochemical industry provides cost-effective solutions and high quality effluent to the recipient water

---

[1] galilno@tx.technion.ac.il.

bodies. The approach of treatment-recycling serves as a trigger to the industrial management, in addition to regulatory requirements, to invest in water treatment facilities.

INTRODUCTION

Process and manufacturing plants usually consume large amounts of water in various operations of production, cleaning and rinsing. Wastewater contains pollutants that are frequently environmentally regulated. An effective way to minimize wastewater and pollutant emissions is to design wastewater recycling, so that the used water could be reused to a maximum extent in the same plant.

Petrochemical complexes are producing large amounts of wastewater, which is characterized by a diversity of pollutants including free and emulsified hydrocarbons, phenol, cresols, xylenols, sulfides, ammonia, and cyanides. The production processes usually include distillation, catalytic cracking, visebreaking, oil and waxes, ethylene, sulfur recovery and other processes. Due to national or regional water shortage, which results in low fresh water consumption, as well as the variety of production processes, petrochemical wastewater in arid or semi-arid regions are characterized by high concentrations of pollutants. They include several periodical streams from gasoline, kerosene and other products washeries, containing up to 12 percent phenols, most of them cresols and xylenols.

Diwan et al. (1995) mentioned a great potential for recycling of effluents to solve water shortage for the industries, since in many cases the cost of treatment is modest compared to overall benefits. Asano et al. (1996) mentioned the status of national policies on wastewater treatment, wastewater reuse characteristics and some wastewater reuse experiences in Japan. Au et al. (1996) reported a great economic efficiency obtained by the use of a low cost filtration system working on petrochemical secondary effluent.

Wijesinghe et al. (1996) reported a study based on the use of secondary effluent as cooling water makeup for inland industry in Australia. Brown and Mountain (1998) reported findings regarding general feasibility of wastewater reuse as cooling tower makeup at power plants in Maryland, USA. Buhrmann et al. (1999) used a spiral reverse osmosis plant to treat mine water and spent cooling water producing a new source of water for a power station.

Angelakes et al. (1999) presented the status of wastewater reclamation and reuse around the Mediterranean basin and discussed existing guidelines and regulations, also presenting the possibility of developing uniform wastewater reuse standards. The potential for the recovery and reuse of cooling water in Taiwan has been reported by Shu-Hai et al. (1999). A brief overview of the reuse of treated industrial wastewater in cooling water systems is provided by Phulwar et al. (1999), including a case study of the reuse of treated effluent as cooling water at a refinery process plant in India. Large wastewater reuse projects in the UK, based on long-term international operation experience on reuse projects for the petrochemical, power and paper industries are discussed by Durham (2000). Yang et al. (2000) introduced a mathematical approach to design an optimal network when multiple pollutants are contained and the treated effluent can be reused to a maximum extent in the same plant.

Zhong and Lai (2009) reported the reuse of effluent from a petrochemical company for make up to the cooling system. Wong (2000) described the pilot testing and implementation of a major advanced wastewater reclamation project to recover secondary effluent from a municipal plant and blowdown from a cooling tower for reuse in a large petroleum plant. Durham (2000) reported about large wastewater reuse projects in the UK based on long term international operation experience on reuse projects for the petrochemical, power and paper industries. In the field of wastewater treatment processes membrane technology, especially membrane bioreactor (MBR) is being applied (Llop et al., 2009, Fratila-Apachitei et al., 2001, Galil et al., 2009).

This chapter deals with a research and development project, which was carried out at a petrochemical complex located at a distance of about two miles from the Mediterranean coast in the Gulf of Haifa, Israel. The program included characterization of the wastewater main stream, as well as lateral streams generated by specific production processes (Galil et al., 1988). Laboratory and pilot plant studies on flocculation-dissolved air flotation (Galil and Wolf, 2000) enabled the design and operation of a full-scale treatment plant. A comparative study of three alternative biological processes: activated sludge, rotating biological contactor and aerated ponds provided the data for a biological treatment process based on two aerated lagoons in series, accomplished by a lime softening-clarification chemical plant (Galil and Rebhun, 1990; Galil and Rebun, 1991). A survey of the biological process occurring in the recirculated cooling system of the industrial complex enabled to operate this system as the recipient of the treated effluent, as well as a polishing nitrification bioreactor (Rebhun and Engel, 1988).

Following the research results and conclusions, the full scale developed solution for treatment and reuse of petrochemical wastewater was based on: (a) multiple stage treatment, achieved by combining physical, chemical and biological processes, creating several technological barriers in order to avoid uncontrolled emissions into the neighboring river and marine environment; (b) maximal recycling of treated effluent and oil, for minimizing disposal of pollutants outside the industrial zone (Galil and Rebhun, 1992).

BASIC CONCEPTS

The implementation of environmental quality regulations, regarding the disposal of effluent to the environment, usually to water bodies, is imposing careful considerations. By lowering the level of pollutants to the values required by the regulations, the treated effluent and some of the constituents separated from the wastewater could be considered for recycling by the petrochemical complex. This would minimize the disposal outside the industrial zone.

In the case of the Haifa petrochemical complex, the research and development project included the following tasks: (a) characterization of the main raw wastewater streams, as well as lateral streams generated by specific production processes; (b) feasibility studies of general treatment of all the wastewater streams versus separate treatment of concentrated streams; the investigated process was based on chemical emulsion-breaking, flocculation and dissolved air flotation (DAF); (c) a comparative study of three alternative biological treatment processes for the removal of dissolved organic matter; (d) a survey of the processes occurring in the water cooling system of the complex, including studies on the use of treated effluent as makeup; (e) characterization of two different types of sludge produced by the wastewater treatment and development of sludge treatment methods.

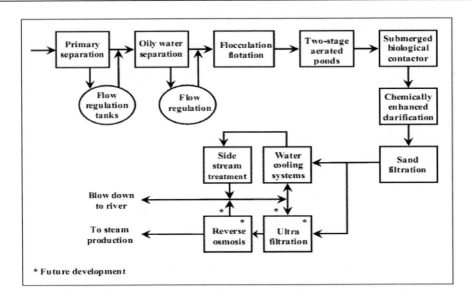

Figure 1. General description of the wastewater treatment-reuse system.

Following the conclusions of the research and development project, the wastewater facilities of the Haifa petrochemical complex include: separate storage and treatment of the concentrated phenol (spent soda) streams; storage and flow regulation (equalization) of the main raw wastewater stream; gravitational oil-water separator (OWS); chemical flocculation and dissolved gas (nitrogen) flotation (DGF); biological treatment for carbonaceous substrate removal; biological treatment by submerged bio-contactors (SBC) for nitrification; chemical precipitation for softening and clarification; sand filtration; effluent reuse as makeup in the water cooling system; blow-down treatment by chemical precipitation-sedimentation before the final disposal to the river; sludge collection, treatment and disposal. A general description of the wastewater treatment-reuse system is described in Figure 1.

DESCRIPTION OF TREATMENT UNITS

Flow Regulation: The main wastewater stream could be influenced by factors such as rain floods and spills caused by unexpected accidents at the production units. For minimizing these influences, two flow regulation tanks with a total capacity of 45,000 m3 were built and connected to the system. The operation of these tanks, having a capacity of about five days of maximal flow, enables the operators to avoid sudden hydraulic or pollutant surges on the treatment units.

Concentrated wastewater streams: Studies carried out by Galil and Rebhun (1988) indicated severe disturbances and inhibition caused by phenols included in the spent soda streams coming from the gasoline and other product washeries. As part of the general project, the concentrated spent-soda wastewater streams were separated from the sewerage system, stored in special tanks and gradually treated. The treatment is based on neutralization and separation between: gases, which are conducted to the flare; an oily phase including the phenols is recycled to the production processes; a water phase containing mainly inorganic salts is drained to wastewater.

Chemical flocculation and flotation (DGF): Laboratory and pilot plant studies have been carried out, developing design and operational parameters for this process. The flotation unit is covered in order to avoid VOC's emissions, therefore nitrogen is used instead of air. The flotation systems consist on three parallel units with a capacity of 200 m3/hr each. The flocculant in use is a cationic polyelectrolyte in a dose of 7 to 10 mg/L. Later studies performed by Galil and Wolf (2000) on this wastewater indicated that the chemical flocculation - DGF could remove efficiently the emulsified phase, which could be aggregated and separated up to the surface. However, it was found that the process could also remove substantial amounts of dissolved organic matter, due to the hydrophobic characteristics of some of the substances, which could bind to the solid surfaces.

Biological treatment: A comparative study has been carried out including activated sludge, rotating biological contactor (RBC) and aerated lagoons (Galil and Rebhun, 1990). These bioprocesses represent different concepts: activated sludge and RBC are considered as intensive processes, developing high concentrations of active biomass and high cell residence time (CRT), while aerated ponds are considered as a partial bioprocess, involving low biomass and low CRT values without biosolids recycling. The aerated ponds alternative was adopted because of the possibility of lowering the investment cost. It was clear that in this case, additional biotreatment would be necessary. This alternative was based on sharing the bioprocess tasks between: (a) the aerated ponds, performing carbonaceous substrate removal (two days detention time); (b) second stage biological treatment by submerged biological contactors (SBC), mainly for nitrification; The experience accumulated over the last ten years shows that this combination has achieved good and reliable biological treatment (Table 1).

Chemical clarification: A chemical contact flocculation-clarification unit, designed for a flow of 600 m^3/hr is operated for efficient separation of biosolids and clarification. A second identical unit works on the treatment of water from inside the cooling system (side stream treatment). Part of the side stream treated effluent goes back to the cooling system, while the remaining effluent is disposed off to the neighboring river (Figure 1). Both contact flocculation-clarification units are operated at pH values of 10.7 by addition of lime for enabling removals of calcium carbonate and magnesium hydroxide. The removal of suspended solids is being enhanced by the use of a cationic polyelectrolyte as aid coagulant.

Filtration: A gravity sand filtration unit operates after chemical enhancement by a cationic polyelectrolyte. The effluent fits all the quality requirements for being reused as make up in the cooling system or for being discharged to the river. In the future the filtration effluent will be treated by ultra filtration, reverse osmosis and reused as make up to steam production for the local power station (Figure 1).

Sludge treatment: The petrochemical complex wastewater treatment system is producing two categories of sludge: (a) oily sludge is produced by oily water separators, by the dissolved gas flotation and also includes sediments from crude oil storage tanks. The oily sludge is gravitationally thickened in long term concrete storage tanks, chemically conditioned and cake-filtered by geo-tubes. The oil is recycled to production and the water phase is returned to wastewater treatment. (b) sludge produced by the biological treatment stages (biosolids) is obtained from the chemical clarification and from the backwash of the sand filters. This sludge is stabilized by land farming and transported to landfill sites. In the future all sources of sludge will be treated by cake filtration and by thermal technologies (Figure 2) for maximizing recyclable materials and improve land utilization.

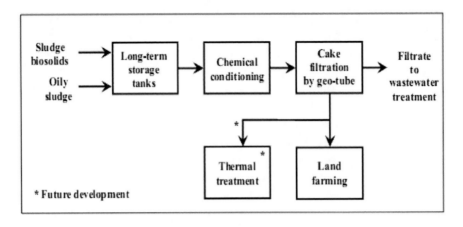

Figure 2. General description of the sludge treatment system.

EFFLUENT QUALITY

Table 1 presents the results obtained as part of a six years (2003 to 2008) monitoring of the last wastewater treatment stages, which are DGF, aerated ponds, submerged biological contactor and chemical clarification followed by sand filtration. The results are expressed in statistical terms which include 50% and 80% probabilities of obtaining values equal to or less than the stated magnitudes. Table 1 also indicates average values and standard deviation. The parameters reported include pH, total organic carbon, total suspended solids, oil, ammonia nitrogen, nitrate nitrogen and phosphates.

Table 1. Effluent quality after different treatment stages

Statistical Parameter	pH	TOC (mg/L)	TSS (mg/L)	OIL (mg/L)	NH$_4$-N (mg/L)	NO$_3$-N (mg/L)	PO$_4$ (mg/L)
DGF EFFLUENT							
50%	7.6	59		16	9.5	0.9	2.0
80%	7.8	81		25	14.0	2.5	2.8
Average	7.6	53		23	10.9	1.7	2.0
St. Dev.	0.3	27		14	8.7	2.8	0.9
AERATED PONDS EFFLUENT							
50%	7.8	28	45	7.4	6.3	0.8	0.7
80%	8.0	43	68	13.7	9.5	2.7	1.4
Average	7.9	33	51	11.4	6.8	2.5	1.0
St. Dev.	2.6	17	27	18.4	4.9	4.7	1.8
SUBMERGED BIOCONTACTOR EFFLUENT							
50%	8.0	14	37	4.1	0.1	32.2	1.3
80%	8.1	19	56	7.6	0.2	42.0	2.0
Average	7.9	17	42	6.4	0.5	32.9	1.5
St. Dev.	0.2	11	24	11.8	2.0	14.7	0.9
SAND FILTRATION EFFLUENT							
50%	8.1	5.7	5.6	1.8	0.1	28.7	0.6
80%	8.2	7.9	8.2	3.4	0.2	37.1	0.8
Average	7.9	6.8	6.4	2.3	0.4	31.7	0.7
St. Dev.	0.2	3.2	3.8	0.8	0.7	15.8	0.4

The final effluent, after sand filtration, contains less than 10 mg/L of TOC, less than 10 mg/L of suspended solids, less than 1 mg/L of ammonia nitrogen and less than 1 mg/L phosphates. This effluent is being reused as make up to the water cooling systems as well as for fire fighting. In the future part of the effluent will be additionally treated and reused for steam production (Figure 1).

CONCLUSIONS

The project involves several technological barriers for protecting river and sea water and for enabling sustainable effluent reuse:

- hydraulic barrier is achieved by the storage-flow regulation tanks;
- physical and chemical barriers include four different treatment stages of gravity separation, chemically enhanced flotation, chemical clarification and sand filtration before reuse or final disposal;
- biological barriers include two separate processes: aerated ponds and submerged biological contactors.

Flexibility, as well as complete independent operation of the treatment units, significantly increased the reliability of producing a final effluent of high and reliable quality. The recycling of oil and sludge has minimized the disposal of contaminants outside the industrial zone.

The treatment-recycle system in the reported petrochemical industry provides cost-effective solutions. The reuse of treated effluent at the Haifa petrochemical complex saves about 2.5 million cubic meters of fresh water per year, which is the equivalent water consumption of a town with a population of 45,000. The cost of this amount of water, if purchased from the national resources would be close to one million US dollars per year.

The cost-effective approach of treatment-recycling serves as a trigger to industrial management, in addition to the regulatory requirements, to invest in water treatment facilities.

ACKNOWLEDGMENT

The project was sponsored by the Oil Refineries, Haifa Ltd., and carried out at the Laboratory for Industrial Wastewater Treatment and Water Renovation at the Faculty of Civil Engineering, Technion - Israel Institute of Technology. During the years 1979 - 1997, Professor Menahem Rebhun was the head of the above Laboratory and had a leading role in this project.

REFERENCES

Asano, T., Maeda, M. and Takaki, M. (1996). Wastewater reclamation and reuse in Japan: Overview and implementation examples. *Water Science Technology 34(11)*, 219-226.

Angelakes, A.H., Marekos, DoMonte, M.H.F., Bontaoux L. and Asano, T. (1999). *Water Research 33(10),* 2201-2217.

Au, D., Zhang, J. and Yi, Y. (1996). Using bundle filters to process petrochemical secondary effluents for industrial reuse. *Water Science Technology 34(10),* 127-131.

Brown, D.H. and Mountain, D. (1998). Wastewater reuse as cooling tower makeup: A pioneering case study in Maryland. *Proc. Annual Meet., Air Waste Mang. Assoc., 91st, CODEN: PAMEE5 ISN,* 1052-6102.

Buhrmann, F., Van der Waldt, M., Hanekom, D. and Finlayson, F. (1999). Treatment of industrial wastewater for reuse, *S. Afr. Desalination 124(1-3),* 263-269.

Diwan, R.C., Bausal, T.K., Garg, M.R., Vilaj, K.and Tiwana, H.S. (1995). Reuse of wastewater for industries. *Environ. Pollut. Prot., Deep and Deep Publications,* New Delhi, India, 109-117.

Durham, B. (2000). Case studies of wastewater reuse for the petrochemical, power and paper industry. *Spec. Publ. R. Soc. Chem. (Membrane Technology in Water and Wastewater Treatment),* 241-247.

Fratila-Apachitei, L.E., Kennedy, M.D., Linton, J.D., Blume, I. and Schippers, J.C. (2001), Influence of membrane morphology on the flux decline during dead-end ultrafiltration of refinery and petrochemical waste water. *Journal of Membrane Science 182(1-2),* 151-159.

Galil, N.I., Rebhun, M. and Brayer, Y. (1988). Disturbances and inhibition in biological treatment of wastewater from an integrated oil refinery. *Water Science Technology 20(10),* 21-29.

Galil, N.I. and Rebhun M. (1990). A comparative study of RBC and activated sludge in biotreatment of wastewater from an integrated oil refinery. *Proc. of the 44th Ind. Waste. Conf.,* Purdue Univ., West Lafayette, 711-717.

Galil, N.I. and Rebhun, M. (1991). Combined treatment by aerated ponds and chemical clarification completed by recirculated cooling systems, *Proc. 45th Ind. Waste Conf.,* Purdue Univ., West Lafayette, 645-654.

Galil, N.I. and Rebhun M. (1992). Multiple technological barriers combined with recycling of water and oil in wastewater treatment of a coastal petrochemical complex. *Water Science Technology 25 (12),* 277-282.

Galil, N.I. and Wolf, D. (2000). Removal of hydrocarbons from petrochemical wastewater by dissolved air flotation. *4th Int. Conf. on Dissolved Air Flotation,* Helsinki, Finland.

Galil, N.I., Ben-David Malachi, K. and Sheindorf, Ch. (2009). Biological nutrient removal by MBR configurations. *Environmental Engineering Science, 26 (4),* 817-824.

Llop, A., Pocurull, E. and Borrull, F. (2009). Evaluation of the Removal of Pollutants from Petrochemical Wastewater Using A Membrane Bioreactor Treatment Plant. *Water, Air, and Soil Pollution 197(1-4),* 349-359.

Phulwar, D. and Amesur, D. (1999). Reuse of wastewater in cooling water system. *Trans. Met. Finish. Assoc., India* 8 (1), 31-34.

Rebhun, M. and Engel, G. (1988). Reuse of wastewater for industrial cooling systems, *Jour. Water Poll. Control Fed.* 60, 232-242.

Shu-Hai, Y., Dyi-Hwa, T., Gia-Luen, G. and Jyh-Jian, Y. (1999). *Resources conservation and recycling 26 (1),* 53-70.

Wijesinghe, B., Kaye, R., Fell, C. and Joseph, D. (1996). Reuse of treated sewage effluent for cooling water makeup: a feasibility study and a pilot plant study. *Water Science Technology 33 (10-11),* 363-369.

Wong, J. M. (2000). Testing and implementation of an advanced wastewater reclamation and recycling system in a major petrochemical plant. *Water Science and Technology 42(5-6),* 23-27.

Yang, M.D., Sykes, R.M. and Merry, C.J. (2000). Estimation of algal biological parameters using water quality modeling and SPOT satellite data. *Ecological Modelling 125(1),* 1-13.

Zhong, X. and Lai, X. (2009). Commercial application of properly treated wastewater discharged from ethylene plant. *China Petroleum Processing and Petrochemical Technology (3),* 25-28.

In: Water Production and Wastewater Treatment
Editor: B. Antizar-Ladislao et al.

ISBN 978-1-61728-503-5
© 2011 Nova Science Publishers, Inc.

Chapter 2

ACTIVATED SLUDGE CHARACTERIZATION: EXTRACTION AND IDENTIFICATION OF HYDROLYTIC ENZYMES

Debora Nabarlatz[,a], Frank Stüber[a], Josep Font[a], Agustí Fortuny[b], Azael Fabregat[a], and Christophe Bengoa[a]*

a Departament d'Enginyeria Química,
Escola Tècnica Superior d'Enginyeria Química,
Universitat Rovira i Virgili. Av. Països Catalans 26 (43007)
Tarragona, Catalonia, Spain
b Departament d'Enginyeria Química, EPSEVG,
Universitat Politècnica de Catalunya. Av. Víctor Balaguer s/n (08800)
Vilanova i la Geltrú, Barcelona, Catalonia, Spain

ABSTRACT

The organic matter in domestic wastewater is mainly composed by lipids, proteins and carbohydrates. Due to that the microorganisms present in activated sludge cannot consume it directly, they produce specific hydrolytic enzymes like proteases and lipases to metabolize the organic fraction. In this sense, the recovery of enzymes from activated sludge is a promising option for the valorisation of this resource, considering the sludge as a raw material capable of generating multiple new biomolecules and products. This chapter deals with the extraction and identification of the several types of hydrolytic enzymes that have been detected in activated sludge. The enzymes quantified were lipase, protease, alkaline and acid phosphatase, L-leu-aminopeptidase, α-glucosidase and α-amylase. The amount of protein released during the treatments was also measured. The method employed for the extraction of enzymes from activated sludge was ultrasonication. The results showed that 30 min of disintegration applying 50 W of ultrasonic power are enough to extract the maximal amount of enzymatic activity. These results were compared with those obtained when 2% v/v Triton X100 (a detergent

[*] Corresponding author. Tel. +34 977558656, Fax. +34 977559667. E-mail: debora.nabarlatz@urv.cat.

currently used to extract membrane proteins) was used as additive. It was observed that the use of Triton X100 increases the amount of protease and acid phosphatase activity extrated, but it has not a significant influence in the extraction of the other enzymes.

INTRODUCTION

Nowadays, the activated sludge generated during wastewater treatment is becoming a serious issue due to several factors like the growth of population, its accumulation in large cities, and the increment in the amount and complexity of the industrial activity. As results from the implementation in 2005 of the Urban Waste Water Treatment Directive 91/271/EEC, the generation of sewage sludge has increased significantly. In Europe, the total amount of sludge generated in urban wastewater treatment plants has increased from 5.5 million (1992) to 10 million tons dry matter in 2007. In Spain, sewage sludge production from 1997 to 2005 increased 40%, rising up to 1.065 million tons in 2006 [1]. As consequence, the amount of activated sludge that is disposed off increases annually and several countries in Europe are implementing a more strict environmental legislation which considers not adequate the actual disposal ways (landfilling and composting). For this reason it is necessary to develop new technologies, firstly to reduce the amount of activated sludge generated that should be disposed off, and secondly to use it as raw material capable to generate biomolecules and energy. The recovery of valuable products from sludge that could be used for the sludge reduction itself or for any other industrial applications are promising.

The domestic wastewater is mainly composed by complex organic matter, from which 60 - 70% is formed by lipids, proteins and polysaccharides. A huge fraction of this organic matter (30 - 85%) is formed by particles larger than 0.1 μm which cannot be directly assimilated by the microorganisms [2]. For this reason, the microorganisms produce hydrolytic enzymes that are released to the media to degrade this organic matter. Up to 80-90% of the microorganisms present in activated sludge cannot be grown using standard cultivation techniques [3] and for this reason several methods have been applied to isolate the hydrolytic enzymes that are produced during the degradation. It was demonstrated that the enzymatic activity (as free form) present in the liquid phase of the activated sludge is almost negligible, and that the extracellular enzymes are attached to the flocs components (e.g. the cell wall of individual cells) by ionic and also hydrophobic interactions [3]. Ultrasound disintegration, alone or combined with detergents or ionic exchange resins is one of the methods with better performance for the recovery of the enzymes maintaining them active [2, 4-11].

The extraction of enzymes from activated sludge collected from municipal wastewater treatment plants was just briefly explored until now, as demonstrated by the fact that less than 15 articles were found to deal with this subject until now. The extraction of enzymes from activated sludge was started in 1995 [4]. In this study it was detected the presence of extracellular enzyme activity of esterase, lipase, leucine aminopeptidase, α- and β-glucosidase, chitinase, and β-glucuronidase. Several authors reported these and other enzymes (13 types in total, overviewed in Table 1) as they are present in activated sludge collected from urban wastewater treatment plants. However, there is a wide range in the amount of enzyme activity recovered that can vary up to three orders of magnitude depending on the source.

Table 1. State of the art for the different enzymes extracted from activated sludge in municipal wastewater treatment plants

Enzyme	Amount detected	Substrate	Unit definition	Author
Esterase	0.035	4-methylumbelliferyl stearate	μmol MUF/h/mg VS	[4]
	140	*p*-nitrophenyl esters (chain length 4-6)	μmol *p*-nitrophenol/min/L	[30]
Lipase	0.005	4-methylumbelliferyl stearate	μmol MUF/h/mg VS	[4]
	0.002	*p*-nitrophenyl-palmitate	μmol *p*-nitrophenol/min/g MLSS	[7]
	350	*p*-nitrophenyl-palmitate	μmol *p*-nitrophenol/min/g VSS	[3]
	1000	4-methylumbelliferyl oleate	μmol MUF/h/g TS	[31]
	90	*p*-nitrophenyl-palmitate	μmol *p*-nitrophenol/L/h	[32]
L-leu-aminopeptidase	0.015	L-leucine-4-methyl-7-coumarinylamide hydrochloride	μmol MCA/h/mg VS	[4]
	9	L-leu-*p*-nitroanilide	μmol *p*-nitroaniline/min/g VS	[2]
	38	L-leu-*p*-nitroanilide	μmol *p*-nitroaniline/L/h	[32]
Protease	0.1	Azocasein, 440 nm	1 mg azocasein/h/mg MLVSS	[29]
Protease (continuation)	80	Casein	μmol L-tyrosine/min/mg protein	[6]
	2210	Casein	μmol L-tyrosine/min/g MLSS	[7]
	8	Azocasein, 340 nm	ΔAbs/min/g VS	[2]
	4000	Azocasein, 440 nm	0.01 ΔAbs/g VSS	[3]
	28	Casein	μmol L-tyrosine/min/g VSS	[8]
	4	Casein	μmol L-tyrosine/min/g VSS	[9]
	9	Casein	μmol L-tyrosine/min/g VSS	[10]
	2.5	Casein	μmol L-tyrosine/min/g VSS	[11]
α-glucosidase	0.005	4-methylumbelliferyl-α-D-glucoside	μmol MUF/h/mg VS	[4]
	2.5	*p*-nitrophenyl-α-D-glucopyranoside	μmol *p*-nitrophenol/min/g VS	[2]
	300	-	μmol glucose/min/g VSS	[8]
	4	-	μmol glucose/min/g VSS	[9]
	2	-	μmol glucose/min/g VSS	[10]
β-glucosidase	0.009	4-methylumbelliferyl-β-D-glucoside	μmol MUF/h/mg VS	[4]
	0.002	*p*-nitrophenyl-β-D-glucopyranoside	units/g MLSS	[7]
	40	*p*-nitrophenyl-β-D-glucopyranoside	μmol *p*-nitrophenol/L/h	[32]
β-glucuronidase	0.005	4-methylumbelliferyl-β-D-glucuronide	μmol MUF/h/mg VS	[4]
Endoglucanase	0.002	Carboxymethyl cellulose	units/g MLSS	[7]
α-amylase	2.7	Amylose azure	μmol Remazol brilliant blue/min/g VS	[2]
	15	-	μmol glucose/min/g VSS	[8]
	150	-	μmol glucose/min/g VSS	[9]
	45	-	μmol glucose/min/g VSS	[10]
	20	-	μmol glucose/min/g VSS	[11]
Alkaline phosphatase	0.2	*p*-nitrophenyl phosphate	μmol *p*-nitrophenol/h/ mg MLVSS	[29]
	38	*p*-nitrophenyl phosphate	μmol *p*-nitrophenol/L/h	[32]
	60	*p*-nitrophenyl phosphate	μmol *p*-nitrophenol/h/ mg MLVSS	[9]

Table 1. (Continued)

Enzyme	Amount detected	Substrate	Unit definition	Author
	17	p-nitrophenyl phosphate	μmol p-nitrophenol/h/ mg MLVSS	[10]
	10	p-nitrophenyl phosphate	μmol p-nitrophenol/h/ mg MLVSS	[11]
Acid phosphatase	0.5	p-nitrophenyl phosphate	μmol p-nitrophenol/h/ mg MLVSS	[29]
	38	p-nitrophenyl phosphate	μmol p-nitrophenol/h/ mg MLVSS	[9]
	12	p-nitrophenyl phosphate	μmol p-nitrophenol/h/ mg MLVSS	[10]
	3	p-nitrophenyl phosphate	μmol p-nitrophenol/h/ mg MLVSS	[11]
Dehydrogenase	0.35	Iodonitrotetrazolium (INT)	μmol INT-formazan /h/mg MLVSS	[29]
Chitinase	0.005	4-methylumbelliferyl-N-acetyl-and-D-glucosaminide	μmol MUF/h/mg VS	[4]

The definition of enzymatic activity is arbitrary and depends strongly on the substrate and the conditions of the reaction used to determine it. For this reason, it is necessary to establish formal protocols with well defined methods (in which the definition of enzymatic activity is clear) suitable to determine the enzymatic activities, because this is a key parameter in the extraction and purification process. The economy of an industrial process for the extraction of enzymes will be determined by the efficiency of the extraction process and the enzymatic activity extracted.

About the possible applications of the extracted enzymes, several studies have been carried out to evaluate the influence of an enzymatic pretreatment step prior to the anaerobic digestion of domestic or industrial wastewater. The results showed that it was possible to remove solids, decrease the COD level and improve the biogas production after the anaerobic digestion. But, for these studies, mainly commercial enzymes (mostly lipases) have been used [12-22] and just in few cases enzymes extracted from sludge were used to treat and improve the degradation of different compounds in certain types of wastewater [23]. On the other side, enzymes such as lipases are starting to be used as a pretreatment step prior to the anaerobic degradation of specific types of polymeric esters like phthalate esters [24], diethyleneglycol terephtalate and poly(ethylene)terephtalate [23]. These studies open the possibilities of application for the different enzymes recovered from activated sludge. This will have two main advantages: first, the recovery of a valuable product from sludge; and second, that these enzymes could be used to improve the degradation of sludge (which will enhance the biogas production during the anaerobic digestion step) or for the degradation of other specific chemical compounds that are difficult to degrade by traditional processes.

The objective of the present chapter is to determine the different types of hydrolytic enzymes and the amount of enzymatic activity present in the activated sludge of an urban wastewater treatment plant, using ultrasound disintegration alone or combined with a non-ionic detergent like Triton X100. The protocols for the determination of the enzymatic activity recovered and the definition of the enzymatic activity itself will be established.

MATERIAL AND METHODS

Sludge Collection and Handling

The activated sludge was collected from the aeration basin in the municipal wastewater treatment plant in Reus, Spain. This plant processes near 20,000 m^3 wastewater/day (the city has 105,000 inhabitants). The samples of activated sludge were taken and transported to the laboratory in 30 min. All the disintegration experiments were carried out the same day, preserving the sludge under aeration at room temperature. The samples of sludge were taken every 2-3 weeks, and the experiments were carried out along 6 months of plant operation. The sludge was used as received, and it was analyzed in order to determine the content in total solids (TS) and volatile suspended solids (VSS) by gravimetric method according to standard methods [25].

Disintegration of Activated Sludge

The disintegration experiments were carried out using an ultrasonic disintegrator UP200S (Hielscher Ultrasonics GmbH, Germany). The experiments were carried out at 24 kHz working frequency, 4 W/cm^2 power intensity (50 W ultrasonic power) and different disintegration times between 1 and 30 min. The volume of sludge used for each test was 200 mL using 400 mL vessels. The disintegration experiments were carried out using sludge alone or combined with a non ionic detergent like Triton X100 (TX100) in concentration 2% v/v (purchased from Sigma Aldrich). These conditions were chosen taking into account preliminary experiments for the recovery of protease and lipase [26, 27]. For all the experiments a water–ice bath was used, maintaining the temperature constant at 5±1°C. Samples of sludge were taken before and after the disintegration process and were centrifuged at room temperature at 10,100 × g for 10 min prior to the analysis. The supernatant was used as the source of enzyme for the determination of the enzymatic activity and the amount of protein. All the disintegration experiments were carried out by duplicate.

Determination of the Enzymatic Activity and Amount of Protein

The enzymes identified and quantified were lipase, protease, alkaline phosphatase, acid phosphatase, L-leu-aminopeptidase, α-glucosidase and α-amylase. All the methods used to determine the enzymatic activity were based on standard protocols from Sigma Aldrich. The amount of protein was quantified following the Bradford method. Absorbance measurements were carried out using an UV-Vis DINKO spectrophotometer (DINTER S.A. Spain). All the experiments were carried out by duplicate.

o   *Lipase activity.* It was determined using *p*-nitrophenyl butyrate as substrate, measuring the release of *p*-nitrophenol by continuous spectrophotometric rate determination. For the experiments, 0.2 mL of enzyme solution were placed in a suitable cuvette, adding 1.8 mL of a solution containing 100 mM NaH$_2$PO$_4$ buffer having 150 mM NaCl and 0.5% v/v TX100 (pH 7.2 at 37°C). It was mixed by inversion and the absorbance at 400 nm was measured at room temperature. The reaction started when 20 μL of 50 mM p-nitrophenyl butyrate (PNPB) prepared in acetonitrile were added to the test, and 20 μL of H_2O were added to the blank. The increase in the absorbance at 400 nm was recorded for approximately 6 min. The ΔAbs_{400nm}/min was calculated using the maximum linear rate for both the test and the blank, considering that 0.0148 is the μmolar extinction coefficient of p-nitrophenol at 400 nm. One unit of enzyme will release 1.0 μmol of p-nitrophenol per minute.

o *Protease activity.* It was analyzed using casein as substrate, measuring by spectrophotometry the concentration of L-tyrosine released by the action of the enzyme. A 0.65% w/v casein solution was prepared in 50 mM potassium phosphate buffer (pH 7.5 at 37°C). 5 mL of this substrate solution were mixed with 1 mL of the enzyme solution and incubated during 10 min at 37°C. Then 5 mL of 110 mM trichloroacetic acid were added to stop the reaction. After 30 min of incubation at 37°C, the reaction mixture was centrifuged at 10,100 × g for 10 min at room temperature. The clear supernatant (2 mL) was mixed with 5 mL of 500 mM Na_2CO_3 and 1 mL of Folin and Ciocalteu's Phenol reagent. This mixture was incubated for 30 min at 37°C and finally centrifuged at 10,100 × g for 10 min at room temperature. The absorbance of this solution was measured at 660 nm (1 cm light path cuvettes) against a blank. The concentration of L-tyrosine was determined by comparison with a calibration curve. The unit definition for the enzymatic activity considers that one unit of protease will hydrolyze casein to produce colour equivalent to 1.0 μmol of L-tyrosine per minute.

o *Acid phosphatase activity.* It was determined by spectrophotometric stop rate determination using p-nitrophenyl phosphate as substrate. For this analysis, 0.5 mL of 90 mM citrate buffer (pH 4.8 at 37°C) and 0.5 mL of 15.2 mM p-nitrophenyl phosphate (PNPP) were added to test tubes (test and blank). The mixture was equilibrated at 37°C, and then 0.10 mL of enzyme solution were added to the test tube. Immediately it was mixed by inversion and incubated at 37°C for exactly 10 min. Then, 4 mL of 100 mM NaOH were added to the test and blank, and finally 0.10 mL of the enzyme solution were added to the blank. The absorbance was measured at 410 nm. The definition of enzymatic activity considers that one unit of enzyme hydrolyzes 1 μmol of p-nitrophenyl phosphate per minute at pH 4.8 at 37°C.

o *Alkaline phosphatase activity.* It was determined using p-nitrophenyl phosphate as substrate, measuring the release of p-nitrophenol by continuous spectrophotometric rate determination. For this test, 1.35 and 1.4 mL of 1 M diethanolamine buffer with 0.5 mM $MgCl_2$ (pH 9.8 at 37°C) were placed in the test and blank cuvette, respectively. 0.15 mL of a 150 mM p-nitrophenyl phosphate solution were added to both cuvettes. The mixture was equilibrated at room temperature, and then 0.05 mL of the enzyme solution were added to the test. The increase in the absorbance at 405 nm was recorded for approximately 10 min. The definition of enzyme activity considers that one unit of enzyme hydrolyzes 1 μmol of p-nitrophenyl phosphate per minute at pH 9.8 at 37°C.

o *Leucine aminopeptidase activity.* It was determined by continuous spectrophotometric rate determination using L-leucine-p-nitroanilide as substrate. To this purpose, 2.8 mL of 50 mM sodium phosphate buffer (pH 7.2 at 37°C) were placed in suitable cuvettes (test and blank), and 0.1 mL of 24 mM L-leucine-*p*-nitroanilide (prepared in methanol) were added to both test and blank. The mixture was equilibrated at room temperature, and 0.10 mL of the enzyme solution and deionized water were added to the test and the blank, respectively. The increase in the absorbance at 405 nm was recorded for approximately 7 min. The definition of enzyme activity considers that one unit of enzyme hydrolyzes 1 µmol of L-leucine-*p*-nitroanilide per minute at pH 7.2 at 37°C.

o *α-amylase activity.* It was determined by colorimetric method using starch as substrate. To this purpose, 1 mL of 1% w/v starch solution prepared in 20 mM sodium phosphate buffer having 6.7 mM NaCl (pH 6.9 at 20°C) were placed in suitable test tubes (for test and blank). The mixture was equilibrated at 20°C. Then 1 mL of enzyme solution was added to the test, and the mixture was incubated for exactly 3 min at 20°C. After that, 1 mL of colour reagent solution was added to the test and the blank, and finally 1 mL of enzyme solution was added to the blank. The colour reagent solution was prepared adding 8 mL of 1.5 g/mL sodium potassium tartrate in 2 M NaOH solution, to 20 mL of 96 mM 3,5-dinitrosalicylic acid solution, and this mixture was diluted to 40 mL with deionized water. The tubes were placed in a boiling water bath for exactly 15 min, and then they were cooled on ice to room temperature. Finally 9 mL of deionized water were added to the test and blank, and the absorbance was measured at 540 nm. A standard curve was prepared using maltose as standard solution, plotting $\Delta A_{540\ nm}$ of the standards vs. mg of maltose. The definition of enzyme activity considers that one unit of enzyme will liberate 1 mg of maltose from starch in 3 min at pH 6.9 at 20°C.

o *α-glucosidase activity.* It was determined by spectrophotometric stop rate determination using *p*-nitrophenyl α-D-glucoside as substrate. 5 mL of 67 mM potassium phosphate buffer (pH 6.8 at 37°C) and 0.20 mL of 3 mM glutathione (reduced solution) were placed in test tubes (for test and blank). 0.20 mL of enzyme solution and 0.20 mL of deionized water were added to the test and blank tube, respectively. The mixture was equilibrated at 37°C, and then 0.5 mL of 10 mM *p*-nitrophenyl α-D-glucoside were added to both (test and blank) tubes. Then, the tubes were incubated for exactly 20 min at 37°C. After this time, 2 mL of the corresponding test and blank were placed into suitable containers, adding 8 mL of 100 mM sodium carbonate solution to each tube. The absorbance was measured at 400 nm. The definition of enzyme activity considers that one unit of enzyme will liberate 1 µmol of D-glucose per minute at pH 6.8 at 37°C.

o *Protein.* The amount of protein was determined following the Bradford method (Bio-Rad). For this assay, 100 µL of the enzyme solution (test) or deionized water (blank) were placed in suitable test tubes, adding 5 mL of Coomasie blue brilliant reagent (Bradford colour reagent, diluted 1:5 with deionized water). The solution was incubated at room temperature for 1 h and the absorbance was measured at 595 nm. The samples containing detergent TX100 were diluted 1:20 to have a detergent concentration compatible with the assay. A calibration curve using bovine serum albumin (BSA) as standard was carried out in the range 0.01 to 1 mg protein/mL.

RESULTS AND DISCUSSION

As it was already mentioned, the objective of this chapter is to determine the presence of several hydrolytic enzymes in activated sludge collected from an urban wastewater treatment plant. To this purpose, several disintegration experiments were carried out, following the optimal experimental conditions found in preliminary studies [26, 27]. Two enzymes were detected in these previous experiments (protease and lipase), which were the most abundantly referenced in the literature. The present chapter extends this study to another five enzymes which are well known of participating in the degradation process. As it was mentioned before, it is difficult to compare the results and extract useful conclusions from the literature. Between them, the lack of details about the definition of enzymatic activity itself and the differences in the protocol and the substrate used to measure the enzymatic activity are of importance. For this reason, with the purpose of extracting the enzymes and to use them for any specific application, it is necessary to perform a detailed study about the availability of each type of enzyme and the optimal protocol for its extraction, maximizing the amount of enzyme activity recovered in each case. The enzymes studied are acid phosphatase, alkaline phosphatase, L-leu-aminopeptidase, α-amylase, protease, lipase, and α-glucosidase. Its presence in the activated sludge give us an idea of the variations in the substrate composition, microbial population, etc., depending on the presence of the different macromolecules in the activated sludge that the microorganisms are able to degrade [28]. Lipase hydrolyzes the lipids and esters present in activated sludge, while acid and alkaline phosphatase hydrolyze different types of phosphate esters. The generic enzyme called protease hydrolyzes different types of proteins, while leucine aminopeptidase is more specific and cuts the bond between leucine and different peptides. Finally, α-amylase and α-glucosidase hydrolyze starch and maltose from cellulose, respectively.

The solids content in the sludge samples was determined by gravimetry according to standard methods. The results are showed in Table 2, together with the sludge characteristics. The total solids content varied between $1.8 - 2.2$ g/L, while the volatile suspended solids (VSS) content varied between $0.87 - 0.92$ g/L for all the samples tested.

Table 2. Characteristics of the activated sludge collected from biological reactor

Activated sludge from WWTP Reus	
TS (g/L)	2.03 ± 0.17
VSS (g/L)	0.90 ± 0.03
VSS/TS	0.44
Organic load (kg DBO5/ (kg TSS * day)	0.91 ± 0.10
Sludge age (days)	3

The variations in the solids content are related to the typical variations in the organic matter composition of activated sludge due to changes in flow, temperature, seasonal changes, city population, etc. which at the end will affect the enzymatic activity content in the activated sludge.

Figure 1 shows the results for the enzymatic activity obtained and the amount of protein recovered when using ultrasonication at different disintegration times. The disintegration experiments were carried out using a water-ice bath to control the temperature during the process ($5\pm1°C$). The enzymatic activity of acid phosphatase, alkaline phosphatase, L-leu-aminopeptidase, α-amylase, protease, lipase and α-glucosidase, is presented in units of enzyme per gram of VSS as well as in units of enzyme per mg of protein. The amount of protein released is also shown in Figure 1 h. As it can be observed, 30 min of disintegration time using 4 W/cm^2 power intensity seems to be adequate to extract the maximal amount of enzyme present in the activated sludge for all the enzymes. However, there are some differences in the amount of the enzymatic activity extracted during the time of disintegration. The amount of enzymatic activity recovered per gram of VSS for acid and alkaline phosphatase, leucine aminopeptidase, α-glucosidase and lipase has an increasing tendency that seems to continue beyond 30 min of disintegration. On the other side, α-amylase and protease showed a maximal amount of enzymatic activity at 20 min of disintegration time, and beyond this point, the activity slightly diminishes. This decrease in the enzyme activity extracted could be explained by the degradation of the enzyme due to ultrasonic disintegration. Acid and alkaline phosphatase yielded a maximum of 7.8 and 3.4 units enzyme/g VSS (0.01 and 0.003 units/mL) respectively when using 30 min of disintegration time. These values are near to that found in the literature (0.0125 units/mL and 0.005 units/mL for acid and alkaline phosphatase, respectively) which were expressed in similar units [29]. Yu et al. reported between $10 - 17$ units /g VSS for alkaline phosphatase and between 3 - 12 units/g VSS for acid phosphatase, respectively [10, 11]. L-leucine aminopeptidase showed a maximal activity of 11 units/g VSS, which is slightly higher than the value found in literature (around 9 units/g VSS) [2]. The results for α-amylase showed a higher enzymatic activity (it was possible to extract up to 174 units/g VSS) which is in the range reported (between $15 - 150$ units/g VSS) [9-11]. The activity of α-glucosidase extracted after 30 min of disintegration (3.9 units/g VSS) was higher than some values found in the literature (2 units/g VSS) [2]. However, Yu et al. had extracted between $2 - 305$ units/g VSS [8-10]. There are several results in the literature for the extraction of lipase, but only few of them are comparable. In the present study it was possible to extract up to 29.5 units/g VSS, which is a lower value than that found in literature (335 units/g VSS) [3]. On the other side, protease yielded up to 25.7 units/g VSS, which is in the range of the results found in the literature (between $2,5 - 28$ units/g VSS) [8-11]. Finally, the maximal amount of protein present in the supernatant after centrifugation is around 0.035 mg/mL, which represents near 4% of the volatile suspended solids present in the activated sludge. If we observe the amount of enzyme recovered per mg of protein, it is possible to detect a maximum in the amount extracted at 10 min of disintegration, and then a steep decrease. However, observing the amount of protein extracted from activated sludge it increases until reaching a maximum at 20 min of extraction for all the cases (see Figures 1 a $-$ g). That indicates that even if the amount of protein extracted increases with disintegration time, the effect of the ultrasonication affects the enzyme and deactivates it.

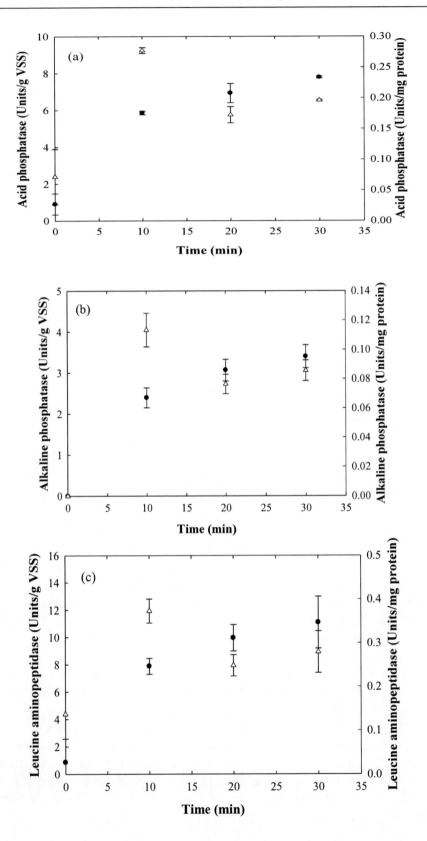

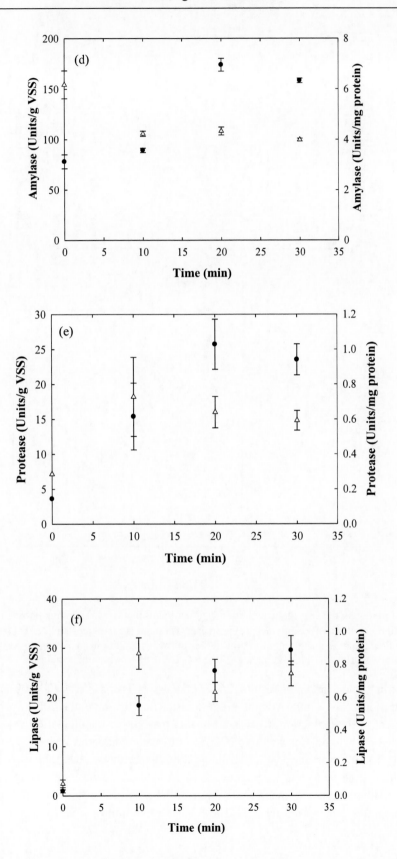

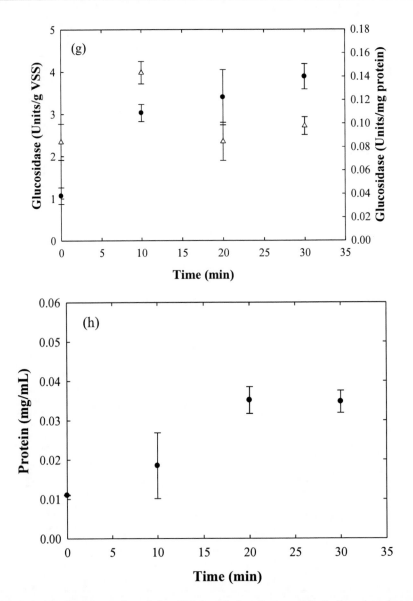

Figure 1. Variation in the enzymatic activity of: (a) acid phosphatase; (b) alkaline phosphatase; (c) leucine aminopeptidase; (d) α-amylase; (e) protease; (f) lipase; (g) α-glucosidase; (h) amount of protein, as function of the disintegration time at the following conditions: 4 W/cm2 power intensity, 5±1°C, 0% v/v TX100. ● Units of enzyme/g VSS; △ Units of enzyme/mg protein.

According to our previous results [26, 27] the use of Triton X-100 (TX100) as additive in a concentration 2% v/v improves the process efficiency for the extraction of protease, but it has no effect in the extraction of lipase. For this reason, the disintegration experiments that were carried out without any additive (0% TX100) were compared with the results obtained when 2% TX100 was used. The disintegration experiments were done using 30 min disintegration time at 5±1°C (see Figure 2 a). As it can be observed, only two enzymes incremented the activity recovered per gram of VSS: protease and acid phosphatase. The activity of protease increased from 11.7 to 53.3 enzyme units/g VSS (356% increase) when

0% and 2% of detergent was used, respectively. The activity of acid phosphatase increased from 15 to 20 enzyme units/g VSS at the same conditions (33% increase). The other enzymes were recovered with near the same activity when the experiments were carried out with or without detergent, indicating that the use of TX100 does not improve significantly its recovery. On the contrary, the activities of lipase or leucine aminopeptidase even descend with the use of TX100 (it decreases between 15-20%).

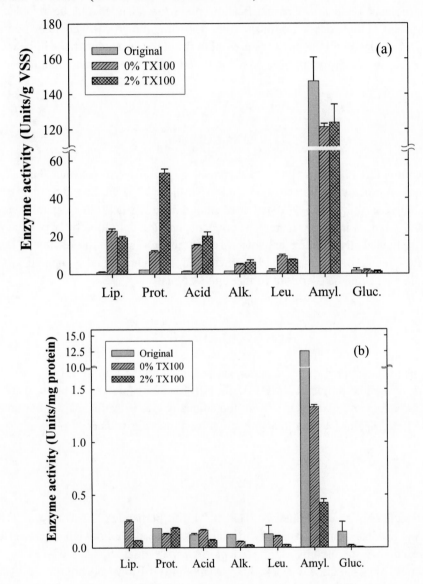

Figure 2. Enzymatic activity recovered after disintegration experiments using 0% v/v and 2% v/v TX100 at 4 W/cm2 power intensity, 5±1°C, 30 min disintegration time. (a) Enzymatic activity expressed in units/g VSS; (b) Enzymatic activity expressed in units/mg protein. Legends: Lip. (lipase); Prot. (protease); Acid (acid phosphatase); Alk. (alkaline phosphatase); Leu. (leucine aminopeptidase); Amyl. (α-amylase); Gluc. (α-glucosidase). Original (supernatant from sludge not disintegrated); 0% TX100 (supernatant from sludge disintegrated without TX100); 2% TX100 (supernatant from sludge disintegrated with 2% TX100).

The results in Figure 2 b showed the same tendencies. As the amount of protein extracted increases with the use of detergent, the amount of enzymatic activity decreases, indicating some deactivation of the enzyme. Only protease showed a little increment in the amount of enzyme extracted with the use of detergent. As it was already mentioned, the use of Triton X100 as additive will be effective depending on the type of enzyme that will be extracted. In this case its use is helpful for the extraction of protease and acid phosphatase, but it may generate problems related to the purification procedure that should be avoided in the subsequent steps of the process. For this reason, the extraction process should be optimized in every particular case for all the enzymes present in the activated sludge that will be recovered, taking into account the degree of purity and the specific enzymatic activity required at the end of the process.

CONCLUSION

The main objective of this chapter was to analyze the different enzymes that take part in the degradation process of the activated sludge. Until now, in the literature there were few references about the enzymology of activated sludge, being difficult to compare them mainly due to the differences in the measurement protocols and the definition of enzymatic activity. This study allowed determining and quantifying the presence of the different hydrolytic enzymes in a standard way that could be measured, reproduced and compared in terms of enzyme units that could be useful for further applications.

ACKNOWLEDGMENTS

The financial support for this research was provided by the European Union Research 6th Framework Program, project REMOVALS, FP6-018525. Authors want to thank Jaume Cabré, Raúl García and Iñaqui Oriol from the company Gestió Ambiental i Abastament S.A. (EDAR de Reus, Spain) for their kind collaboration during this project.

REFERENCES

[1]   Carbonell, G.; Pro, J.; Gómez, N.; Babýn, M. M.; Fernandez, C.; Alonso, E.; Tarazona, J. V. Sewage sludge applied to agricultural soil: Ecotoxicological effects on representative soil organisms. *Ecotoxicol. Environ. Saf.* 2009, *72*, 1309-1319.

[2]   Cadoret, A.; Conrad, A.; Block, J. C. Availability of low and high molecular weight substrates to extracellular enzymes in whole and dispersed activated sludges. *Enzyme Microb. Technol.* 2002, *31*, 179-186.

[3]   Gessesse, A.; Dueholm, T.; Petersen, S. B.; Nielsen, P. H. Lipase and protease extraction from activated sludge. *Water Res.* 2003, *37*, 3652-3657.

[4]   Frolund, B.; Griebe, T.; Nielsen, P. H. Enzymatic Activity in the Activated-Sludge Floc Matrix. *Appl. Microbiol. Biotechnol.* 1995, *43*, 755-761.

[5] Frolund, B.; Palmgren, R.; Keiding, K.; Nielsen, P. H. Extraction of extracellular polymers from activated sludge using a cation exchange resin. *Water Res.* 1996, *30*, 1749-1758.

[6] Jung, J.; Xing, X. H.; Matsumoto, K. Kinetic analysis of disruption of excess activated sludge by Dyno Mill and characteristics of protein release for recovery of useful materials. *Biochem. Eng. J.* 2001, *8*, 1-7.

[7] Jung, J.; Xing, X. H.; Matsumoto, K. Recoverability of protease released from disrupted excess sludge and its potential application to enhanced hydrolysis of proteins in wastewater. *Biochem. Eng. J.* 2002, *10*, 67-72.

[8] Yu, G.; He, P.; Shao, L.; Lee, D. Enzyme activities in activated sludge flocs. *Appl. Microbiol. Biotechnol.* 2007, *77*, 605-612.

[9] Yu, G.; He, P.; Shao, L.; Lee, D. Extracellular enzymes in sludge flocs collected at 14 full-scale wastewater treatment plants. *J. Chem. Technol. Biot.* 2008, *83*, 1717-1725.

[10] Yu, G.; He, P.; Shao, L.; Zhu, Y. Extracellular proteins, polysaccharides and enzymes impact on sludge aerobic digestion after ultrasonic pretreatment. *Water Res.* 2008, *42*, 1925 - 1934.

[11] Yu, G.; He, P.; Shao, L.; Zhu, Y. Enzyme extraction by ultrasound from sludge flocs. *J. Environ. Sci.* 2009, *21*, 204 - 210.

[12] Barjenbruch, M.; Kopplow, O. Enzymatic, mechanical and thermal pre-treatment of surplus sludge. *Adv. Environ. Res.* 2003, *7*, 715-720.

[13] Cammarota, M. C.; Teixeira, G. A.; Freire, D. M. G. Enzymatic pre-hydrolysis and anaerobic degradation of wastewaters with high fat contents. *Biotechnol. Lett.* 2001, *23*, 1591-1595.

[14] Jeganathan, J.; Nakhla, G.; Bassi, A. Hydrolytic pretreatment of oily wastewater by immobilized lipase. *J. Hazard. Mater.* 2007, *145*, 127-135.

[15] Jordan, S. N.; Mullen, G. J. Enzymatic hydrolysis of organic waste materials in a solid-liquid system. *Waste Manage.* 2007, *27*, 1820-1828.

[16] Leal, M.; Freire, D. M. G.; Cammarota, M. C.; Sant'Anna, G. L. Effect of enzymatic hydrolysis on anaerobic treatment of dairy wastewater. *Process Biochem.* 2006, *41*, 1173-1178.

[17] Parmar, N.; Singh, A.; Ward, O. P. Enzyme treatment to reduce solids and improve settling of sewage sludge. *J. Ind. Microbiol. Biotechnol.* 2001, *26*, 383-386.

[18] Roman, H. J.; Burgess, J. E.; Pletschke, B. I. Enzyme treatment to decrease solids and improve digestion of primary sewage sludge. *Afr. J. Biotechnol.* 2006, *5*, 963-967.

[19] Recktenwald, M.; Wawrzynczyk, J.; Dey, E. S.; Norrlow, O. Enhanced efficiency of industrial-scale anaerobic digestion by the addition of glycosidic enzymes. *J. Environ. Sci. Health., Part A.* 2008, *43*, 1536 - 1540.

[20] Wawrzynczyk, J.; Recktenwald, M.; Norrlow, O.; Dey, E. S. Solubilisation of sludge by combined chemical and enzymatic treatment. *Afr. J. Biotechnol.* 2007, *6*, 1994-1999.

[21] Valladao, A. B. G.; Freire, D. M. G.; Cammarota, M. C. Enzymatic pre-hydrolysis applied to the anaerobic treatment of effluents from poultry slaughterhouses. *Int. Biodeterior. Biodegrad.* 2007, *60*, 219-225.

[22] Kim, H. J.; Kim, S. H.; Choi, Y. G.; Kim, G. D.; Chung, T. H. Effect of enzymatic pretreatment on acid fermentation of food waste. *J. Chem. Technol. Biot.* 2006, *81*, 974-980.

[23] Zhang, J. F.; Gong, J. X.; Shao, G. Q.; Qin, J. J.; Gu, Z. Y. Biodegradability of diethylene glycol terephthalate and poly(ethylene terephthalate) fiber by crude enzymes extracted from activated sludge. *J. Appl. Polym. Sci.* 2006, *100*, 3855-3859.

[24] Gavala, H. N.; Yenal, U.; Ahring, B. K. Thermal and enzymatic pretreatment of sludge containing phthalate esters prior to mesophilic anaerobic digestion. *Biotechnol. Bioeng.* 2004, *85*, 561-567.

[25] APHA. *Standard Methods for the Examination of Water and Wastewater.* American Public Health Association. American Water Association: Washington, 1999.

[26] Nabarlatz, D.; Vondrysova, J.; Jenicek, P.; Stüber, F.; Font, J.; Fortuny, A.; Fabregat, A.; Bengoa, C. Extraction of enzymes from activated sludge. In *Waste Management and the Environment IV. WIT Transactions on Ecology and the Environment*; M. Zamorano, et al.; Ed. WIT Press: Southampton, 2008; pp 249 - 257.

[27] Nabarlatz, D.; Vondrysova, J.; Jenicek, P.; Stüber, F.; Font, J.; Fortuny, A.; Fabregat, A.; Bengoa, C. Extraction of protease and lipase from activated sludge by ultrasound and magnetic stirring disintegration. In *18th International Congress of Chemical and Process Engineering*. Process Engineering Publisher: Prague, Czech Republic, 2008.

[28] Voet, D.; Voet, J.; Pratt, C. *Fundamentals of Biochemistry: Life at the molecular level.* 2nd ed. Editorial Medica Panamericana: Madrid, Spain, 2006; pp 1130.

[29] Goel, R.; Mino, T.; Satoh, H.; Matsuo, T. Enzyme activities under anaerobic and aerobic conditions inactivated sludge sequencing batch reactor. *Water Res.* 1998, *32*, 2081-2088.

[30] Boczar, B. A.; Forney, L. J.; Begley, W. M.; Larson, R. J.; Federle, T. W. Characterization and distribution of esterase activity in activated sludge. *Water Res.* 2001, *35*, 4208-4216.

[31] Schade, M.; Lemmer, H. Lipase activities in activated sludge and scum - Comparison of new and conventional techniques. *Acta Hydroch. Hydrob.* 2005, *33*, 210-215.

[32] Li, Y.; Chrost, R. J. Microbial enzymatic activities in aerobic activated sludge model reactors. *Enzyme Microb. Technol.* 2006, *39*, 568-572.

In: Water Production and Wastewater Treatment
Editor: B. Antizar-Ladislao et al.

ISBN 978-1-61728-503-5
© 2011 Nova Science Publishers, Inc.

Chapter 3

DGGE AND 16S rDNA SEQUENCING ANALYSIS OF BACTERIAL COMMUNITIES IN A MEMBRANE BIOREACTOR FOR THE REMOVAL OF PHENOL FROM OIL REFINERY WASTEWATER

Fernanda R. Pinhati[a], Aline F. Viero[a],
Eduardo M. Del Aguila[a], Ana Paula R. Torres[b],
Joab T. Silva[a], and Vânia M. F. Paschoalin[a1]*

[a]Universidade Federal do Rio de Janeiro, Instituto de Química,
Av. Athos da Silveira Ramos, 149 - Bloco A, sala 545,
Cidade Universitária, 21941-909, Rio de Janeiro, RJ, Brazil
[b]Petrobras-CENPES, Gerência de Biotecnologia e Tratamentos Ambientais,
Av. Horácio de Macedo, 950 Cidade Universitária,
21941-915 Rio de Janeiro, RJ, Brazil

ABSTRACT

The stability of the activated sludge bacterial community present in a submerged membrane bioreactor (SMBR) fed with petroleum refinery wastewater was investigated. The changes in the activated-sludge bacterial community during adaptation from low- to high-phenol loading were analyzed using a 16S rDNA-based technique. Amplicons from the V3 variable regions of bacterial 16S rDNA were analyzed by denaturing gradient gel electrophoresis (DGGE) and sequencing. The phenol removal efficiency of the SMBR bioreactor was 98% during acclimation (15 mg phenol L^{-1}), high-organic loading (85 mg phenol L^{-1}), and recovery (15 mg phenol L^{-1}) steps. The cluster analysis of DGGE fingerprints showed higher similarity between the community structure of the bacterial population in the SMBR when the community structure of 'native' sludge was compared to bacterial communities during the high-phenol and recovery steps, with Cs of 76.7 and 63.4%, respectively. The fingerprint data combined with statistical tools showed that the bacterial community could adapt to the adverse environmental conditions during

---

[1] *Corresponding author: e-mail: paschv@iq.ufrj.br, tel +55 21 2562 7362; fax: +55 21 2562 7266.

wastewater treatment operations, sustaining the high quality of the effluents and maintaining stability of the SMBR in response to high-phenol-shock loadings. Seven prominent bands excised from DGGE fingerprints from the phenol-shock bands were successfully reamplified and sequenced, allowing the identification of predominant bacteria in the sludge. The phylogenetic analysis indicated that the isolates fell into two major lineages of the Bacteria domain: the Alpha and Gamma proteobacteria classes.

INTRODUCTION

Phenolic compounds are the major pollutants resulting from many industrial processes, including refining petroleum, synthesizing resins, and manufacturing explosives (Geng et al. 2006). Phenol is toxic to many biochemical functions and to marine life, even at low concentrations (Prieto et al. 2002). In human beings, phenols can cause liver and kidney damage and blood pressure drop (Barrios-Martinez (2006), and are toxic by ingestion, contact, or inhalation. Brazilian law specifies the concentration of 0.5 mg L^{-1} as the limit for discharge of phenol in effluents (Conama, 2005).

Granular or biological activated-carbon filtration, ozonation, solvent extraction, and membrane-filtration processes are used to remove phenolic compounds from wastewater (Nuhoglu and Yalcin, 2005; Barrios-Martinez et al. 2006). However, the microbial-based process for phenol removal from industrial wastewater has generated significant interest because phenols and other aromatic compounds can be used as the sole carbon and energy source by many microorganisms. Biological treatment is a desirable alternative to traditional physical and chemical methods because of its low cost, reliable operational stability, and efficient destruction/reduction of pollution (Jiang et al. 2004). Although phenol is inhibitory at high concentrations, biological techniques are widely used for treatment of wastewater or soil containing moderate levels (5–500 mg L^{-1}) of this compound (Barrios-Martinez et al. 2006). Biodegradation of phenol is often a prerequisite for the treatment of mixed pollutants, and phenol concentration can be accepted as an indicator of the removal efficiency of pollutant compounds from industrial wastewater, including refinery effluents (Margesin et al. 2005).

Conventional wastewater treatment in oil refinery wastewater plants comprises several steps, generally consisting in oil/water separation, biological treatment and filtration/adsorption as an optional additional step. The process generally produces good results, although the activated sludge used in the biological treatment step is poorly suited to deal with large changes in flow rate and/or composition (Jiang et al. 2004). Activated sludge from aerobic wastewater-treatment plants is formed by a complex consortium of microorganisms, all of which are required to achieve the desired biological conversions. The microbial consortium from activated sludge has been exhaustively studied in order to understand the specific role of each microbial population in the biological processes and the effect of the microbial diversity on the overall performance (Amann et al. 1997; Liu et al. 2007; Schwartz et al. 2000).

Membrane bioreactors (MBRs), which can be defined as integrating a biological degradation system of waste products with membrane filtration (Molina-Muñoz et al. 2007), has many advantages over conventional wastewater treatment technologies, including high quality of effluent, small footprint, less excess sludge, and ease of operation (Ueda and

Horan, 2000). The use of MBRs is a very suitable technology for decentralized wastewater management and satellite wastewater-treatment systems (Lobos et al. 2005). The development of cost-effective manufacturing of membranes and increasingly stringent regulations for the discharge of effluents have accelerated the application of membrane technology in wastewater treatment and reuse (Choi et al. 2005). Many full-scale wastewater treatment plants using MBRs are already in operation, and the number of installations of MBRs is expected to increase. The water quality of MBR effluent is suitable for a variety of water-reuse applications, and is suitable, after disinfection, for a number of non-potable but otherwise unrestricted uses (Laera et al. 2005; Gobel et al. 2007).

In the submerged MBR (SMBR) process, the membrane is immersed directly in the aeration tank. By applying low vacuum or by using the static head of the mixed liquor, effluent is driven through the membrane, leaving the solids behind. The advantages of the SMBR process for wastewater treatment include high sludge concentration, high quality of effluent, long contact time between the activated sludge and organic pollutants, and complete separation of the hydraulic retention time (HRT) and sludge retention time (SRT) (Chiemchaisri et al. 1992). Moreover, highly treated water in an SMBR is free from bacteria and has the potential for municipal and industrial reuse (Schneider and Tsutiya, 2001).

Studies on the effects of shock loadings in MBR fed with industrial wastewater are few (Banerjee, 1997; González et al. 2001; Jou and Huang, 2003, Hsien and Lin, 2005), especially on oil refinery wastewater, which contains many volatile aromatic compounds, polycyclic aromatic hydrocarbons, and inorganic compounds. Because of the diversity and complexity of refinery wastewater, phenols have been accepted as a suitable compound to provide an indication of the performance of biodegradation (Barrios-Martinez, 2006). Viero et al. (2008) studied the effects of organic- shock loadings with respect to the organic matter, ammonia-nitrogen, and phenol removal efficiencies, and proved the ability of the SMBR to manage high-strength feed during long-term exposure, achieving high efficiencies in removing phenols and ammonia-nitrogen. However, the changes in the microbial community during shock loading have not been assessed.

Most living bacteria have not yet been isolated and characterized (Torsvik et al. 1990; Giovannoni et al. 1991), because most of them cannot be cultured by standard techniques (Liu et al. 2007). For example, the culturable fraction of the bacteria present in wastewater-treatment reactors was estimated to be typically around 15 – 20% (LaPara et al. (2002), and the microbial communities found in refinery activated-sludge systems are still uncharacterized. Recently, several molecular techniques have been developed to study microbial communities. Methods based on direct PCR amplification of 16S rRNA gene and analysis of the amplified fragment by temperature-gradient gel electrophoresis (TGGE) or denaturing-gradient gel electrophoresis (DGGE) have been frequently used to examine the microbial diversity of environmental samples and to monitor changes in microbial communities (Amann et al. 1995). DGGE methods are relatively simple and produce results in relatively short time (Miura et al. 2007). They are based on the separation of the amplified fragments according to their nucleotide sequences, which are specie-specific. DGGE has provided important information about the diversity of microorganisms in natural and engineered habitats, including those microbial species previously unknown because of the limitations of culture-based approaches (Wagner and Loy, 2002; Cortés-Lorenzo et al. 2006). This technique has been frequently used to study the ecology of biological processes in MBR-based wastewater treatment plants, and to compare communities from different reactors or from the same reactor operated under different conditions (Witzig et al. 2002; Stamper et al. 2003; Miura et al. 2007; Molina-Muñoz et al. 2007).

In this study, we investigated the changes over time in the bacterial community present in the activated sludge from an SMBR fed with oil refinery effluent, during long-term phenol-shock loadings, by comparing the DGGE fingerprints of the V3 hyper-variable region of the 16S rDNA produced from total DNA extracted periodically from the activated sludge present in the bioreactor.

MATERIAL AND METHODS

SMBR Operation

The reactor construction and operation have been described previously (Viero et al. 2008). In brief, a mini-reactor consisting of a cylindrical acrylic tank with a working volume of 4.4 L was used. The polyetheremide membranes (average pore diameter of 0.15 ± 0.09 μm and total surface area $2.78 \times 10^{-2} m^2$) were produced by wet spinning, using the phase-inversion process. The bioreactor was operated at 25°C under a hydraulic retention time (HRT) of 10 h, air flow rate 2.5 L min^{-1}, filtration time 5 min, backwashing time 6.25 min, air backwashing pressure 3.0 bars, and liquid permeate flux 15–17 L m^{-2} h^{-1} bar^{-1}. The reactor was fed with a mixture of effluents collected from a petroleum refinery, consisting of an oily stream (OS) from the oil desalting process mixed with acid wastewater, and oily water drained from crude-oil storage tanks. A phenolic wastewater (PW) drained from the bottoms of cracked-gasoline tanks was added to increase the content of recalcitrant compounds content in the feed. The NH_4^+-N content in the PW and OS was 562.5 mg L^{-1} and 110 mg L^{-1}, respectively.

Activated Sludge and Oil-Refinery Wastewater

The activated sludge (10 g L^{-1} of total suspended solids after sedimentation) was collected in a Brazilian oil refinery wastewater-treatment plant. The sludge was acclimated for 33 days in the SMBR processing the regular oily wastewater. During acclimation and recovery, the SMBR operated with the wastewater flow rates regularly used in the refinery (15 mg L^{-1} phenol). After acclimation, the SMBR was fed with a mixture of oil wastewater (OS) and phenolic wastewater, showing mean CN^{-1} concentrations of 0.34 mg L^{-1}; Cl^{-1}, 1084 mg L^{-1}; and NH_4^+-N concentrations of 110 mg L^{-1}; S^{-2} of 2.23 mg L^{-1}, respectively. At the stage of high organic-loading operation, the phenol concentration was raised to 85 mg L^{-1}.

Analytical Methods

Samples of effluent were collected in an oil refinery in Brazil. The initial effluent and the effluent samples collected periodically from the SMBR reactor were assayed for chemical oxygen demand (COD) and concentrations of phenol, CN^{-1}, Cl^{-1}, NH_4^+-N and S^{-2} (Standard

Methods, 1998), using the Water Testing Kits (Chemetrics Inc) as recommended by the manufacturer.

Sampling of Activated Sludge

After acclimation (day 34), a sample of the activated sludge present in the SMBR was collected to characterize the 'native' sludge. During the high-loading-rate shock (days 35 to 63), activated sludge samples were collected each day, and during the last phase (days 64 to 90), when the loading-rate feed in the process was similar to the acclimation period, activated-sludge samples were taken every two days. Samples of activated sludge were collected by centrifugation at 2,000 g for 15 min, and the pellets were stored at -20 $^{\circ}$C prior to DNA extraction.

DNA Extraction from Sludge Samples

DNA was extracted from activated-sludge samples according to the method of Melvin & Hobson (1994), with some modifications. Each sludge pellet (0.5 g wet weight) was suspended in 1mL of TESC buffer (10mM Tris, 0.1mM EDTA and 0.1mM NaCl), pH 8.3, and shaken vigorously. After incubation for 2 h at –80ºC, 5 µL of DMSO (dimetyl sulfoxide) were added, and the suspension was again incubated at room temperature for 1 min. Subsequently, 500 µL of 5M guanidine thiocyanate and 500 µL of phenol:chloroform:isoamyl alcohol (25:24:1 v/v) were added. After centrifugation, the aqueous phase was transferred to a new tube and 30 µL of 3M sodium acetate was added. Total nucleic acids were precipitated with 2.5 volumes of 100% ethanol (-20ºC), dried, suspended in sterile double-distilled water, and then stored at –20ºC.

PCR Amplification

The V3 hypervariable region of the 16S rRNA gene, corresponding to nucleotide positions from 968 to 1401 (*Escherichia coli*), was amplified using the universal bacterial primers 968f (5'-AACGCGAAGAACCTTAC-3') containing a 40-bp GC clamp (5'-CGCCCGCCGCGCGCGGCGGGCGGGGCGGGGGCACGGGGGG-3') added to its 5'-end, and 1401r (5'-CGGTGTGTACAAGACCC-3') described by Nübel et al. (1996).

The PCR mixture comprised 5 µl of the DNA preparation extracted from sludge samples, 50 pmol of each universal primer, 5 µl of 10X PCR buffer (Invitrogen), 0.1µM $MgCl_2$, 0.2mM of each deoxynucleoside triphosphates (Invitrogen), and sterile ultrapure water, to a final volume of 50 µl. Negative controls consisting of sterile ultrapure water instead of the sample were included in each batch of samples. PCR was performed in a Perkin Elmer Gene Amp® PCR System 2400, with an initial denaturation step of 94 °C for 7 min, followed by 25 cycles of a denaturation step at 94ºC for 1 min, a primer annealing step at 60ºC for 1 min, an extension step at 72ºC for 1 min, and a final step of 72ºC for 7 min. Prior to the DGGE analysis, the presence of the PCR product of 433 bp was confirmed by electrophoresis in a

1.2% agarose gel stained for 15 min with 0.5 µg/ml ethidium bromide. A 100-bp DNA ladder digest (Invitrogen) served as the molecular size standard.

DGGE Assays

DGGE banding profiles of the V3 region of the 16S rDNA amplified by PCR with the 968f-GC/1401r primers were obtained using the Dcode Universal Mutation Detection System (Bio-Rad Dcode, Hercules, CA, USA) at 50 V and 60°C for 14 h in 0.5X TAE buffer (20 mM Tris-acetate 10 mM sodium acetate, 0.5 mM disodium EDTA, pH 7.4). The PCR products (30 µl) were loaded on 6% (w/v) polyacrylamide gels containing a linear gradient of the denaturants urea and formamide (45 to 65%), increasing from the top to the bottom of the gel [100% denaturant corresponding to 7 M urea and 45% (v/v) formamide]. Two gels were run to accommodate all the samples. A sample showing multiple bands in earlier experiments was loaded in the first and last slots of each gel to facilitate alignment and comparison between gels. After electrophoresis, gels were stained with SYBR green I nucleic acid gel stain (1:10.000 dilution; Molecular Probes, USA) for 60 min and observed/documented under UV light with the MiniBisPro System (BioAmerica Inc).

Analysis of DGGE Fingerprints

Cluster analysis was used to estimate the relatedness of the DGGE profiles representing the activated-sludge bacterial community in the SMBR. Band patterns generated by DGGE were normalized, compared, and clustered using the Gel Compar II v. 5.0 software (Applied Maths, Belgium). Bands were automatically detected and matched, with additional manual fine tuning of the band designations. Dendrograms relating band pattern similarities were automatically calculated with the Dice coefficient and UPGMA algorithms (*Unweighted pair group method with arithmetic mean*). The significance of UPGMA clustering was estimated by calculation of the cophenetic correlation coefficients.

Sequencing of DGGE Bands

After DGGE, bands of interest were excised from the gel and the DNA from each band was extracted using the QIAEX II GEL Extraction Kit (QIAGEN, Hilden, Germany). Subsequently, an aliquot (3 µl) was used to amplify the DGGE bands using the primers 968F (without the GC clamp) and 1401R, under the same amplification conditions. The amplified bands were purified using the Wizard SV Gel and PCR Clean-Up System (Promega, WI, USA). The DNAs recovered were used for automated sequencing in an ABI PRISM 3100 Avant Genetic Analyzer. DNA sequences were used to classify bacteria to the genus level by using the biocomputing tool Sequence-Match from the Ribosomal Database Project (http://rdp.cme.msu.edu/seqmatch).

RESULTS AND DISCUSSION

Evaluating the Efficiency of SMBR

The SMBR was operated for 90 days, fed with refinery wastewater (RW) showing mean values of chemical oxygen demand (COD) and phenol of 616 mg L^{-1} and 15 mg L^{-1}, respectively. The RW was additionally characterized: CN^{-1} (0.34 mg L^{-1}), Cl^{-1} (1084 mg L^{-1}), NH_4^+-N (110 mg L^{-1}) and S^{-2} (2.23 mg L^{-1}). The stock phenol wastewater (PW) showed mean values of COD, phenols and NH_4^+-N of 55.754 mg L^{-1}, 628 mg L^{-1} and 562.5 mg L^{-1}, respectively. Both the PW and RW were generated in the same oil refinery where the activated sludge was collected.

The average phenol removal by the SMBR was always higher than 98% (Figure 1A), and reached values greater than 99.3% when the phenol concentration in the feed was less than 15 mg L^{-1}, as in the recovery phase. Notably, phenol removal efficiency remained high even during the high-organic-loading operation phase, when the phenol concentration was raised to 85 mg L^{-1} in the feed, but the phenol in the SMBR permeate was raised to the still-low concentration of 0.35 mg L^{-1} (Figure 1B), within the specifications laid down by Brazilian legislation for the waste effluent (Conama, 2005), which established that concentrations of phenol in effluents must be less than 0.5 mg L^{-1}.

The average removal efficiency of phenol obtained in this study (98%) was similar or superior to those reported in the literature.

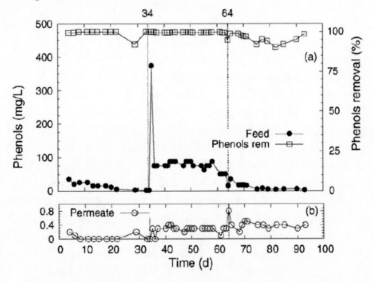

Figure 1. Reactor performance. A) Phenol concentration in the feed and phenol removal efficiency. B) Phenol concentration in the permeates.

This observed efficiency is even greater if we consider that the influent contained significant amounts of NH_4^+-N, which is potentially toxic to sludge microbes and could reduce the efficiency of removal of phenols and organic matter. The removal efficiencies were high, considering that the hydraulic retention time employed was 10 h. Vázquez et al. (2006) described a phenol biodegradation process for coke wastewater treatment using a laboratory-scale activated sludge plant composed of a 20 L volume aerobic reactor, which achieved 96% efficiency with a hydraulic retention time (HRT) of 15 h. A similar membrane bioreactor performance was also described by Barrios-Martinez et al. (2006) who reported a phenol removal efficiency of 100% during the treatment of a synthetic wastewater containing phenols at concentrations of 1000mg L^{-1} using adapted biomass.

The ability to remove large amounts of phenol, together with the good retention of other organic substances, demonstrated the proper performance of the SMBR. This method should be viewed as an alternative to the traditional physical and chemical methods for phenol removal, generally considered to be costly and dangerous to handle (H_2O_2, O_3).

Communities Structure Analysis

The influence of the phenol-shock loading on the SMBR bacterial community was studied by DGGE. Bacterial community changes were detected by isolation of total DNA from activated sludge from SMBR during a 93-day time course of sampling. Twenty-four samples were analyzed: 01 collected at day 34, after acclimatization of the sludge, 12 samples during the phenol-shock loading (days 35 to 63), and 11 samples during the recovery period (days 64 to 93). DGGE banding profiles of the PCR-amplified V3 region of the 16S rDNA were produced from bacterial community DNA extracted from the above activated-sludge samples. Experiments designed to establish the repeatability of DNA extraction and PCR amplification found a 90% to 95% similarity in triplicate independent samples, as determined by analysis of the DGGE patterns (results not shown).

The analysis of complex microbial communities by DGGE technique is limited by the difficulty to extract and amplify by PCR the DNA of unknown communities (Gelsomino et al. 1999) and the possibility of formation of chimeric PCR products (Wang and Wang, 1997), reducing the variability of microorganisms contained in each sample. However, the DGGE fingerprints obtained from the sludge samples collected during the 93 days of SMBR continuous operation detected a great genetic variety of the microorganisms (Figure 2A). The community structure was remarkably dynamic. None of the bands was universally present in the samples, and 24 band classes were detected in over 72% of them, compared to 6 band classes being represented in 18% or less of the samples. DGGE fingerprints were of medium complexity, as 11–22 bands per lane were recorded, distributed in a total of 33 different band classes. This number is within the range reported by previous studies on sludge from MBRs (Stamper et al. 2003; van der Gaast et al. 2006; Molina-Muñoz et al. 2007), but bacterial communities found in aerobic wastewater-treatment systems based on conventional activated sludge or submerged filter biofilms, are usually more complex (Wagner and Loy, 2002; Gómez-Villalba et al. 2006). Bacterial diversity in MBRs has been also found to be strongly influenced by bioreactor volume (van der Gaast et al. 2006), and thus the small volume pilot-scale bioreactor used in this study is expected to naturally support lower levels of diversity than full-scale MBRs.

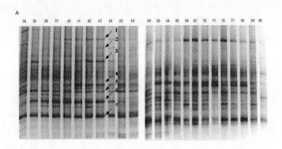

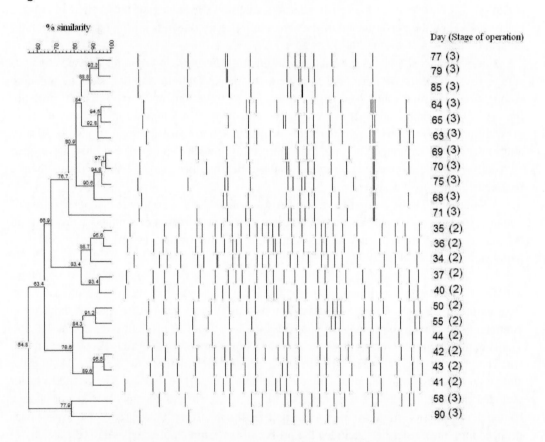

Figure 2. DGGE banding profiles of the V3 region of 16S rDNA produced from bacterial community DNA extracted from different samples of the activated sludge present in MBR during shock loading. A) DGGE was performed as described in Material and Methods, and stained with SYBR Green I. Acclimated activated sludge (lane 34), high phenol-shocked sludge (lanes 35 to 63), and recovered sludge (lanes 64 to 91). Arrows indicate the bands that were sequenced. B) Clustering of the DGGE profiles obtained with universal V3 primer using UPGMA method and Dice's similarity coefficient computed using Gel Compar II v. 5.0 (Applied Maths, Belgium). The scale bar indicates the percentage of similarity.

The results suggested that the bacterial community structure was dynamic and able to adapt to environmental changes. Several researchers have reported that the bacterial community structure of laboratory-scale activated-sludge reactors seeded with sludge from domestic wastewater treatment plants was not static, but constantly changed. Interestingly, this dynamic behavior of the bacterial community of laboratory-scale bioreactors is not observed in full-scale biological treatment plants (Godon et al. 1997; Eichner et al. 1999; Boon et al. 2000; Forney et al. 2001).

LaPara and colleagues (2002), examining the bacterial community structure of seven full-scale biological plants treating pharmaceutical wastewater, showed that the community was stable under normal operating conditions. A stable community structure in full-scale biological treatment plants compared to laboratory-scale activated-sludge reactors could be explained by the equilibrium model of island biogeography, which seeks to establish and explain the factors affecting the species richness of a particular isolated community (Curtis et al. 2003). A consortium of bacterial species is required for achieving the desired biological conversions, and the performance of these reactors largely depends on the bacterial diversity present (Saikaly and Oerther 2004).

This dynamic behavior in the bacterial community structure in laboratory-scale activated-sludge reactors could be attributed to several biotic and abiotic factors, such as resource competition (Huisman and Weissing, 1999; 2001), predation, and new selective pressure imposed on domestic sludge. It is recognized in ecology that competition for three or more growth-limiting resources may generate oscillations and chaotic fluctuations in species abundances (Huisman and Weissing, 2002). Recently, Saikaly and Oerther (2004) developed an ecology-based mathematical model to describe the mechanism behind these chaotic bacterial community structures.

Although the DGGE technique alone does not allow for the complete characterization of complex communities such as that inhabiting wastewater-treatment sludge, it provides an efficient tool to monitor the dynamics of their species composition, as influenced by external parameters (Lyautey et al. 2005).

The hierarchical grouping of bacterial communities carried out using UPGMA method and Dice's similarity coefficient computed using Gel Compar II v. 5.0 (Applied Maths, Belgium) (Fig. 2B), allowed the identification of four clusters that reflect changes in bacterial community following the change in concentration of phenol in effluent fed into the reactor. The community present during the operation at a high phenol loading (day 35 to 63, stage 2) was comprised by two clusters. The first one included the "native" sludge (day 34) and the sludge community from samples collected at days 35, 36, 37 and 40. The second cluster included the samples collected at days 41, 42, 43, 44, 50 and 55. In contrast, the sludge bacterial community from samples collected in the recovery phase (days 64 to 90) was grouped into one cluster that included the profile of the sample collected at day 63 (last day of operation of the high-phenol-loading regimen), and formed three sub-clusters. The fourth cluster was constituted from profiles of the samples collected at day 58 (high-phenol loading) and 90 (recovery), sharing 77.9% similarity, and clustering away from the rest of the samples. These profiles are characterized by a low number of band classes (17 and 9, respectively) and may represent stages of decrease in microbial diversity under changing environmental conditions.

Most of the fingerprints from samples collected during the phenol-shock loading (days 35 to 63) and recovery (days 64 to 90) stages were grouped together, and showed a 54.8% overall similarity. The similarity between the profiles from the high-phenol loading and recovery stages was 63.4% and 76.7%, respectively. As can be observed, genetic diversity decreased during the course of the treatment because, probably, some of the original microorganisms present in the acclimated sludge were selected during the high-phenol-loading step. The plasticity of the microbial community ensured the efficiency of phenol degradation and the successful performance of the SMBR (Fernández et al. 1999). Individual persistent species responsible for these bands would be likely candidates for incorporation into a seed culture and improve bioreactor performance, particularly during startup of wastewater treatment (Stamper et al. 2003).

Communities Shifts During Phenol-Shock Loadings

Dice's similarity coefficient (Cs) computed using Gel Compar II v. 5.0 (Applied Maths, Belgium) was used to evaluate the similarity of the DGGE fingerprints from sludge samples collected during the SMBR operation. The Cs for the "native" sludge (day 34) in comparison to sludge collected at day 63 or day 90 was 49.8% and 88.2%, respectively. A decrease in similarity was observed between the acclimated sludge (34 day) and that collected at the end of the phenol-shock loading (day 63), however, the Cs increased when the acclimated sludge was compared to the recovery loading, on the last operating day (day 90).

Dynamic changes in SMBR communities may be related to the toxicity of phenol to the sludge microorganisms. In petrochemical wastewater treatment plants, phenolic compounds, even at low concentrations, can inhibit microbial growth. Uygur and Kargi, (2004) reported variable inhibition of nutrient removal from wastewater by a sequencing bath reactor (SBR) at different phenol concentrations. Phenol toxicity to microorganisms may be related to the reduction of observed bands in the DGGE samples taken during the high phenol-loading (Fig. 2B, days 41 to 55) or even during the recovery loading (Fig. 2B, days 64 to 85), which may select some resistant species during these periods. However, the structure of bacterial communities in the batch bioreactor was virtually stable throughout the process, according to the analysis of the indexes of similarity comparing the bacterial community present in the SMBR at the high phenol load and recovery load with the 'native' sludge (76.7% and 63.4%) and the large number of bands that remained in the DGGE fingerprints throughout the SMBR operation.

Activated sludge, similarly to the other diverse ecosystems such as sediments and soils, has DGGE banding patterns that are very complex to interpret. Moreover, analyses of similarity are necessary to examine and compare the DGGE fingerprints generated. However, the bands in a DGGE fingerprint do not necessarily give an accurate picture of the number and abundance of the corresponding species within the microbial community. One organism may produce more than one DGGE band because of multiple, heterogeneous rRNA operons (Cilia et al. 1996). On the other hand, partial 16S rDNA sequences amplification does not always allow discrimination between species, since one DGGE band may represent several species with identical partial 16S rDNA sequences (Naeem and Li, 1997). In addition, in a mixture of target rDNAs with different concentrations, the less-abundant sequences cannot be sufficiently amplified to be observed. For this reason, the banding pattern reflects only the most abundant rDNA types in the microbial community (Huisman and Weissing, 1999). Therefore, the similarity index calculated from the DGGE fingerprints of amplified 16S rDNA sequences must be interpreted as an indication and not an absolute measure of the degree of complexity in a bacterial community (Curtis and Sloan, 2004). In our study, the DGGE fingerprints were related to samples taken from the same "native sludge" exposed to different concentrations of phenol, and not from environmental samples collected in diverse ecosystems. The equal band intensities in samples collected during SMBR operation at the same feed condition indicated the absence of preferential amplification. Furthermore, there is no evidence of chimera or heteroduplex formation, since no additional bands were detected in the DGGE profiles.

The PCR-DGGE results presented herein indicate that functionally stable wastewater treatment bioreactors also have stable microbial community structures and are capable of adapting in response to perturbations. We believe that PCR-DGGE combined with another nucleic acid-based technique (e.g., ARDRA and *in situ* hybridization) can be used in future research to develop a mechanistic understanding of the relationships between reactor operational strategies, microbial community structure, and reactor performance.

Phylogenetic Analysis

A total of seven bands from the shock-loading period (day 43 – Fig. 2A, indicated by arrows) were isolated from the DGGE gels, reamplified, and sequenced. The resulting nucleotide sequences were compared to those filed in the RPD database. Table 1 shows the identified sequences, which are mostly related to the Alpha-proteobacteria (bands 1, 3, 4 and 5) and Gamma-proteobacteria (bands 2, 6 and 7). Sequencing of DGGE bands corresponding to the dominant population in the sludge community profiles showed the prevalence of genus *Acetobacter* in all the experiments, in spite of the different operation conditions applied.

Table 1. Seven prominent bands present in DGGE profiles of the V3 region of the 16S rDNA from activated sludge present in MBR during shock loading (Fig. 2A, indicated by arrows) were excised from the gel, and the isolated DNA was amplified by PCR using primers 968F (without the GC clamp) and 1401R, and sequenced in an ABI PRISM 3100 Avant Genetic Analyzer. Nucleotide sequences were used to identify the putative donator by using SeqMatch from the Ribosomal Database Project (http://rdp.cme.msu.edu/seqmatch). Accession number is from GenBank

Band	Phylum	Class	Order	Family	Genus	Accession number
1	Proteo-Bacteria	Alpha-proteobacteria	Rhodospirillales	Acetobacteraceae	*Acetobacter*	AP011121
2	Proteo-Bacteria	Gamma-proteobacteria	Chromatiales	Halothiobacillaceae	*Thiofaba*	DQ415810
3	Proteo-Bacteria	Alpha-proteobacteria	Rhodospirillales	Acetobacteraceae	*Acetobacter*	AP011163
4	Proteo-Bacteria	Alpha-proteobacteria	Rhodobacterales	Acetobacteraceae	*Acetobacter*	AP011121
5	Proteo-Bacteria	Alpha-proteobacteria	Rhodospirillales	Acetobacteraceae	*Acetobacter*	AP011135
6	Proteo-Bacteria	Gamma-proteobacteria	Xanthomonadales	Xanthomonadaceae	*Aquimonas*	GQ354936
7	Proteo-bacteria	Gamma-proteobacteria	Xanthomonadales	Xanthomonadaceae	*Thermomonas*	GQ389149

Geng et al. (2006) previously described the genus *Acinetobacter* as a novel phenol-degrading bacterium isolated from an activated sludge from an industrial wastewater treatment plant. The authors used a culture-enrichment technique. Jiang et al. (2004) used both culture-based and culture-independent technique to investigate the bacterial diversity cultivated in a sequencing batch reactor. The phylogenetic analysis indicated that the isolates felt into three major lineages of the Bacteria domain: the Beta and Gamma proteobacteria, and gram-positive high- G+C bacteria. In the present study, we showed that in the dominant populations in the sludge community profiles, there was a prevalence of Alpha and Gamma proteobacteria. Although the Alpha proteobacteria comprised the majority, the presence of Gamma proteobacteria agrees with the previous work of Bramucci et al. (2003), who also found this class using methodologies entirely based on the culture approach. In our study, the bacteria could not be unambiguously identified to species level, suggesting that most of the bacteria in our SMBR sludge have not been cultured or identified.

CONCLUSIONS

This study demonstrated the performance of a membrane bioreactor (SMBR) using previously activated sludge, for the degradation of an industrial effluent from an oil refinery, containing high phenol concentration (85 mg L-1). The good performance of the SMBR was accompanied by changes in the structure of bacterial communities present in the sludge. The use of PCR-DGGE allowed monitoring of these changes in the bacterial communities. Dominant members of the bacterial community in the SMBR were identified as belonging to the Alpha and Gamma proteobacteria. The integration of the fingerprint data with statistical tools showed that the bacterial community could adapt to the adverse environmental conditions during operation wastewater-treatment operation, sustained high effluent quality functionally keeping the reactor wastewater treatment stable in response to changing characteristics of wastewater effluent.

The finding that operation and environmental parameters mostly influenced the evolution of the structure of the microbial populations in the SMBR, and the impact of these community features on bioreactor performance and quality of the sludge, contributes to the understanding of the community-function relationships, and will aid in improving the performance of the bioreactors.

REFERENCES

Amann, R. I.; Ludwig, W.; Schkeifer K. H. (1995). Phylogenetic identification and in situ detection of individual microbial cells without cultivation. *Microbiology, 59,* 143-169.

Amann, R.; Glockner, F. O.; Neef, A. (1997). Modern methods in subsurface microbiology: in situ identification of microorganisms with nucleic acid probes. *FEMS Microbiology Reviews, 20,* 191-200.

Banerjee, G. (1997). Treatment of phenolic wastewater in RBD reactor, *Water Research, 31,* 705-714.

Barrios-Martinez, A.; Barbot, E.; Marrot, B.; Moulin, P.; Roche, N. (2006). Degradation of synthetic phenol-containing wastewater by MBR. *Journal of Membrane Science, 281,* 288-296.

Bramucci, M.; Kane, H.; Chen, M.; Nagarajan, V. (2003). Bacterial diversity in an industrial wastewater bioreactors. *Applied Microbiology Biotechnology, 62*, 594-600.

Boon, N. J.; Goris, P.; De Vos, W.; Verstraete, K.; Top, E. M. (2000). Bioaugmentation of activated sludge by an indigenous 3-chloroanilinedegrading Comamonas testosteroni strain. *Applied Environmental Microbiology, 66,* 2906-2913.

Cilia, V.; Lafay, B.; Christen, R. (1996). Sequence heterogeneities among 16S ribosomal RNA sequences, and their effect on phylogenetic analyses at the species level. *Molecular Biology Evolution. 13,* 451-461.

Cortés-Lorenzo, C.; Molina-Muñoz, M.L.; Gómez-Lillalba, B.; Vilchez, R.; Ramos, A.; Rodelas, B. (2006). Analysis of community compostion of biofilms in a submerged filter system for the removal of ammonia and phenol from industrial wastewater. *Biochemical Society Transactions, 334,*165-168.

Choi, H.; Kim, H.-S.; Yeom, L.-C.; Dionysiou, D. D. (2005). Pilot plant study of an ultrafiltration membrane system for drinking water treatment operated in the feed-and-bleed mode, *Desalination, 172,* 281-291.

Chiemchaisri, C.; Wong, Y. K.; Urase, T.; Yamamoto, K. (1992). Organic Stabilization and Nitrogen Removal in Membrane Separation Bioreactor for Domestic Wastewater Treatment. *Water Science and Technology, 25,* 231-240.

CONAMA, (2005). Resolução 357, *Diário Oficial da União*, *53,* 58-63.

Curtis, T. P.; Head, I. M.; Graham, D. W. (2003). Theoretical Ecology for engineering biology. *Environmental Science and Technology, 37*, 64-70.

Curtis, T. P. and Sloan W. T. (2004). Prokaryotic diversity and its limits: microbial community structure in nature and implications for microbial ecology. *Current Opinion in Microbiology, 7*, 221-226.

Eichner, C. A.; Erb, R. W.; Timmis, K. N.; Wagner-Dobler, I. (1999). Thermal gradient gel electrophoresis analysis of bioprotection from pollutant shocks in the activated sludge microbial community. *Applied Environmental Microbiology, 65,* 102-109.

Fernández, A.; Huang, S.; Seston, S.; Xing, J.; Hickey, R.; Criddle, C.; Tiedje, J. (1999). How stable is stable? Function versus community composition. *Applied Environmental Microbiology, 65,* 3697-3704.

Forney, L. J.; Liu, W. T.; Guckert, J. B.; Kumagai, Y.; Namkung, E.; Nishihara, T.; Larson, R. J. (2001). Structure of microbial communities in activated sludge: Potential implications for assessing the biodegradability of chemicals. *Ecotoxicology and Environmental Safety, 49,* 40-53.

Gelsomino, A.; Keijzer-Wolters, A. C.; Cacco, G.; van Elsas, J. D. (1999). Assessment of bacterial community structure in soil by polymerase chain reaction and denaturing gradient gel electrophoresis. *Journal of Microbiological Methods, 38,* 1-15.

Geng, A.; Soh, A. E. W.; Lim, C. J.; Loke, L. C. T. (2006). Isolation and characterization of a phenol-degrading bacterium from an industrial activated sludge. *Applied Microbiology Biotechnology, 71,* 728-735.

Giovannoni, S. J.; Britschgi, T. B.; Moyer, C. L.; Field, K. G. (1991). Genetic diversity in Sargasso Sea bacterioplankton, *Nature, 345,* 60-63.

Gobel, A.; McArdell, C. S.; Joss, A.; Siegrist, H.; Giger, W. (2007). Fate of sulfonamides, macrolides and trimethoprim in different wastewater treatment technologies. *Science Total Environment, 372,* 361-371.

Godon, J. J.; Zumstein, E.; Dabert, P.; Habouzit, F.; Moletta, R. (1997). Microbial 16S rDNA diversity in an anaerobic digester. *Water Science Technology, 36,* 49-55.

Gómez-Vilalba, B.; Calvo, C.; Vilchez R.; González-López J.; Rodelas, B. (2006). TGGE analysis of the diversity of ammonia-oxidizing and denitrifying bacteria in submerged filter biofilms for the treatment of urban wastewater. *Applied Microbiology Biotechnology, 72,* 393-400.

González, G.; Herrera, G.; García, M. T.; Peña, M. (2001). Biodegradation of phenolic industrial wastewater in a fluidized bed bioreactor with immobilized cells of *Pseudomonas putida, Bioresource Technology, 80,* 137-142.

Hsien, T.-Y. and Lin, Y.-H. (2005). Biodegradation of phenolic wastewater in a fixed biofilm reactor, *Biochemical Engineering Journal. 27,* 95-103.

Huisman, J. and Weissing, F. J. (1999). Biodiversity of plankton by species oscillations and chaos. *Nature, 402,* 407-410.

Huisman, J. and Weissing, F. J. (2001). Biological conditions for oscillations and chaos generated by multispecies competition. *Ecology, 82,* 2682-2695.

Huisman, J. and Weissing, F. J. (2002). Oscillations and chaos generated by competition for interactively essential resources. *Evolutionary Ecology Research, 17,* 175-181.

Jiang, H-L.; Tay, J-H.; Maszenan, A. M.; Tay, S. T. L. (2004). Bacterial diversity and function of aerobic granules engineered in a sequencing batch reactor for phenol degradation. *Applied Environment Microbiology, 70,* 6767-6775.

Jou, C.-J. G. and Huang, G.-C. (2003). A pilot study for oil refinery wastewater using a fixed-film bioreactor. *Advances in Environmental Research, 7,* 463-469.

Laera, G.; Pollice, A.; Saturno, D.; Giordano, C.; Lopez, A. (2005). Zero net growth in a membrane bioreactor with complete sludge retention. *Water Research, 39,* 5241-5249.

LaPara, T. M.; Nakatsy, C. H.; Pantea, L. M.; Allegan, J. E. (2002). Stability of the bacterial communities supported by a seven-stage biological process treating pharmaceutical wastewater as revealed by PCR-DGGE. *Water Research, 36,* 638-646.

Liu, X.-C.; Yang, M.; Zhang, Y. (2007). Microbial community comparison of different biological processes for treating the same sewage. *Word Journal Microbiology Biotechnology, 23,* 135-143.

Lobos, J.; Wisniewshi, C.; Heran, M.; Grasmick, A. (2005). Effects of starvation conditions on biomass behaviour for minimization of sludge production in membrance bioreactors. *Water Science Technology, 51,* 35-44.

Lyautey, E.; Lacoste, B.; Ten-Hage, L.; Rols, J-L.; Garabetian, F. (2005). Analysis of bacterial diversity in river biofilms using 16S rDNA PCR-DGGE: methodological settings and fingerprints interpretation. *Water Research, 39,* 380-388.

Margesin, R.; Fonteyne, P. A.; Redl, B. (2005). Low-temperature biodegradation of high amounts of phenol by Rhodococcus spp. and basidiomycetous yeasts, *Research in Microbiology, 156,* 68-75.

Melvin, W. T. and Hobson, P. N. (1994). Identification of anaerobic digester bacteria using a polymerase chain reaction method. *Bioresource Technology, 47,* 73-80.

Miura, Y.; Hiraiwa, M. N.; Ito, T.; Itonaga, T.; Watanabe, Y.; Okabe, S. (2007). Bacterial community structures in MBRs treating municipal wastewater relationship between community stability and reactor performance. *Water Research, 41*, 627-37.

Molina-Muñoz, M.; Poyatos, J. M.; Vílchez, R.; Hontoria, E.; Rodelas, B.; González-López, J. (2007). Effect of the concentration of suspended solids on the enzymatic activities and biodiversity of a submerged membrane bioreactor for aerobic treatment of domestic wastewater. *Applied Microbiology Biotechnology, 73*, 1441-1451.

Naeem, S. and Li, S. B. (1997). Biodiversity enhances ecosystem reliability. *Nature 390*, 507-509.

Nuhoglu, A. and Yalcin, B. (2005). Modelling of phenol removal in a batch reactor, *Process Biochemistry, 40*, 1233-1239.

Nubel, U.; Engelen, B.; Felske, A.; Snaidr, J.; Wieshuber, A.; Amann, R. I.; Ludwig, W.; Backhaus, H. (1996). Sequence heterogeneities of genes encoding 16S rRNAs in *Paenibacillus polymyxa* detected by temperature gradiente gel eletrophoresis. *Journal of Bacteriology, 178*, 5636-5643.

Prieto, M. B.; Hidalgo, A.; Serra, J. L.; Llama, M. J. (2002). Degradation of phenol by Rhodococcus erytropolis UPV-1 immobilized on Biolite in a packed-bed reactor, *Journal of Biotechnology, 97*, 1-11.

Saikaly, P. E. and Oerther, D. B. (2004). Bacterial competition in activated sludge: Theoretical analysis of varying solids retention times on diversity. *Microbial Ecology, 48*, 274-284.

Schneider, R.P. and Tsutiya, M.T. (2001). Membranas Filtrantes para o Tratamento de Água, Esgoto e Água de Reuso. 1 edition, São Paulo, Brasil, Associação Brasileira de Engenharia Sanitária e Ambiental-ABES, 234.

Schwartz, M. W.; Brigham, C. A.; Hoeksema, J. D.; Lyons, J. D.; Mills, M. H.; van Mantgeni, P. J. (2000). Linking biodiversity to ecosystem function: implications for conservation ecology. *Oecologia, 122*, 297-305.

Stamper, D. M.; Walch, M.; Jacobs, R. N. (2003). Bacterial Population changes in a membrance bioreactor for graywater treatment monitored by denaturing gradient gel electrophoretic analysis of 16S rRNA gene fragments. *Applied Environmental Microbiology, 69*, 852-860.

Standard Methods for the Examination of Water and Wastewater. (1998). American Public Health Association and American Water Works Association and Water Pollution Control Federation, 20th edition, Washington, DC.

Torsvik, V.; Goksoyr, J.; Daae, F. L. (1990). High diversity in DNA of soil bacteria, *Applied Environmental Microbiology, 56*, 782-787.

Ueda, T. and Horan, N. J. (2000). Fate of indigenous bacteriophage in a membrane bioreactor. *Water Research, 34*, 2151-2159.

van der Gaast, C. J.; Reid, J. B. E.; Bailey, M. R. T.; Judd, S. J. (2006). Bacterial diversity is determined by volume in membrane bioreactors. *Environment Microbiology, 8*, 1048-1055.

Vázquez, I.; Rodríguez, J.; Marañón, E.; Castrillón, L.; Fernández, Y. (2006). Simultaneous removal of phenol, ammonium and thiocyanate from coke wastewater by aerobic biodegradation. *Journal of Hazardous Materials, 137*, 1773-1780.

Viero, A. F.; Melo, T. M.; Torres, A. P. R.; Ferreira, N. M.; Sant'Anna Jr. G. L.; Borges, C. P.; Santiago, V. M. J. (2008). The effects of long-term feeding of high organic loading in a submerged membrane bioreactor treating oil refinery wastewater. *Journal of Membrane Science, 319*, 223-230.

Wang, G.C.-Y. and Wang, Y. (1997). Frequency of formation of chimeric molecules as a consequence of PCR coamplification of 16S rRNA genes from mixed bacterial communities. *Applied Environmental Microbiology, 63*, 4645-4650.

Wagner, M. and Loy, A. (2002). Bacterial community composition and function in sewage treatment systems. *Current Opinion in Biotechnology, 13*, 218-227.

Witzig, R.; Manz, W.; Rosenberger, S.; Krugerb, U.; Kraumeb, M.; Szewzyk, U. (2002). Microbiological aspects of a bioreactor with submerged membranes for aerobic treatment of municipal wastewater. *Water Research, 36,* 394-402.

Uygur, A. and Kargi, F. (2004). Phenol inhibition of biological nutrient removal in a four-step sequencing batch reactor. *Process Biochemistry, 39*, 2123-2128.

In: Water Production and Wastewater Treatment
Editor: B. Antizar-Ladislao et al.

ISBN 978-1-61728-503-5
© 2011 Nova Science Publishers, Inc.

Chapter 4

BIOSORPTION OF CD (II) AND NI (II) FROM AQUEOUS SOLUTIONS BY *CYSTOSEIRA INDICA*

M.M. Montazer-Rahmati [a]*, *P. Rabbani* [a] and *A. Abdolali* [a]

a School of Chemical Engineering, College of Engineering,
University of Tehran, Tehran, Iran, 11155-4563

ABSTRACT

Toxic heavy metal contamination of industrial wastewater is an important environmental problem. Many industries, such as automotive, electroplating, battery manufacturing, mining, electric cable manufacturing, tannery, steel and textile industries release various concentrations of heavy metals such as nickel, cadmium, lead, mercury and copper, etc. into natural waters. These heavy metals are toxic to the aquatic ecosystem and human health even at low concentrations as a result of accumulation in organisms beyond tolerance levels. In this chapter, different methods for uptake of heavy metal ions from aqueous solutions are introduced and biosorption as an effective and low cost method of removing nickel and cadmium ions from synthetic wastewater is discussed. For metal biosorption, brown algae possessing a high content of ioniziable functional groups such as carboxyl, alcohol and amino groups specifically have been previously identified as very promising biosorbents for removing heavy metal ions from synthetic and natural aqueous solutions. The biosorption of brown marine algae, Cystoseira indica, both intact and pretreated by crosslinking with formaldehyde (FA) has been studied. Experimental results have been obtained from batch equilibrium tests. The optimum sorption conditions have been determined and results show that the highest biosorption capacities (19.42 mg/g and 10.06 mg/g for Cd (II) and Ni (II), respectively) onto FA-treated Cystoseira indica (2g/L) are obtained at an optimum pH of 5.5 and 6.0 for Cd (II) and Ni (II), respectively. In the experiments carried out, the initial metal concentration was 0.5 mmol/L, while contact time was about 120 min. One-way ANOVA and one sample t-tests were performed on experimental data to evaluate the statistical significance of biosorption capacities after five sorption and desorption cycles. To describe the biosorption isotherms, the Langmuir, Freundlich, Toth, and Radke-Prausnitz isotherm models were applied. The results fit well to the Radke-Prausnitz and the Toth

---

*Corresponding author. Tel.: +98-21-61113217 Fax: +98-21-66957784. E-mail address: mrahmati@ut.ac.ir.

isotherms for Cd (II) and Ni (II), respectively. The kinetic data were fitted by models including pseudo-first-order and pseudo-second-order. The pseudo-second-order kinetic model describes the biosorption of cadmium and nickel ions quite well.

1. INTRODUCTION

Heavy metals are major pollutants that are released into the natural environment as wastes from industrial processes and have resulted in a number of environmental problems. Cadmium and nickel are among the heavy metals that are used widely. Cadmium is extremely toxic even at low concentrations [1-3]. The industrial uses of these metals are in plastics, alloy preparation, wood treating, and covered metalworking operations, paint pigments, mining, ceramics, electroplating and batteries; therefore, they pose a significant potential hazard to the environment and human beings [4]. Since heavy metals cannot be annihilated in the natural environment, there is a need for new technologies that can remove and recover heavy metals from wastewaters [3, 5]. At present, a number of technologies such as adsorption, chemical precipitation, electroplating, and ion exchange are used for the treatment of wastewater streams containing heavy metals [2, 4]. But when heavy metal concentrations in the wastewater are low, these methods are not effective and are very expensive when the concentration of heavy metals in the effluent is very low [6]. Biosorption has been found to be a feasible economical alternative as a wastewater treatment process for metal removal [6-8]. It has been reported that the biomass of brown algae has a metal binding capacity higher than the other types of biosorbents such as fungi, bacteria and yeast [1, 9].

The mechanism of binding metal ions by algal biomass may depend on the species and ionic charges of the metal ions, the algal organisms, the chemical composition of the metal ion solution and other external environmental factors such as pH and temperature.

The purpose of this chapter is to study cadmium (II) and nickel (II) removal from aqueous solutions by both intact and pre-treated brown algae from the Persian Gulf. The biosorption process was analyzed through batch experiments. The influence of pH, modification and contact time was studied. Also sorption and desorption experiments were carried out. In order to investigate the sorption behaviour, various kinetic and isotherm models were studied.

1.1. Physico-Chemical Methods for Heavy Metal Removal

Different treatment techniques for wastewater containing heavy metals have been developed in recent years both to decrease the amount of wastewater produced and to improve the quality of the treated effluent. Although various treatments such as chemical precipitation, coagulation–flocculation, floatation, ion exchange and membrane filtration can be employed to remove heavy metals from contaminated wastewater, they have their inherent advantages and limitations in application [10].

1.1.1. Chemical Precipitation

As metals enter the treatment process, they are in a stable, dissolved aqueous form and are unable to form solids. The goal of metal treatment by hydroxide precipitation is then to adjust the pH (hydroxide ion concentration) of the water so that the metals will form insoluble precipitates. Once the metals precipitate and form solids, they can then be removed easily, and the water, now having a low metal concentration, can be discharged.

Metal precipitation is primarily dependent upon two factors: the concentration of the metal, and the pH of the water. Heavy metals are usually present in wastewaters in dilute quantities (1-100 mg/L) and at neutral or acidic pH values (< 7.0). Both of these factors are disadvantageous with regard to metal removal. However, when one adds caustic to water containing dissolved metals, the metals react with hydroxide ions to form metal hydroxide solids.

Some variations in the exact values of the metal concentrations will occur due to the presence of other substances in the wastewater. Compounds such as cyanide or ammonia can inhibit precipitation of metals, and limit their removal to the point where discharge limits can be exceeded. Also, not all metals have the same minimum solubility. Therefore, in a wastewater containing various metals, as a general rule, pH should be adjusted to an average value of approximately 9.

However, the metals now exist in another phase or state (i.e., as small solid particles). Metal removal is not complete until these metal solids are physically removed from the wastewater, typically by subsequent sedimentation and filtration.

Metal removal occurs through the use of several unit operations:

In the first step the wastewater enters the rapid mix unit. The goal of the rapid mix operation is to first raise the wastewater pH to form metal hydroxide particles, as discussed above. After the addition of caustic, the next step is to add aluminium or iron salts, or organic polymers (coagulants) directly into the wastewater. These polymers attach to the solid metal particles.

The small metal hydroxide particles become entangled in these polymers, causing the particle size to increase (form flocs), thus promoting the settling process.

Once particles become enmeshed in the polymer, they are allowed to settle so that they can be removed from the wastewater. The particles settle since they are heavier than water. Settling occurs in the sedimentation tanks.

Sedimentation tanks, in contrast to rapid mixing units, are designed to have no mixing and to provide a calm flow for settling.

Water emerging from the sedimentation basin is routed to the filtration unit.

The filtration unit is designed to trap those particles that did not settle in the sedimentation basin (because they were too small) or did not have sufficient time to settle and were carried out of the basin.

Water entering the filtration unit is passed through silica sand, diatomaceous earth, carbon, or cloth to capture the remaining metal hydroxide particles. Metal particles stick to the filtering material and are removed from the water. Filtration completes the metal treatment process. Only now should the pH be reduced for discharge, if necessary, or the pH can now be adjusted for water reuse.

The solids produced in the sedimentation stage (and possibly solids from filtration) are denoted as a sludge and periodically removed. In diatomaceous earth and fiber filters, the entire filter media (diatomaceous earth, filter cartridge) is dumped with the captured metal hydroxide solids. This sludge may be sent to a dewatering stage to remove excess water and leave only solids. The water from the dewatering stage may not be completely free of metals and should be piped to the rapid mix tank.

The sludge now contains the precipitated metal hydroxide solids, made up of identifiable quantities of heavy metals, which are regulated according to applicable guidelines. The solids produced from heavy metal wastewater treatment must then be disposed of as a hazardous waste.

The applicability of hydroxide precipitation in a closed system was studied to remove Cd (II) and Cu (II) ions from synthetic wastewater [7]. Inorganic cations (Ca (II) and Na) were employed as ligand-sharing agents for EDTA (Ethylene Diamine Tetraacetic Acid) and NTA (Nitrilo Triacetic Acid). It was reported that Ca (II) was the only cation that could effectively bond with both ligands to form hydroxide precipitates of the complexed metals. Another study by Papadopoulos et al. [11] pertains to experiments carried out for Ni (II) removal from a low-strength real wastewater using hydroxide precipitation.

1.1.2. Membrane Filtration

Membrane filtration has received considerable attention for the treatment of inorganic effluents, since it is capable of removing not only suspended solid and organic compounds, but also inorganic contaminants such as heavy metals. Depending on the size of the particles that can be retained, various types of membrane filtration such as ultra-filtration (UF), nano-filtration (NF) and reverse osmosis can be employed for heavy metal removal.

UF utilizes permeable membranes to separate heavy metals, macromolecules and suspended solids from inorganic solutions based on the pore size (5–20 nm) and molecular weight of the compounds to be separated (1000–100,000). These unique capabilities enable UF to allow the passage of water and low-molecular weight solutes, while retaining the macromolecules, having a size larger than the pore size of the membrane [12].

Depending on the membrane characteristics, UF has a removal efficiency of more than 90% with a metal concentration ranging from 10 to 112 mg/L at pH values ranging from 5 to 9.5 and at pressures in the range of 2–5 bars. Although UF needs a lower driving force and smaller space, this method has high operating costs.

1.1.2.1. Reverse Osmosis

Reverse osmosis (RO) is a separation process that uses pressure to force a solution through a membrane that retains the solute on one side and allows the pure solvent to pass to the other side. More formally, it is the process of forcing a solvent from a region of high solute concentration through a membrane to a region of low solute concentration by applying a pressure in excess of the osmotic pressure. This is the reverse of the normal osmosis process, which is the natural movement of solvent from an area of low solute concentration, through a membrane, to an area of high solute concentration when no external pressure is applied. The membrane is semi-permeable, meaning it allows the passage of solvent but not of solute.

The membranes used for reverse osmosis have a dense barrier layer in the polymer matrix where most separation occurs. In most cases the membrane is designed to allow only water to pass through this dense layer while preventing the passage of solutes (such as salt ions). This process requires that a high pressure be exerted on the high concentration side of the membrane [13, 14].

1.1.2.2. Nanofiltration

Nanofiltration has unique properties compared with UF and RO membranes. Its separation mechanism involves steric (sieving) and electrical (Donnan) effects. A Donnan potential is created between the charged anions in the NF membrane and the co-ions in the effluent to reject the latter [15]. The significance of this membrane lies in its small pore and membrane surface charge, allowing charged solutes smaller than the membrane pores to be rejected along with the bigger neutral solutes and salts.

Ahn et al. [16] worked on Ni (II) ion removal from real electroplating wastewater using NTR-7250 membranes in order to evaluate polyvinyl alcohol as the skin materials of the NF membrane. They found that the removal of Ni (II) depended on the initial metal concentrations and the applied pressure. Moreover, from their experiments, it was observed that beyond a pressure of 2.9 bars, the removal of Ni (II) did not improve with increasing pressure, therefore it was suggested that 2.9 bars was the optimum pressure for NF application to remove Ni (II) ions from wastewater.

A comparative study of Cu (II) and Cd (II) removal from synthetic wastewater using nanofiltration (NF) and reverse osmosis (RO) has been conducted [17]. At the same initial metal concentration, while NF was capable of removing only 90% of Cu (II) and 97% of Cd (II); 98% of Cu (II) removal and 99% of Cd (II) removal could be achieved using RO. These results indicate that both types of membrane filtration are effective for metal removal from contaminated wastewater. Nevertheless, NF requires lower pressures than RO, making NF more preferable due to its lower operating costs.

Depending on the membrane specifications, NF can effectively remove heavy metal ions with a concentration of approximately 2000 ppm at a wide pH range of 3–8 and at pressures of 3–4 bars. However, NF is less intensively investigated than UF and RO for the removal of heavy metals [18].

1.1.3. Coagulation–Flocculation

Coagulation–flocculation can be employed to treat wastewater. Principally, the coagulation process destabilizes colloidal particles by adding a coagulant and results in sedimentation. To increase the particle size, coagulation is followed by the flocculation of the unstable particles into bulky floccules [19]. The general approach for this technique includes pH adjustment and involves the addition of ferric/alum salts as the coagulant to overcome the repulsive forces between particles [20].

In general, coagulation–flocculation can treat inorganic effluents with a metal concentration of less than 100 mg/L or higher than 1000 mg/L.

Improved sludge settling, dewatering characteristics, bacterial inactivation capability, sludge stability are reported to be the major advantages of lime-based coagulation. In spite of its many advantages, the coagulation–flocculation process has disadvantages such as high operating costs due to chemical consumption. The increased volume of sludge generated from the coagulation–flocculation process may hinder its adoption as a global strategy for wastewater treatment. This can be attributed to the fact that the toxic sludge must be converted into a stabilized product to prevent heavy metals from leaking into the environment [21].

To overcome such problems, electro-coagulation may be a better alternative than the conventional coagulation, as it can remove the smallest colloidal particles and produce just a small amount of sludge [22,23]. However, this technique also creates a floc of metallic hydroxides, requiring further purification and making the recovery of valuable heavy metals impossible.

1.1.4. Ion-Exchange

Ion exchange is a reversible chemical reaction wherein an ion (an atom or molecule that has lost or gained an electron and thus acquired an electrical charge) from solution is exchanged for a similarly charged ion attached to an immobile solid particle. These solid ion exchange particles are either naturally occurring inorganic zeolites or synthetically produced organic resins. The synthetic organic resins are the predominant type used today because their characteristics can be tailored to specific applications.

An organic ion exchange resin is composed of high-molecular-weight polyelectrolytes that can exchange their mobile ions for ions of similar charge from the surrounding medium. Each resin has a distinct number of mobile ion sites that set the maximum quantity of exchanges per unit of resin.

Ion exchange reactions are stoichiometric and reversible, and in that sense they are similar to other solution phase reactions.

Unlike chemical precipitation, ion exchange does not present any sludge disposal problems [24], thus lowering the operating costs for the disposal of the residual metal sludge. Other advantages of ion exchange include convenience for fieldwork since the required equipment is portable, the speciation results are reliable and the experiments can be done quickly. Resins also have certain ligands that can selectively bond with certain metal cations, making ion exchange easy to use and less time-consuming [25].

Despite these advantages, ion exchange also has some limitations in treating wastewater laden with heavy metals. Prior to ion exchange, appropriate pretreatment systems for secondary effluent such as the removal of suspended solids from wastewater are required. In addition, suitable ion exchange resins are not available for all heavy metals, while the capital and operating costs are high [26].

1.1.5. Adsorption

Recently, adsorption has become one of the alternative treatment techniques for wastewater laden with heavy metals [27]. Basically, adsorption is a mass transfer process by which a substance is transferred from the liquid phase to the surface of a solid, and becomes bound by physical and/or chemical interactions [10]. Due to its large surface area, high adsorption capacity and surface reactivity, adsorption using activated carbon can remove metals from inorganic effluents.

Activated carbons are more effective in the removal of heavy metals due to some specific characteristics that enhance the use of activated carbon for the removal of contaminants including heavy metals from water supplies and wastewater [28]. Natural materials that are available in large quantities or certain waste products from industrial operations [29] and agricultural by-products [30, 31] may have potential as inexpensive adsorbents. Generally, adsorbents can be assumed as low cost if they require little processing, are abundant in nature, or are a by-product or waste material from another industry [32].

In general, technical applicability and cost-effectiveness are the key factors that play major roles in the selection of the most suitable adsorbent to treat inorganic effluents.

1.1.6. Evaporation

Evaporation is a process in which the effluent is heated as much as possible and the concentration of solids in it increases as a result of partial evaporation. The steam produced can be used for power generation or changed to liquid to be reused again.

For evaporation of effluents, a large place is needed leading to high investment costs. Besides the high fixed and operating costs, this process is very time consuming.

In this method, metals are not separated individually, so a concentrated sludge consisting of all the metals is produced. Therefore, an auxiliary method such as ion-exchange is required for separating particular metals.

However, all the methods discussed so far have several disadvantages; which include incomplete metal removal and toxic sludge generation or other waste products that require disposal. On the other hand, the use of artificially prepared ion exchange resins is effective, but too expensive to be applied on industrial scale. These techniques, apart from being expensive, have other disadvantages such as high reagent and energy requirements.

For this reason, the potential of a new method of removing heavy metals using biosorbents may provide an important breakthrough [33].

In Table 1, the different heavy metal uptake methods are compared and their advantages and disadvantages are presented.

1.1.7. Biosorption

Heavy metal removal from wastewater by the adsorption process has a short history compared to other methods of water purification [34]. The potential of algae biosorption is beginning to be recognized both for the recovery of valuable metals and also for reducing pollution [35].

The potential of adsorption was first observed by Lowitz in 1785 and was soon applied as a process for removal of color from sugar during refining.

In the second half of the nineteenth century, American water treatment plants used non-activated charcoal filters for water purification. In 1929 the first granular activated carbon (GAC) units for treatment of water supplies were constructed in Hamm, Germany, and in 1930 at Bay City, Michigan. Inasmuch as the cost of activated carbon was so high as to limit its use in adsorption, a number of studies for a low-cost and readily available adsorbent led to the investigation of agricultural and biological materials as potential metal sorbents. Biosorption is the ability of certain types of microbial biomass to adsorb heavy metals from aqueous solutions. Biosorbents may be viewed as natural ion-exchange materials that primarily contain weakly acidic and basic groups [34].

In recent decades, several investigators [9, 36-38] have reported the ability of metal removal of natural materials such as rice, coconut husks, peat moss, peanut skin, waste tea leaves, sugar cane bagasse, carrot and orange peels, and so on. Many studies have shown that nonliving plant biomass materials are effective for the removal of trace metals from the environment [39].

Live or dead biomass can be used as an adsorbent for removal of toxic metal ions from aqueous solutions. The efficiency of dead cells in biosorbing metal ions may be greater, equivalent to, or less than that of living cells and may depend on factors such as biosorbent properties, the pre-treatment method used, and the type of metal ion being studied.

Table 1. Summary of the applicability of various physico–chemical techniques for wastewater treatment [10]

Type of treatment	Target of removal	Advantages	Disadvantages
Chemical precipitation	Heavy metals, divalent metals	Low capital cost, simple operation	Sludge generation, extra operational cost for sludge disposal
Coagulation–flocculation	Heavy metals and suspended solids	Shorter time to settle out suspended solids, improved sludge settling	Sludge production, extra operational cost for sludge disposal
Evaporation	Heavy metals and suspended solids	Using the generated steam in utilities	Sludge production, Subsequent treatments are required to improve the removal efficiency of heavy metals, high cost
Ion exchange	Dissolved compounds, cations/anions	No sludge generation, less time consuming	Not all ion exchange resins are suitable for metal removal, high capital cost
Ultrafiltration	High molecular weight compounds (1000–10000)	Smaller space requirement	High operational cost, prone to membrane fouling
Nanofiltration	Sulphate salts and hardness ions such as Ca(II) and Mg(II)	Lower pressure than RO (7–30 bar)	Costly, prone to membrane fouling
Reverse osmosis	Organic and inorganic compounds	High rejection rate, able to withstand high temperature	High energy consumption due to high pressure required (20–100 bar), susceptible to membrane fouling
Biosorption	Heavy metals	Efficient in very low concentration of heavy metals in dead and alive biomasses, low cost, simple operation and less time consuming	Subsequent treatments are required to improve the removal efficiency of heavy metal for tapped water

The use of dead cells over live cells offers the following advantages:

- The metal removal system is not subject to toxicity limitations
- There is no requirement for growth media and nutrients
- The biosorbed metal ions can be easily desorbed and biomass can be reused and
- The dead biomass-based treatment systems can be subjected to the traditional adsorption models in use.

As a result, use of dead biomass has been a preferred choice of numerous studies on biosorption of toxic metal ions from aqueous solutions [40].

In biosorption, the metal binding on the active surface sites takes place via various mechanisms such as complexation, coordination, chelating, physical and/or chemical adsorption, ion-exchanging and microprecipitation. A large number of microorganisms like bacteria, fungi, yeast and marine algae constitute potential biosorbents. A number of studies [41-45] demonstrated that among the many possible biosorbents, marine algae especially brown algae are excellent biosorbents for metals. Among biosorbent materials, algae have proved to be both economical and eco-friendly, as they are abundantly available, have regeneration and metal recovery potential, lower volume of chemical and/or biological sludge to be disposed of, high efficiency in dilute effluents and high surface area to volume ratio. Their use provides a cost effective solution for industrial wastewater management. The brown algae are an important assembly of plants that are classified in about 265 genera with more than 1500 species [46].

The biorecovery of heavy metals can be affected by physico-chemical parameters of the solution such as pH, ion strength and temperature and by other characteristics of the biomass like concentration, presence of organic and inorganic functional groups and chemical modification (pre-treatment) [37,47-50]. Even though the brown algae are one of the most commonly used biosorbents for heavy metal recovery, they may cause a secondary pollution due to organic substances release, for example, alginate dissolving from biosorbents during the biosorption process. This phenomenon may hinder their industrial application. Also the leaching of some adsorbtive components may lead to a loss of biosorption capacity [51]. Some studies [51-53] have shown that surface modification by calcium chloride, formaldehyde and glutaraldehyde can prevent leaching of adsorptive components from biomass and increase the stability of the biosorbent material. Polyethylene imine (PEI) is well known for its metal chelating characteristics due to the presence of a large number of amine groups in a molecule and it is often used to modify the adsorbent surface to increase the adsorption capacity [9]. The results obtained indicate that the pretreated algae have a better potential for the removal of heavy metals from wastewaters [54].

The carboxylic groups are generally the most abundant acidic functional groups in brown algae. They constitute the highest percentage of titrable sites (typically greater than 70%) in dried brown algal biomass. The adsorption capacity of the algae is directly related to the presence of these sites on the alginate polymer, which itself comprises a significant component (up to 40% of the dry weight) of the dried seaweed biomass. Furthermore, the majority of metals of interest (i.e. Cd^{2+}, Co^{2+}, Cu^{2+}, Zn^{2+}, Ni^{2+} and Pb^{2+}) display maximal or near maximal sequestration at pHs near the apparent dissociation constant of carboxylic acids observed in brown algal biomass (near 5). The role of carboxylic groups in the adsorption process has been clearly demonstrated by a reduction in heavy metal ion removal by dried blown algae.

In general, biosorption by brown algae is efficient at very low concentrations of heavy metals using dead and living biomass, is low cost, is simple and less time consuming in operation.

2. DISCUSSSION

2.1. Materials and Preparation of Pre-Treated Biomass

Stock metal solutions were prepared by dissolving cadmium and nickel nitrate, $Cd(NO_3)_2.4H_2O$ and $Ni(NO_3)_2.6H_2O$ (Merck, Germany) in double distilled water (DDW). All the reagents were obtained from Merck (Germany).

Samples of brown marine algae, Cystoseira indica, were collected from the coastal areas of the Persian Gulf, Iran. They were washed with tap water to remove sand and other impurities and were sun-dried for 48 h. The biomass was crushed and sieved (RETSCH AS-200, Germany) to a particle size of 0.5-1.0 mm and then washed with DDW and dried in an oven (Heraeus CH 20P, Germany) at 80°C for 24 h. This material will be referred to as intact biomass. Surface modification by FA can prevent leaching of the adsorptive components from biomass and increase the stability of the biosorbent material [51]. For preparation of the pre-treated algae by 10% FA, 10 g/L of unwashed biomass was stirred with the solution at 25°C and at 100 rpm for 1 h. The pre-treated biomass was washed several times with de-ionized water and then dried in the oven at 60°C overnight. The dried biomass was then sieved to get a uniform particle size of 0.5-1.0 mm.

2.2. Batch Biosorption Experiments

The biosorption experiments were carried out in a series of 100ml Erlenmeyer flasks containing metal nitrate solutions with a metal concentration of 0.5 mmol/L of each metal ion, 0.06g (2g/L) of biomass and a buffer solution to adjust the pH. Contents of the Erlenmeyer flasks were shaken in the incubator shaker (INFORS multitron, Switzerland) at 25°C and at 150 rpm for 2 h. After this time, the biomass was separated from the solution using a centrifuge (Sigma 203, Germany) at 4000 rpm for 15 min. The concentration of metal in the remaining solution was measured by an ICP-OES (Inductively Coupled Plasma-Optical Emission Spectrometer) (Perkin Elmer-Optima 2100, USA).

The amount of cadmium and nickel adsorbed q (mg/g), by FA-treated Cystoseira indica was calculated using the following equation [45]:

$$q = \frac{v\left(C_i - C_f\right)}{m} \tag{1}$$

where C_i and C_f (mg/L) are the initial and final metal ion concentrations in the solution, respectively, v (L) is the solution volume and m (g) is the mass of the biosorbent.

2.3. Effect of pH

Zeta potential measurements showed that the immobilized biosorbent was negatively charged in the pH range of 3.0-8.0 [55]. An additional possible explanation why sorption increases with increasing pH is that the solubility of many metals in solution decreases with increasing pH. A further possible explanation of increasing sorption with increasing pH is that hydrolyzed species have a lower degree of hydration, i.e., less energy is necessary for removal or reorientation of the hydrated water molecules upon binding. With a further increase of pH (6–9), the solubility of metals decreases enough for precipitation to occur. This should be avoided during sorption experiments because otherwise distinguishing between sorption and precipitation metal removal becomes difficult [56].

Experiments were conducted with FA-treated *Cystoseira indica* for cadmium (II) and nickel (II) biosorption in batch systems. The adsorption characteristics of cadmium (II) and nickel (II) at various pH values in the range of 2.5-7.0 were examined. Experiments were not conducted beyond a pH of 7.0 to avoid metal precipitation as mentioned before. As shown in Fig. 1, biosorption of these metals are highly pH-dependent and adsorption of cadmium and nickel is highest at pH values of 5.5 and 6.0, respectively, and then decreases as the pH increases. Therefore, it is obvious that modification causes an increase in metal biosorption.

The pH dependency of metal sorption is explained considering the nature of biosorbents. The cell wall of brown algae mainly contains a large number of surface functional groups, among which carboxyl is generally the most abundant acidic functional group. At low pH values, cell wall ligands are protonated and compete significantly with metal ions for binding. With increasing pH, more ligands such as amino and carboxyl groups would be exposed leading to attraction between these negative charges and metal ions. In addition, at low pH values, the concentration of H_3O^+ far exceeds that of metal ions and hence occupies the binding sites on the cell walls, leaving metal ions unbound. When the pH values are increased, the competing effect of H_3O^+ decreases and positively charged metal ions take up the free binding sites, therefore metal sorption increases [52, 54].

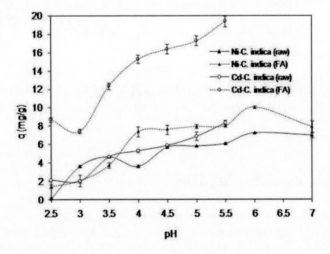

Figure 1. Effect of pH on Cd (II) and Ni (II) biosorption by intact and FA-treated C. indica biomass (Cd and Ni conc.: 0.5 mmol/L; contact time: 2 h; T: 25°C; biomass dosage: 2g/L).

2.4. Sorption and Desorption Experiments

Because of economic reasons, regeneration of biomass seems to be necessary. For desorption of Cd (II) and Ni (II) ions from biomass, three desorbing agents 0.1M CaCl$_2$, 0.1M

CH₃COOH and 0.1M NaCl have been used [35]. The biomass biosorption capacity was tested in five repeated cycles at an optimum pH of 5.5 and 6.0 for Cd (II) and Ni (II), respectively. Figure 2 indicates that the biosorption capacity of the biomass is good after 5 cycles. To test the significance and adequacy of the model, statistical testing of the model in the form of analysis of variance (ANOVA) and the one-sample t-test were done. For a 5% level of significance, F and critical F values are 0.55 and 3.89 for Cd (II) (p value = 0.59) and 2.32 and 3.80 for Ni (II) (p value = 0.141), respectively. These values show the variation of sorption capacities among the three desorbing agents not to be significant after 5 cycles. For a 5% level of significance, t values for NaCl, CH₃COOH and CaCl₂ desorbing agents are 0.61, 1.66 and 4.44 for Cd (II) and 0.85, 1.42 and 3.91 for Ni (II), respectively and the critical t is 3.18 for both. Results show that the effect of CaCl₂ on the biosorbent is significant and CaCl₂ causes an increase in the sorption capacity. Hence, CaCl₂ is recommended as a good desorbent for elution and desorption of cadmium and nickel from the biosorbent. Of course the much lower cost of NaCl should also be taken into consideration.

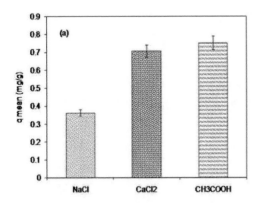 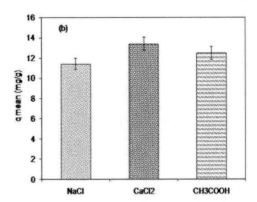

Figure 2. Effect of desorping agents on metal biosorption onto FA-treated C. indica biomass at optimum pH (T: 25°C; sorption contact time: 45 min; desorption contact time: 20 min; 5 cycles) (a) Cd (II) conc.: 0.05 mmol/L and (b) Ni (II) conc.: 1 mmol/L.

2.5. Effect of Initial Concentrations

The adsorption concentrations increased with an increase in the initial metal ion concentration. This was most probably due to an increase in the initial ion concentrations providing more chance for biosorbent contact.

2.6. Effect of Biosorbent Dosage

Biosorbent dosage seemed to have a great influence on the biosorption process. The dosage of biomass added into the solution determines the number of binding sites available for adsorption.

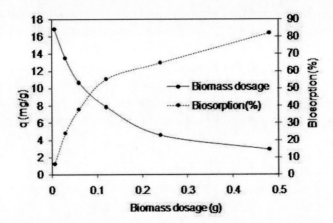

Figure 3. Effect of biomass dosage on biosorption of Ni (II) onto FA-treated C. indica biomass (Ni conc.: 1.0 mmol/L; Temperature: 25°C; Contact time: 3h; pH: 6.0).

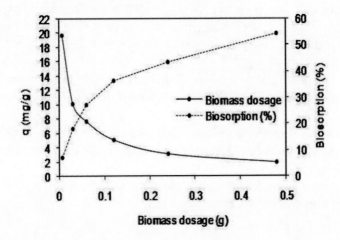

Figure 4. Effect of biomass dosage on biosorption of Cd (II) onto FA-treated C. indica biomass (Cd conc.: 0.5 mmol/L; Temperature: 25°C; Contact time: 3h; pH: 5.5).

Linear regression has been frequently used to evaluate the model parameters; however, the non-linear method is to be preferred because this method is more suited to the error structure of the data. The error of the estimates of the parameters can only be calculated consistently from a non-linear fitting procedure [57].

The effect of biomass dosage on Ni and Cd ion removal is indicated in Figs. 3 and 4.

2.7. Biosorption Isotherms

For optimization of the biosorption process design, it is necessary to acquire the appropriate correlation for the equilibrium curve. In this chapter, the relationship between metal biosorption capacity and metal concentration at equilibrium has been described by two-parameter sorption isotherm models: Langmuir and Freundlich and three-parameter isotherm models: Toth and Radke-Prausnitz. The results of the other models described herein are not given in these tables. The constants, residual root mean square error (RMSE), chi-square test (χ^2) and correlation coefficient (R^2) of two and three–parameter models are given in Tables 2 and 3, respectively.

All model parameters are evaluated by non-linear regression using the MATLAB® software. Furthermore, RMSE, χ^2 and R^2 are used to measure the goodness of fit. RMSE and χ^2 can be defined as:

$$RMSE = \sqrt{(\frac{1}{m-2})\sum_{i=1}^{m}(q_{i,exp} - q_{i,cal})^2} \tag{2}$$

$$\chi^2 = \sum_{i=1}^{m}\frac{(q_{i,exp} - q_{i,cal})^2}{q_{i,exp}} \tag{3}$$

where $q_{i,exp}$ and $q_{i,cal}$ are the observation from the batch experiment and the estimate from the isotherm for the corresponding $q_{i,exp}$, respectively, and m is the number of observations in the experimental isotherm. The smaller RMSE value indicates a better curve fitting, moreover, if the data from the model are similar to the experimental results, χ^2 will be a small number [58].

Two-parameter isotherms: Several mathematical models have been developed to quantitatively express the relationship between the extent of sorption and the residual solute concentration.

The most widely used model is the Langmuir adsorption isotherm model. Virtually all theoretical treatments of adsorption phenomena are based on or can be readily related to the analysis developed by Langmuir [8].

This model provides a simple mechanistic picture of the adsorption process and gives rise to a relatively simple mathematical expression, which follows:

$$q_e = q_m\frac{bC_e}{1+bC_e} \tag{4}$$

where q_m is the maximum metal biosorption and b ($k_{adsorption}/k_{desorption}$) is the adsorption equilibrium constant (L/mg). These constants are related to monolayer adsorption capacity and energy of adsorption, respectively [58].

Maximum monolayer adsorption capacity (q_m) was obtained as 19.56 mg/g and 16.17 mg/g for Cd (II) and Ni (II) sorption, respectively. The b values of Cd (II) and Ni (II) biosorption are estimated from the isotherms to be 0.05 L/mg and 0.04 L/mg, respectively.

The term q_m is presumed to represent a fixed number of surface sites in the sorbent, and it should, therefore, be constant and temperature-independent. This term is only determined by the nature of the sorbent.

The Langmuir model was originally derived for the adsorption of gases onto activated carbon with several assumptions:

1. There is a limited area available for adsorption,
2. The adsorbed solute material on the surface is only one molecule in thickness, and
3. Adsorption is reversible and an equilibrium condition is achieved.

The two parameters of the Langmuir isotherm reflect the maximum uptake and the affinity of the component for the sorbent. As it was shown for the biosorption of heavy metals, metal ion removal is eventually limited by the fixed number of active sites and a resulting plateau can be observed. This phenomenon is well depicted by Langmuir isotherms.

The Freundlich equation is an empirical expression based on biosorption on a heterogeneous surface.

The Freundlich model is recognized as the earliest empirical equation and is shown to be consistent with an exponential distribution of active centers, characteristic of heterogeneous surfaces. This isotherm model is presented as follows [58]:

$$q_e = k_F C_e^{1/n} \qquad (5)$$

where k_F (L/g) is the Freundlich constant which is an important constant indicating a relative measure for adsorption efficiency and n is the Freundlich exponent. The magnitude of n is an indication of the favorability of adsorption. Values of n larger than 1 indicate favorable adsorption [59]. It is assumed that the stronger binding sites are occupied first. The k_F and n values in the Freundlich equation are calculated as 0.007 L/g, 0.56 L/g, and 0.52 and 1.27 for Cd (II) and Ni (II), respectively.

From Table 2, it is apparent that equilibrium data of Cd (II) biosorption are fitted well by the Freundlich isotherm, the values of R^2 of the Freundlich and Langmuir isotherm models are 0.996 and 0.897, respectively, and for Ni (II) the Langmuir isotherm gave a better fit than the Freundlich isotherm based on the values of R^2 of the Langmuir isotherm model (0.997) which is higher than that of the Freundlich isotherm (0.995) although not significantly so (only the third decimal is different).

Since the Freundlich and Langmuir isotherm models do not provide any clues about the mechanism of biosorption, the equilibrium data are tested with the Dubinin–Radushkevich isotherm model. Dubinin and Radushkevich have reported that the characteristic biosorption curve is related to the porous structure of the sorbents. The Dubinin–Radushkevich (D-R) equation is generally expressed as follows:

$$q_e = q_{DR} \exp\left(-B_{DR} \varepsilon_{DR}^2\right) \qquad (6)$$

$$\varepsilon_{DR} = RT \ln\left(1 + \frac{1}{C_e}\right) \qquad (7)$$

where ε_{DR}, the Polanyi potential, is a constant related to the biosorption energy, R is the gas constant (8.314 kJ/mol) and T is the absolute temperature (K). q_{DR} and B_{DR} are the D-R isotherm constants in mg/g and mol^2/kJ^2, respectively.

The Polanyi sorption theory assumes a fixed volume of sorption space close to the sorbent surface and the existence of a sorption potential over these spaces. The mean free energy of biosorption (E) can be calculated from the following equation:

$$E = \frac{1}{\sqrt{2B_{DR}}} \tag{8}$$

Three-parameter isotherms: The Toth isotherm, derived from the potential theory, is expressed as:

$$q_e = \frac{q_{m,T} b_T C_e}{\left[1 + (b_T C_e)^{1/n_T}\right]^{n_T}} \tag{9}$$

where b_T is the Toth model constant and n_T is the Toth model exponent. It is obvious that for $n_T = 1$ this isotherm reduces to the Langmuir equation.

The Toth model constant b_T and exponent n_T values for Cd (II) and Ni (II) are found to be 0.10 L/mg, 3.67 L/mg, and -0.16 and -0.21, respectively.

The Radke-Prausnitz isotherm can be represented as [60]:

$$q_e = \frac{a_{R-P} r_{R-p} C_e^{\beta_{R-P}}}{a_{R-P} + r_{R-P} C_e^{\beta_{R-P}-1}} \tag{10}$$

where a_{R-P} and r_{R-P} are Radke-Prausnitz model constants and β_{R-P} is the Radke-Prausnitz model exponent.

The Radke-Prausnitz isotherm constants, a_{R-P} and r_{R-P} for Cd (II) and Ni (II) are calculated as -0.27 mg/g and 1.02 mg/g, and 0.0004 L/g and 0.37 L/g, respectively.

As the results shown in Table 3 indicate, the experimental results of Cd (II) biosorption are fitted quite well by the Radke-Prausnitz isotherm model and Ni (II) biosorption data are correlated well by the Toth model as confirmed by small values of RMSE and χ^2, and R^2 values close to 1.0.

Khan's isotherm is as follows:

$$q_e = \frac{q_{m,K} b_K C_e}{(1 + b_K C_e)^{a_K}} \tag{11}$$

where b_K is the Khan model constant and a_K is the Khan model exponent.

The Redlich–Peterson isotherm approximates the Henry's law at low sorbate concentrations, and at high concentrations it behaves like the Freundlich isotherm. It is given as [58]:

$$q_e = \frac{K_{RP} C_e}{1 + a_{RP} C_e^{\beta_{RP}}} \tag{12}$$

where K_{RP} and a_{RP} are the Redlich–Peterson model constants in L/g and L/mg, respectively and β_{RP} is the Redlich–Peterson model exponent lying between 0 and 1.

Table 2. Isotherm constants of the two-parameter models for Cd (II) and Ni (II) biosorption on FA-treated *C. indica* biomass at 25°C

Equilibrium model	Metal	
	Cadmium	Nickel
Langmuir		
q_m (mg/g)	19.56	16.17
b (L/mg)	0.05	0.04
R^2	0.897	0.997
RMSE	7.75	2.38
χ^2	18.74	2.57
Freundlich		
K_F	0.007	0.56
n	0.52	1.27
R^2	0.996	0.995
RMSE	5.62	1.72
χ^2	10.77	1.42

Table 3. Isotherm constants of the three-parameter models for Cd (II) and Ni (II) biosorption on FA-treated C. indica biomass at 25°C

Equilibrium model	Metal	
	Cadmium	Nickel
Toth		
$q_{m,T}$ (mg/g)	2.619	0.061
b_T (L/g)	0.101	3.671
n_T	-0.16	-0.21
R^2	0794	0.999
RMSE	7.339	1.778
χ^2	32.576	1.268
Radke-Prausnitz		
a_{R-P} (L/g)	-0.273	1.02
r_{R-P} (L/mg)	0.0004	0.37
β_{R-P}	2.55	0.99
R^2	0.994	0.866
RMSE	2.41	3.12
χ^2	1.75	9.62

The Sips isotherms is a combination of the Langmuir and Freundlich isotherm type models and is expected to describe heterogeneous surfaces much better. At low sorbate concentrations it reduces to the Freundlich isotherm, while at high sorbate concentrations it predicts a monolayer adsorption capacity characteristic of the Langmuir isotherm. The model can be written as [58]:

$$q_e = \frac{K_s C_e^{\beta_s}}{1 + a_s C_e^{\beta_s}} \qquad (13)$$

where K_S and a_S are the Sips model constants in L/g and L/mg, respectively and β_S is the Sips model exponent.

The foregoing analysis of isotherm models shows that the best fit for Cd (II) and Ni (II) biosorption is produced by three-parameter isotherm models.

2.8. Effect of Contact Time

As the adsorption process proceeds, the sorbed solute tends to desorb back into the solution. Eventually the rates of adsorption and desorption will attain an equilibrium state. When the system reaches sorption equilibrium, no further net adsorption occurs. The time at which adsorption equilibrium occurs was determined.

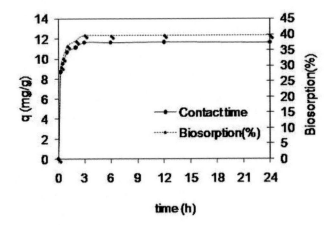

Figure 5. Effect of contact time on biosorption of Ni (II) onto C. indica (Ni conc.: 1.0 mmol/L; Temperature: 25°C; Biomass dosage: 2g/L; pH: 6.0).

The adsorption rate tests were performed on an equilibrium batch basis. 0.06 g/L of the biomass was contacted with a solution bearing a metal concentration of 100 mg/L. The biomass was kept in contact with the metal-bearing solution for different time periods (15, 30, 60 min, 2, 3, 6, 12 and 24 hr). Time zero samples were also taken in these samples for which the biomass was directly separated from the metal-bearing solution within less than one minute of contact time.

The very fast sorption and settling of the anaerobic biomass make this material suitable for continuous flow water treatment systems.

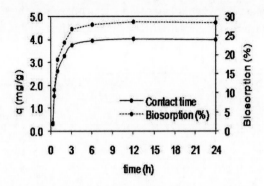

Figure 6. Effect of contact time on biosorption of Cd (II) onto C. indica (Cd conc.: 0.25 mmol/L; Temperature: 25°C; Biomass dosage: 2g/L; pH: 5.5).

From experimental data represented in Fig. 5, the process of biosorption of Ni (II) reached the equilibrium state after approximately 3 h of contact time. This process was rather fast at first and 90% of total biosorption of nickel (II) occurred in the first 60 min. After 1 h, the rate of biosorption was slower and at last no further significant adsorption was noted beyond 3 h. A similar trend for the biosorption of Cd (II) is shown in Fig. 6. It can be seen that equilibrium was achieved within about 3 hours.

2.9. Kinetic Analysis

Adsorption kinetics provides valuable information about the mechanism of adsorption and subsequently helps the investigation of the controlling mechanism in the biosorption process which could lie either in the mass transfer or the chemical reaction step [24]. Rate of metal ion removal, which is required for selecting optimum operating conditions for the full scale batch process, can be obtained from a kinetic analysis [61]. Different models can describe biosorption kinetics; two common semi-empirical kinetic models based on adsorption equilibrium capacity are the pseudo-first order model proposed by Lagergren and the pseudo-second order model proposed by Ho and McKay [62].

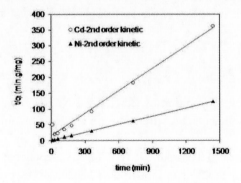

Figure 7. Linearized pseudo-second-order kinetic model for Cd (II) and Ni (II) ions removal by C. indica biomass at the optimum pH (Cd conc.: 0.25 mmol/L; Ni conc.:1mmol/L; T: 25°C; Biomass dosage: 2 g/L).

Table 4. Comparison between adsorption rate constants, the estimated qe and the coefficients of correlation associated with the pseudo-first-order and the pseudo-second-order kinetic models at 25°C

Metal	Pseudo-first-order kinetic model			Experimental value	Pseudo-second-order kinetic model		
	q_e (mg/g)	K_1	R^2	q_e (mg/g)	q_e (mg/g)	K_2	R^2
Cadmium	5.111	0.023	0.963	3.80	4.219	3.79E-3	0.986
Nickel	5.73	0.023	0.830	11.65	11.67	4.32E-3	0.999

In batch systems, adsorption kinetics is most widely described by either the pseudo-first-order or the pseudo-second-order kinetic models. The linearized pseudo-first-order kinetic model takes the following form [50, 60]:

$$q_t = q_e - q_e \exp(-K_1 t) \tag{14}$$

where q_t and q_e are the amounts of metal adsorbed at time t and equilibrium, respectively, and K_1 (min^{-1}) is the first-order reaction rate constant.

The pseudo-second-order kinetic model considered in this chapter is given as [50, 60]:

$$\frac{t}{q_t} = \frac{1}{K_2 q_e^2} + \frac{t}{q_e} \tag{15}$$

where K_2 (g mg^{-1} min^{-1}) is the second-order reaction rate constant.

The experimental data presented in Fig. 7 are fitted by the pseudo-second-order kinetic model while the parameters of both models are tabulated in Table 4. It is obvious that the coefficient of correlation (R^2: 0.986 and 0.999 for cadmium and nickel biosorption, respectively) for the pseudo-second-order kinetic model is higher in comparison with the pseudo-first-order kinetic model (R^2: 0.963 and 0.830) and the calculated value of q_e for the pseudo-second-order kinetic model is closer to the experimental value.

2.10. Conclusions

The present chapter on biosorption of Cd (II) and Ni (II) from aqueous solutions using brown algae, *C. indica*, in intact and FA-treated form suggests the following:

- The adsorption of Cd (II) and Ni (II) ions is dependent on pH. Comparison of cadmium (II) and nickel (II) biosorption capacities of brown algae in intact and chemically-modified forms indicates that the maximum sorption capacity of FA-treated *C. indica* for Cd (II) at an optimum pH of 5.5 is 19.42mg/g and the maximum

Ni (II) biosorption capacity at an optimum pH of 6.0 is 10.06 mg/g (C_i=0.5mmol/L for both Cd (II) and Ni (II) and 2g/L biomass is used in either case).

- Sorption and desorption cycles have no adverse effect on the biosorption capacity and $CaCl_2$ is a desirable desorbent in this case.

- Among the two-parameter biosorption isotherms, the Langmuir model better describes the Ni (II) biosorption and the Freundlich model fits the experimental data of Cd (II) biosorption quite well. The maximum monolayer biosorption capacity of FA-treated *C. indica* for Ni (II) and Cd (II) are 16.17 mg/g and 19.56 mg/g, respectively. Among the three-parameter isotherms, the Toth isotherm best describes the adsorption of Ni (II) and the Radke-Prausnitz model is found to provide the closest fit to the biosorption data of Cd (II).

- The pseudo-second-order kinetic model fits the experimental data quite well (R^2: 0.986 and 0.999 for Cd (II) and Ni (II) biosorption, respectively).

- It may be concluded that the FA-treated *C. indica* can be used as a low cost and abundant source for Cd (II) and Ni (II) removal from aqueous solutions.

REFERENCES

[1]   Cruz, C.C.V.; Costa, A.C.A.; Henriques, C.A.; Luna, A.S. *Bioresour. Technol.* 2004, *91*, 249-257. Kinetic modeling and equilibrium studies during cadmium biosorption by dead *Sargassum* sp. biomass

[2]   Kaewsarn, P.; Yu, Q. *Environ. Pollut.*, 2001, *112*, 209-213. Cadmium (II) removal from aqueous solutions by pre-treated biomass of marine algae *Padina* sp.

[3]   Sari, A.; Tuzen, M. *J. Hazard. Mater.*, 2008, *152*, 302-308. Biosorption of Pb (II) and Cd (II) from aqueous solution using green alga (*Ulva Lactuca*) biomass.

[4]   Lodeiro, P., Cordero, B.; Barriada, J.L.; Herrero, R.; Sastre de Vicente, M.E. *Bioresour. Technol.*, 2005, *96*, 1796-1803. Biosorption of cadmium by biomass of brown marine macroalgae.

[5]   Lodeiro, P., Barriada, J.L.; Herrero, R.; Sastre de Vicente, M.E. *Environ. Pollut.*, 2006, *142*, 264-273. The marine macroalga *Cysroseira baccata* as biosorbent for cadmium (II) and lead (II) removal: Kinetic and equilibrium studies.

[6]   Esteves, A.J.P.; Valdman, E.; Leite, S.G.F. *Biotechnol. Lett.*, 2000, *22*, 499-502. Repeated removal of cadmium and zinc from an industrial effluent by waste biomass *Sargassum* sp.

[7]   Kapoor, A.; Viraraghavan, *T. Bioresour. Technol.*, 1995, *53,* 195-206. Fungal biosorption–an alternative treatment option for heavy metal bearing wastewaters: a review.

[8]   Volesky, B. *Hydrometallurgy*, 2001, *59*, 203-216. Detoxification of metal-bearing effluents: biosorption for the next century.

[9]   Deng, S.; Ting, Y.P. *Water Res.*, 2005, *39*, 2167-2177. Characterization of PEI-modified biomass and biosorption of Cu(II), Pb(II) and Ni (II).

[10]   Kurniawan, T. A.; Chana, G. Y. S.; Lo, C. W.; Babel, S. *Chem. Eng. J.*, 2006, *118,* 83–98. Physico–chemical treatment techniques for wastewater laden with heavy metals.

[11]   Papadopoulos, A.; Fatta, D.; Parperis, K.; Mentzis, A.; Harambous, K. J.; Loizidou, M. *Sep. Purif. Technol.,* 2004, *39*, 181–188. Nickel uptake from a wastewater stream produced in a metal finishing industry by combination of ion-exchange and precipitation methods.

[12]   Dialynas, E.; Diamadopoulos, E. *Desalination*, 2009, *238*, 302–311. Integration of a membrane bioreactor coupled with reverse osmosis for advanced treatment of municipal wastewater.

[13]   Ozaki, H.; Sharma, K.; Saktaywin, W. Desalination, 2002, 144, 287–294. Performance of an ultra-low pressure reverse osmosis membrane (ULPROM) for separating heavy metal: effects of interference parameters.

[14]   Qin, J. J.; Wai, M. N.; Oo, M.H.; Wong, F. S. *J. Membr. Sci.,* 2002, *208*, 213–221.A feasibility study on the treatment and recycling of a wastewater from metal plating.

[15]   Bruggen, B.; Vandecasteele, C. *Environ. Pollut.* , 2003, *122*, 435–445. Removal of pollutants from surface water and groundwater by nanofiltration: overview of possible applications in the drinking water industry.

[16]   Ahn, K. H.; Song, K.G.; Cha, H. Y.; Yeom, I. T. *Desalination,* 1999, *122*, 77–84. Removal of ions in nickel electroplating rinse water using low-pressure nanofiltration.

[17]   Qdais, H. A.; Moussa, H. *Desalination,* 2004, *164*, 105–110. Removal of heavy metals from wastewater by membrane processes: a comparative study.

[18]   Wang, Z.; Liu, G.; Fan, Z.; Yang, X.; Wang, J.; Wang, S. *J. Membr. Sci.*, 2007, *305*, 185–195. Experimental study on treatment of electroplating wastewater by nanofiltration.

[19]   Semerjian, L.; Ayoub, G. M. *Adv. Environ. Res.*, 2003, *7*, 389–403. High-pH-magnesium coagulation–flocculation in wastewater treatment.

[20]   Licsk′o, I. *Water Sci. Technol.*, 1997, *36*, 103–110. Realistic coagulation mechanisms in the use of aluminium and iron(III) salts.

[21]   Ayoub, G. M.; Semerjian, L.; Acra, A.; El Fadel, M.; Koopman, B. *J. Environ. Eng.*, 2001, *127 (3)*, 196–207. Heavy metal removal by coagulation with seawater liquid bittern.

[22]   Vik, E. I.; Carlsoon, D. A.; Eikum, A. S.; Gjessing, E. T. *Water Res.,* 1984, *18*, 1355–1360. Electrocoagulation of potable water.

[23]   Elimelech, M.; O'Melia, C. R. *Environ. Sci. Technol.*, 1990, *24*, 1528–1536. Kinetics of deposition of colloidal particles in porous media.

[24]   Dobrevsky, I.; Todorova-Dimova, M.; Panayotova, T. *Desalination,* 1996, *108,* 277–280. Electroplating rinse wastewater treatment by ion exchange.

[25]   Korngold, E.; Belayev, N.; Aaronov, L. *Sep. Purif. Technol.*, 2003, *33 (2),* 179–187. Removal of chromates from drinking water by anion exchangers.

[26]   Ahmed, S.; Chughtai, S.; Keane, M. A. *Sep. Purif. Technol.,* 1998, *13*, 57–64. The removal of cadmium and lead from aqueous solution by ion exchange with Na–Y zeolite.

[27]   Lo, W. H.; Chua, H., Lam, K. H.; Bi, S. P. *Chemosphere,* 1999, *39 (15),* 2723–2736. A comparative investigation on the biosorption of lead by filamentous fungal biomass.

[28]   Valdimir, S.; Danish, J. M. *J. Colloid Interf. Sci.,* 2002, *250,* 213-220. Characterization and metal sorptive properties of oxidized active carbon.

[29] Youssef, A. M.; El-Nabarawy, T. H.; Samra, S. E. *Colloids Surf. Eng.,* 2004, *235,* 153-160. A Physicochem Sorption properties of chemically-activated carbons 1. Sorption of cadmium(II) ions.

[30] Kadirvelu, K.; Thamaraiselvi, K.; Namasivayam, C. *Bioresour. Technol.,* 2001, *76,* 63-65. Removal of heavy metals from industrial wastewaters by adsorption onto activated carbon prepared from an agricultural solid waste.

[31] Ranganathan, K. *Bioresour. Technol.,* 2000, *73,* 99-103. Chromium removal by activated carbons prepared from Casurina equisetifolia leaves.

[32] Babel, S.; Kurniawan, T. A. *J. Hazard. Mater. B,* 2003, *97,* 219-243. Low-cost adsorbents for heavy metals uptake from contaminated water: a review.

[33] Hanif, M. A.; Nadeem, R.; Zafar, M. N.; Akhtar K.; Bhatti, H. N. *J. Hazard Mater.* 2007, *145,* 501–505. Kineticstudies for Ni (II) biosorption from industrial wastewater by Cassia fistula (Golden Shower) biomass.

[34] Hawari, A. H.; Mulligan, C. N.; *Bioresour. Technol.* 2006, *97,* 692–700. Biosorption of lead(II), cadmium(II), copper(II) and nickel(II) by anaerobic granular biomass.

[35] Naddafi, K.; Nabizadeh, R.; Saeedi, R.; Mahvi, A.H.; Vaezi, F.; Yaghmaeian, K.; Ghasri, A.; Nazmara, S. *J. Hazard. Mater.* 2007, *147,* 785-791. Biosorption of lead(II) and cadmium(II) by protonated *Sargassum glaucescens* biomass in a continuous packed bed column.

[36] Williams, C. J.; Aderhold, D.; Edyvean, R. g. J. *J. Water Res.* 1998, *32,* 216-224. Comparison between biosorbents for the removal of metal ions from aqueous solution.

[37] Romera, E.; Gonzalez, F.; Balleter, A.; Blazquez, M. L.; Munoz, J. A. *J. Bioresour. Technol.* 2008, *99,* 4684-4693. Biosorption of heavy metals by *Fucus spiralis.*

[38] Ricordel, S.; Taha, S.; Cisse, I.; Dorange, G. *J. Sep. Purif. Technol.* 2001, *24,* 389-401. Heavy metals removal by adsorption onto peanut husks carbon: characterization, kinetic study and modeling.

[39] Pejic, B.; Vukcevic, M.; Kostic, M.; Skundric, P.; *J. Hazard. Mater.* 2009, *164,* 146–153. Biosorption of heavy metal ions from aqueous solutions by short hemp fibers: Effect of chemical composition.

[40] Kapoor, A.; Viraraghavan, T. *Bioresour. Technol.* 1998, *63,* 109-113. Biosorption of heavy metals on aspergillus niger: effect of pretreatment.

[41] Davis, T. A.; Volesky, B. *J. Water Res.* 2005, *39,* 239-247. Biosorption of La, Eu and Yb using Sargassum biomass.

[42] Davis, T. A.; Volesky, B.; Mucci, A. *J. Water Res.* 2003, *37,* 4311-4330. A review of the biochemistry of heavy metal biosorption by brown algae.

[43] Hashim, M.; Chu, K. H. *J. Chem. Eng.* 2004, *97,* 249-255. Biosorption of cadmium by brown, green and red seaweeds.

[44] Tsui, M. T. K.; Cheung, K. C.; Tam, N. F. Y.; Wong, M. H. *J. Chemosphere.* 2006, *65,* 51-57. A comparative study on metal sorption by brown seaweed.

[45] Vijayaraghavan, K.; Palanivelu, K.; Velan, M. *J. Sep. Purif. Technol.* 2005, *44,* 53-59. Biosorption of cobalt(II) and nickel(II) by seaweeds: batch and column studies.

[46] Bold, H. C.; Wynne, M. J. *Introduction to the Algae Structure and Reproduction; Second Edition*; Prentice-Hall, Inc.: Englewood Cliffs, New Jersey 1985; Vol. 1, pp 516-525.

[47] Kalyani, S.; Srinivasa Rao, P.; Krishnaiah, A. *J. Chemosphere.* 2004, *57,* 1225-1229. Removal of nickel(II) from aqueous solution using marine algae as sorbing biomass.

[48] Khani, M. H.; Keshtkar, A. R.; Ghandchi, M.; Pahlavanzadeh, H. *J. Hazard. Mater.* 2008, *150,* 612-618. Equilibrium, kinetic and thermodynamic study of the biosorption of uranium onto *Cystoseira Indica* algae.

[49] Schiewer, S.; Wong, M. H. *J. Chemosphere.* 2000, *41,* 271-282. Ion strength effect in biosorption of metals by marine algae.

[50] Chen, Z.; Ma, W.; Han, M. *J. Hazard. Mater.* 2008, *155,* 327-333. Biosorption of nickel and copper onto treated alga (*Undria Pinnatifida*): Application of isotherm and kinetics study.

[51] Yang, L.; Chen, P. *J. Bioresour. Technol.* 2008, *99,* 297-307. Biosorption of hexavalent chromium onto intact and chemically modified *Sargassum* sp.

[52] Matheickal, J.T.; Yu, Q. *J. Bioresour. Technol.* 1999, *69,* 223-229. Biosorption of lead(II) and copper(II) from aqueous solutions by pre-treated biomass of Australian marine algae.

[53] Leusch, A.; Holan, Z. R.; Volesky, B. *J. Chem. Tech. Biotechnol.* 1995, *62,* 279-288. Biosorption of heavy metals (Cd, Cu, Ni, Pb, Zn) by chemically rein-forced biomass of marine algae.

[54] Luo, F.; Liu, Y. H.; Li, X. M.; Xuan, Z. X.; Ma, J. T. *J. Chemosphere.* 2006, *64,* 1122–1127. Biosorption of lead ion by chemicallymodified biomass of marine brown algae Laminaria japonica.

[55] Akar, T; Kaynak, Z.; Ulusoy, S; Yuvaci, D.; Ozsari, G.; Akar, S. T.; *J.Hazard. Mater.* 2009, *163,* 1134–1141. Enhanced biosorption of nickel(II) ions by silica-gel-immobilized waste biomass: Biosorption characteristics in batch and dynamic flow mode.

[56] Schiewer, S.; Volesky, B. *J. Environ. Sci. Technol.* 1995, *29,* 3049– 3058. Modeling of the proton-metal ion exchange in biosorption.

[57] Gerringa, L. J. A.; Herman, P. M. J.; Poortvliet, T. C. W. *J. Mar. Chem.* 1995, *48,* 131–142. Comparison of the linear Van den Berg/Ruzic transformation and a non-linear fit of the Langmuir isotherm applied to Cu speciation data in the estuarine environment.

[58] Vijayaraghavan, K.; Padmesh, T. V. N.; Palanivelu, K.; Velan, M. *J. Hazard. Mater.* 2006, *B133,* 304-308. Biosorption of nickel(II) ions onto *Sargassum wightii*: Application of two-parameter and three- parameter isotherm models.

[59] Daneshvar, N.; Salari, D.; Aber, S. *J. Hazard. Mater.* 2002, *94,* 49–61. Chromium adsorption and Cr(VI) reduction to trivalent chromium in aqueous solutions by soya cake.

[60] Basha, S.; Murthy, Z. V. P. *J. Process Biochem.* 2007, *42,* 1521-1529. Kinetic and equilibrium models for biosorption of Cr(VI) on chemically modified seaweed, *Cystoseira indica*.

[61] Alyüz, B.; Veli, S. *J. Hazard. Mater.* 2009, *167,* 482-488. Kinetics and equilibrium studies for the removal of nickel and zinc from aqueous solutions by ion exchange resin.

[62] Ho, Y. S.; McKay, G. *J. Proc. Biochem.* 1999, *34,* 451–459. Pseudo-second order model for sorption processes.

In: Water Production and Wastewater Treatment
Editor: B. Antizar-Ladislao et al.

ISBN 978-1-61728-503-5
© 2011 Nova Science Publishers, Inc.

Chapter 5

MULTICOMPONENT REMOVAL OF HEAVY METALS FROM AQUEOUS SOLUTION USING LOW-COST SORBENTS

Hilda Elizabeth Reynel-Avila,
Didilia Ileana Mendoza-Castillo,
Virginia Hernández-Montoya,
and Adrián Bonilla-Petriciolet [*1]

Instituto Tecnológico de Aguascalientes, Aguascalientes, México, 20256

ABSTRACT

Recently, some materials from natural or industrial origin have been received attention as possible sorbents for the removal of heavy metals from water due to their acceptable sorption behavior, low cost and large availability. Most of the heavy metals sorption studies using low-cost sorbents are concerned with monometallic systems. However, the industrial wastewaters usually contain more than one metallic specie and, therefore, it is necessary to study and understand the sorption behavior under competitive conditions (i.e., when several metallic species are present). This chapter provides a brief overview of various low-cost sorbents that have been used as sorbent for heavy metal removal in aqueous solution under competitive conditions. The discussion is especially focused on the results reported for sorption studies using some sorbents from different origin, their relative advantages and sorption capacities in multimetallic solutions. Finally, the description and the application of classical multicomponent sorption models are provided including some guidelines for a reliable parameter estimation procedure.

---

[1] * Corresponding author: petriciolet@hotmail.com

1. Introduction

Industrial wastewaters are important source of environmental pollution due to the high content of heavy metal ions. These metals are toxic, non-biodegradable, can be incorporated relatively easy in the food chain, and tend to accumulate causing several diseases and health disorders in humans, and other living organisms [1,2]. In particular, cadmium (Cd^{+2}), lead (Pb^{+2}), nickel (Ni^{+2}), mercury (Hg^{+2}), zinc (Zn^{+2}), copper (Cu^{+2}) and chromium (Cr^{+3}) are the most common metals found in effluents of a large number of industries. The toxicity of these heavy metals has been well documented in literature and their presence in water resources and wastewaters is a potential risk for the environment and public health [1-4]. Thus, it is necessary to design technically and economically feasible processes to minimize the heavy metal pollution and to reduce the risk associated to it.

To date, several studies have focused on the development of effective and low-cost strategies for heavy metal removal from water. The conventional approaches include: ion-exchange, reverse osmosis, evaporation, chemical precipitation, electrochemical treatment, coagulation, solvent extraction, chemical oxidation-reduction, and sorption [1,3,5]. Unfortunately, some methods show technical limitations, are expensive and ineffective when the metal concentrations are in the range of $1 - 100$ mg/L. Besides, available technologies may show high sensitivity to operational conditions, high energy consumption, and also produce large quantity of residual sludge [3,5].

The sorption process is one of the most important methods for treatment of wastewaters polluted by heavy metal ions. This technology offers several advantages for facing water pollution and is even better than other techniques due to its effectiveness, feasibility, versatility, simplicity of design, easiness of operation, possibility of metal recovery, and low cost if a proper sorbent is used [6,7]. Activated carbon is the most known sorbent and has been used for a long time to remove various pollutants including heavy metal ions [4,7,8]. However, the synthesis and regeneration cost of commercial carbons have encouraged the application of low-cost renewable materials.

In this context, natural materials, biomasses and wastes from industrial or agricultural operations that are available in large quantities and require little processing, may be used as low-cost sorbents for improving water quality [1,4,5,7]. These sorbents, which can be used either directly or after a suitable pre-treatment, may show competitive sorption capacities and offer more advantages than commercial activated carbons [1,4,5]. In fact, its use in water treatment has become a current tendency in sorption research and is an attractive approach for the field of environmental engineering.

Reviews of the feasibility and application of a wide variety of low-cost sorbents for the treatment of polluted water by heavy metal ions can be found in Bailey et al. [1], Wan Ngah and Hanafiah [2], Sud et al. [4], Wang and Chen [5], Demirbas [7] and Babel and Kurniawan [8]. These sorbents include ashes, zeolites, clays, biomasses, industrial wastes, and others. In the majority of these works the sorption of a single metal ion has been studied principally and a limited emphasis has been given to the study of multicomponent systems. However, the industrial effluents contain several metallic species and, as a consequence, it is necessary to evaluate the behavior of available sorbents under these conditions. Note that the simultaneous removal of heavy metal ions from solutions containing two or more species plays an important role for the design and operation of water purification processes, because multicomponent sorption studies are useful to identify the competitive effects on sorbent behavior between several metal species. When two or more metal ions are present in solution, they may increase, decrease or may not change the metal-ion sorption capacity of the sorbent [9,10]. Herein, it is convenient to remark that the study, analysis and the interpretation of multicomponent sorption process have also proved to be complex because sorption process is affected by several factors and there are various mechanisms involved in the removal of metal ions, which may occur simultaneously [11]. Actually, experimental sorption data on multimetallic systems are very limited and further studies are necessary to improve the knowledge of multicomponent sorption for the removal of hazardous metallic species using low-cost sorbents.

This chapter provides a brief overview of low-cost sorbents for multicomponent heavy metal removal in aqueous solution. The sorption behavior of various sorbents, including industrial by-products, wastes and natural materials, are discussed and analyzed. Finally, the application of multicomponent sorption models for data correlation is described, and the principal aspects for a reliable modeling procedure are highlighted.

2. DESCRIPTION OF LOW COST SORBENTS USED IN THE REMOVAL OF HEAVY METALS FROM MULTICOMPONENT MIXTURES

In contrast to single-metal sorption studies, a limited number of low-cost sorbents has been studied for heavy metal removal under competitive conditions in multimetallic aqueous systems. Tables 1 and 2 present a summary of the most representative low-cost sorbents used to remove heavy metal ions in multicomponent systems. These tables show the studied metallic species and the sorption experimental conditions. The sorbents include natural polymers, incineration wastes, materials from biological origin, minerals and sediments, industrial by-products and wastes. Note that this chapter does not cover the use of biological sorbents such as bacteria, yeasts and fungi under competitive conditions. For interested readers, an excellent review of the application of several biosorbents for removal of heavy metals from aqueous solutions has been reported by Wang and Chen [5].

Basically, a multicomponent solution may exhibit three possible types of sorption effects under competitive conditions: a) synergism: the sorption of a sorbate increases when there are other sorbates in the mixture, b) antagonism: the sorption of a sorbate decreases when there are other sorbates in the mixture, and c) non-interaction: the mixture has no effect on the sorption of each sorbate in the mixture. In literature, the analysis of competitive effects is based on the ratio of the sorption capacity of one metal ion in the presence of the other metal ions in multicomponent solution, $q_{ei,mix}$, to the sorption capacity of same metal ion when it is present alone in the solution, $q_{ei,0}$ [12-14]. Using this approach, when $q_{ei,mix} / q_{ei,0} > 1$ sorption is promoted by the presence of other metal ions (synergism); if $q_{ei,mix} / q_{ei,0} = 1$ the metals have no effect on each other (non-interaction); and if $q_{ei,mix} / q_{ei,0} < 1$ sorption is suppressed by other metal ions (antagonism). Typically, this analysis is applied for characterizing and studying the sorbent behavior under competitive conditions.

With illustrative purposes, a set of sorption studies of various low-cost sorbents are discussed in the following. This discussion comprises the sorbent description and its behavior and competitive effects in multimetallic solutions. The results of data modeling and some aspects about mechanisms involved in the removal of heavy metal ions are also considered. Finally, the sorption capacities of these sorbents under competitive conditions will be compared and discussed in the section 3.

2.1. Alginate

Alginate is a polysaccharide distributed widely in the cell walls of brown algae. It has been extensively used as immobilization material for various applications, and few studies have tested its behavior as a heavy metal sorbent. Specifically, calcium alginate beads obtained from brown algae have been used for the simultaneous removal of Cu^{+2}, Cd^{+2} and Pb^{+2} ions in binary solutions [15,16]. Sorption experiments were performed at pH 4.5 and 25 °C with metal concentrations up to 10 mmol/L. The sorbent dosage was 1 mg/mL and the particle size was 0.7 mm. Experimental data revealed that Cu^{+2} and Pb^{+2} ions are sorbed preferably more than Cd^{+2} ions. These results suggest antagonistic competitive effects especially for Cd^{+2} ions. In particular, the sorption behavior of alginate for Pb^{+2} ions is less sensitive to the presence of both Cu^{+2} and Cd^{+2} ions in solution. In this study, Langmuir and Sips multicomponent models were used for data regression and the results indicated that the non-modified Langmuir model provided the best correlation of experimental data. Papageorgiou et al. [16] suggested that the main mechanism involved in the sorption of heavy metal ions using alginate is considered to be ion exchange.

2.2. Ashes

Incineration wastes from natural or anthropogenic sources have good sorption properties and have been used for multicomponent removal of heavy metals [10,14,17-19]. These wastes include rice husk ash, volcanic ash, bagasse fly ash, and others (see Tables 1 and 2). Specifically, Srivastava et al. [14] reported the application of bagasse fly ash for the simultaneous removal of Cd^{+2} and Ni^{+2} ions from water. Bagasse fly ash is a waste of sugar industry and is obtained from bagasse-fired boilers. The results of X-ray spectrum of this waste indicated the presence of alumina, silica, calcium oxide, calcium metasilicate, and calcium silicate while FTIR analysis suggested the presence of silanol, aldehydes, ketones, lactones and carboxyl-carbonate groups, which are useful for heavy metal removal. This sorbent was used without treatment in sorption experiments and its BET surface area was $\cong$ 169 m^2/g. Multimetallic removal studies were carried out at 30 °C and pH 6 using metal concentrations from 0.1 to 1.7 mmol/L and a sorbent dosage of 10 mg/mL. Results indicated that the equilibrium uptake of one ion (Cd^{+2} or Ni^{+2}) decreased with increasing concentrations of other ion. For all tested conditions, there is an antagonistic sorption effect between Cd^{+2} and Ni^{+2} ions. Comparing the sorbent behavior, these studies revealed that the preference for Ni^{+2} is greater than Cd^{+2}. The sorption data were fitted to several models including Langmuir, Freundlich and Redlich-Peterson multicomponent isotherms. In particular, the extended Freundlich model provided the best correlation of experimental data in comparison to the other models. These authors concluded that as the solution pH increases, the metal sorption improves due to electrostatic attraction.

Table 1. Summary of sorption studies in binary systems for heavy metal removal from aqueous solution using low-cost sorbents

Sorbent	Metal ions studied	Conditions [1]		Ref.
		T, °C	pH	
Alginate	Cd^{+2} - Cu^{+2}, Pb^{+2} - Cd^{+2}, Cu^{+2} - Pb^{+2}	25	4.5	15,16
Bagasse fly ash	Cd^{+2} - Ni^{+2}	30	6	14
Bone char	Cd^{+2} - Cu^{+2}, Cd^{+2} - Zn^{+2}, Cu^{+2} - Zn^{+2}	20	4.9	20,22,23
Carbonized sewage sludge	Hg^{+2} - Pb^{+2}, Cu^{+2} - Hg^{+2}, Cr^{+3} - Hg^{+2}, Cu^{+2} - Pb^{+2}, Cu^{+2} - Cr^{+3}, Pb^{+2} - Cr^{+3}	25	3 - 5	46
Chicken feathers	Cu^{+2} - Zn^{+2}, Zn^{+2} - Ni^{+2}, Cu^{+2} - Ni^{+2}	25	NS	24
Chitosan	Cu^{+2} - Zn^{+2}, Zn^{+2} - Ni^{+2}, Cu^{+2} - Ni^{+2}, Cu^{+2} - Hg^{+2}	20 - 25	2 - 5	27,28
Crab shell	Pb^{+2} - Cd^{+2}, Cd^{+2} - Cr^{+3}, Pb^{+2} - Cr^{+3}	30	5	30
Iron oxide-coated sediment	Cu^{+2} - Ni^{+2}	20	5	33
Lignin	Cu^{+2} - Zn^{+2}, Cd^{+2} - Cu^{+2}, Cd^{+2} - Zn^{+2}	25	4.5	12
Olive pomace	Cd^{+2} - Cu^{+2}	25	4 - 5	34
Olive mill waste	Pb^{+2} - Cd^{+2}, Cu^{+2} - Pb^{+2}, Cd^{+2} - Cu^{+2}	20	7	35
Olive stone waste	Cd^{+2} - Cu^{+2}, Cu^{+2} - Ni^{+2}, Cu^{+2} - Pb^{+2}, Cd^{+2} - Ni^{+2}, Pb^{+2} - Ni^{+2}, Pb^{+2} - Cd^{+2}	20	5.5	36
Orange wastes	Cd^{+2} - Zn^{+2}, Pb^{+2} - Cd^{+2}, Pb^{+2} - Zn^{+2}	NS	4	37
Pine bark	Cd^{+2} - Cu^{+2}, Cu^{+2} - Ni^{+2}, Cu^{+2} - Pb^{+2}, Cd^{+2} - Ni^{+2}, Pb^{+2} - Cd^{+2}, Pb^{+2} - Ni^{+2}	NS	4	45
Peat	Cd^{+2} - Cu^{+2}, Cd^{+2} - Zn^{+2}, Cu^{+2} - Zn^{+2}, Cu^{+2} - Ni^{+2}, Cu^{+2} - Cr^{+3}, Cd^{+2} - Cr^{+3}, Cu^{+2} - Pb^{+2}, Pb^{+2} - Cd^{+2}, Pb^{+2} - Zn^{+2}	20 - 25	4 - 6	38-42,44
Rice husk ash	Cd^{+2} - Zn^{+2}, Cd^{+2} - Ni^{+2}	30	6	17,18

[1] NS indicates that the pH or temperature is not specified in the reference.

Table 2. Summary of sorption studies in ternary, quaternary and quinary systems for the removal of heavy metals in aqueous solution using low-cost sorbents

Sorbent	Metal ions studied	Conditions [1]		Ref.
		T, °C	pH	
Bone char	Zn^{+2} - Cd^{+2} - Cu^{+2}	20	4.9	23
Chicken feathers	Cu^{+2} - Pb^{+2} - Hg^{+2}, Cu^{+2} - Pb^{+2} - Zn^{+2} - Cd^{+2} - Ni^{+2}	25 - 45	1.9 - 5.6	25
Crab shell	Pb^{+2} - Cd^{+2} - Cr^{+3}	30	5	30
Clinoptilolite	Cu^{+2} - Cd^{+2} - Ni^{+2} - Pb^{+2}	NS	6.2	31
Lignin	Zn^{+2} - Cd^{+2} - Cu^{+2}	25	4.5	12
Low-grade phosphate rock	Cu^{+2} - Zn^{+2} - Pb^{+2}	30	NS	32
Olive mill waste	Cu^{+2} - Cd^{+2} - Pb^{+2}	20	7	35
Peat	Zn^{+2} - Cd^{+2} - Cu^{+2}, Cu^{+2} - Cd^{+2} - Pb^{+2}, Pb^{+2} - Zn^{+2} - Cd^{+2}	20 - 25	4.5 - 6	13,39
Pine bark	Cu^{+2} - Cd^{+2} - Ni^{+2}, Cu^{+2} - Cd^{+2} - Pb^{+2}, Cd^{+2} - Ni^{+2} - Pb^{+2}, Ni^{+2} - Cu^{+2} - Pb^{+2}, Cu^{+2} - Cd^{+2} - Ni^{+2} - Pb^{+2}	NS	4	45
Rice husk ash	Cd^{+2} - Ni^{+2} - Zn^{+2}	30	6	10
Volcanic lava ash	Cd^{+2} - Cu^{+2} - Cr^{+3}	20	6	19

[1] NS indicates that the pH or temperature is not specified in the reference.

On the other hand, rice husk ash is an agricultural waste obtained during the burning of rice husk. This low-cost sorbent has been tested in both binary and ternary solutions of heavy metals. For example, Srivastava et al. [10,17,18] reported the simultaneous removal of Cd^{+2}, Ni^{+2} and Zn^{+2} from binary and ternary mixtures using rice husk ash. This sorbent was obtained from a paper mill industry and was used in sorption experiments without treatment. This waste has a surface area of 36.44 m^2/g and contains several functional groups as -CO-, -OH, -Si-OH-, -SiH, -C-OH- that may interact with heavy metals. Multicomponent sorption experiments were performed at 30 °C and pH 6 using different metal concentrations (0.1 – 1.7 mmol/L). Equilibrium studies indicated that the combined effect of both binary and ternary mixtures on sorption behavior is of antagonism, where the equilibrium uptake of each ion decreases with increasing concentration of other ions. In general, for binary systems, the sorption capacity of rice husk ash for Cd^{+2} is less than Ni^{+2}, and the sorbed amount of Zn^{+2} is larger than Cd^{+2}. It appears that, under competitive conditions, the Ni^{+2} sorption was less affected by the presence of Cd^{+2} ions in comparison to the inhibition exerted in the reverse situation; while the sorption capacity of rice husk ash for Cd^{+2} is less than Zn^{+2}. In ternary mixture, the affinity of rice husk ash for Zn^{+2} is higher than the Ni^{+2} and Cd^{+2} ions. Several non-modified and modified multicomponent models were used for data correlation. The extended Freundlich model offers the best fits for both sets of binary experimental data; while Sheindorf-Rebuhn-Sheintuch model provided the best regression of ternary experimental sorption data in comparison to the other models. Finally, it appears that the removal of these metal ions using rice husk ash is a combination of two mechanisms: chemisorption and electrostatic attractions.

The volcanic lava ash has been also studied as an alternative low-cost sorbent for heavy metal removal from wastewaters [19]. This siliceous material is released into the atmosphere from volcanoes in quantity which is estimated up to 150 million tons per year. The sorption capabilities of this waste were tested in multimetallic experiments using a mixed solution of three ions: Cd^{+2}, Cu^{+2} and Cr^{+3}. Sorption experiments were performed at pH 6 and 20 °C employing different equimolar concentrations of each metal (0.025 – 0.1 mmol/L). In this study, Cu^{+2} ions were sorbed preferably more than Cd^{+2} and Cr^{+3} ions at tested conditions. Authors commented that at low initial metal concentration, the sorption behavior was found comparable with those from single-metal tests (i.e., under these conditions, no competitive effects were found). However, the multicomponent isotherms were not performed and, as a consequence, the maximum sorption capacities for competitive conditions are unknown. According to author's discussion, the lava ash is a material of complex structure and heterogeneous composition, where several mechanisms may act in the removal of heavy metal.

2.3. Bone Char

Recently, the interest in the application of materials from biological origin (plant or animal) in heavy metal removal has increased. In particular, animal bones are composed in 65 – 70% of inorganic material, mainly hydroxyapatite. This hydroxyapatite in bones is useful for sorbing organic and inorganic species from aqueous solutions, including heavy metal ions. Bone char is a heterogeneous sorbent which is derived from the pyrolisis of animal bones. It mainly contains carbon and hydroxyapatite randomly distributed on the surface [20].

Traditionally, this sorbent has been used to decolorize sugar solutions in the sugar industry. But, recent studies have shown that bone char has significant sorption capacities for various metal ions [20,21]. However, few studies have been performed under competitive conditions [21-23]. Reported studies have tested the sorption behavior of bone char using binary and ternary solutions of Cu^{+2}, Cd^{+2} and Zn^{+2} ions [20-23]. Several kinetic and equilibrium sorption experiments were carried out by Cheung et al. [22] and Cheung et al. [23] to assess the influence of co-ion and its concentration on the metal uptake of bone char at pH 4.9 and 20 °C using metal concentrations from 0.1 − 6 mmol/L. These studies revealed an antagonistic effect of Cu^{+2}, Cd^{+2} and Zn^{+2} ions in both binary and ternary solutions. The sorption of Cd^{+2} and Zn^{+2} ions was negatively impacted by Cu^{+2} ions, especially at high concentrations of the systems. Cd^{+2} or Zn^{+2} ions were competing with and being displaced by the Cu^{+2} ions in the multicomponent systems. In binary solution Cd^{+2}-Zn^{+2}, the uptake was higher for Cd^{+2} ions. It appears that the presence of Cd^{+2} has a more competitive effect on Cu^{+2} sorption than Zn^{+2}. However, the sorption capacities for the Cu^{+2} were higher than the Cd^{+2} and Zn^{+2}, and the sorption capacity for Cd^{+2} was also higher than Zn^{+2}. Overall, the sorbed amount of all metal ions in binary systems was higher than those reported for ternary solutions. Mass transfer equations were used to model the multicomponent sorption behavior in these binary and ternary systems obtaining satisfactory fits [20-23]. With respect to the removal mechanisms, these studies proposed that the sorption of metal ions on bone char may involve ion exchange, surface sorption and chelation.

2.4. Chicken Feathers

The fibrous proteins contained in some animal processing wastes are abundant resources to obtain potential sorbents for heavy metal removal from water. The chemical composition of these proteins involves carboxyl, hydroxyl and amine-groups that may act as binders for metal ions. In particular, the keratin is a protein that contains functional groups useful for the sorption of metal species [24-26]. Chicken feathers are an important source of this protein because they consist of about 91% keratin. This feather keratin is a by-product in the poultry industry and is available in significant amounts because a chicken has about 5 to 7% of its body weight in feathers. Sorption processes using chicken feathers have proven to be effective and economically feasible to remove heavy metals from water. However, most of the studies on the removal of heavy metals ions using chicken feathers have been focused on the uptake of single metals, and few studies have reported the removal of heavy metals in multicomponent systems [24,25]. Details of multicomponent sorption studies using chicken feathers are given in Tables 1 and 2.

For example, Al-Asheh et al. [24] studied the removal of binary systems composed of Cu^{+2}, Zn^{+2} and Ni^{+2} ions using metal concentrations from 0.3 to 1.7 mmol/L at 25 °C. Chicken feathers were used in sorption experiments without treatment. This study indicated that the sorption of all metal ions was suppressed by the presence of the other ion in all binary systems tested, and the level of suppression in the metal sorption increased as the concentration of the other metal ion in the system increased. The removal of Zn^{+2} and Cu^{+2} ions was significantly affected by the presence of Ni^{+2} ion especially at high metal concentrations in both Zn^{+2}-Ni^{+2} and Cu^{+2}-Ni^{+2} solutions, while the presence of Cu^{+2} ions appears to have a significant effect on Zn^{+2} sorption. Authors concluded that the competitive removal of these metal ions may be attributed to the electronegativity of each metallic species. Finally, Langmuir, Freundlich and Sips multicomponent equations were used for data correlation employing the parameters obtained from single-solute systems. Freundlich model provided the better fit for all sorption data, while Langmuir model showed the worst performance.

In other study, Kar and Misra [25] reported the removal of Cu^{+2}, Pb^{+2} and Hg^{+2} in a ternary metal solution containing 2 mg/L of each metal at three pH values: 1.9, 4.5 and 5.6. The sorbent behavior was tested using metal removal percentages and authors reported that the removal percentage was of the following order: $Pb^{+2} > Hg^{+2} > Cu^{+2}$. It appears that the sorption of Pb^{+2} or Cu^{+2} onto chicken feathers is better since the atomic weight of these metal ions is higher. For the case of Hg^{+2}, they suggested that this metal may form an anionic complex in solution and thus chicken feathers showed better sorption behavior at lower pH, unlike Pb^{+2} and Cu^{+2}. In addition, metal removal studies were carried out using a multicomponent solution with an initial concentration of 2 mg/L of Cu^{+2}, Pb^{+2}, Zn^{+2}, Cd^{+2} and Ni^{+2} at three different pH values: 4.2, 5, and 5.6. The highest metal removal was obtained at pH 5.6 and the removal percentage was: $Pb^{+2} > Cu^{+2} > Cd^{+2} > Zn^{+2} > Ni^{+2}$. Kar and Misra [25] noted that chicken feathers removed very low amounts of Zn^{+2}, Cd^{+2} and Ni^{+2} under these conditions. Unfortunately, these authors do not report the multicomponent isotherms and as a consequence, the maximum sorption capacities under competitive conditions are unknown. This study suggested that the metal removal by keratin may occur by a combination of both physisorption and chemisorption.

2.5. Chitosan

Chitosan is a partially acetylated glucosamine polymer and it is produced cheaply from deacetylation of chitin, which is one of the most abundant polymers in the nature and is the major component of crustacean shells that are wastes of seafood processing industries [27-29]. Several authors have found that chitosan has unique sorption and chelating properties for a number of heavy metal ions. In fact, the removal of various metallic species has been studied extensively using raw and chemically modified chitosan, principally in single-metal systems [1]. For the case of competitive removal of heavy metals, Juang and Shao [27] reported the sorption of Cu^{+2}, Ni^{+2} and Zn^{+2} ions in binary solutions using glutaraldehyde cross-linked chitosan beads obtained from lobster shell wastes. This sorbent has a surface area of 60 m^2/g. Experiments were carried out at 25 °C and different pH conditions using initial metal concentrations of 0.77 – 17 mmol/L and a sorbent dosage of 1 mg/mL. This study revealed a preferential sorption of Cu^{+2} ions on chitosan beads and an antagonistic competitive effect was determined for these binary systems. Cu^{+2} sorption appears to be preferred in the binary systems Cu^{+2}-Ni^{+2} and Cu^{+2}-Zn^{+2}, while the removal of Zn^{+2} is favored in the binary solution of Ni^{+2}-Zn^{+2}. A simplified model was developed for sorption data regression by considering possible competitive reactions, including the protons in the solutions. The amino and hydroxyl groups on chitosan were identified as active sites for heavy metal removal.

In other study, Vieira et al. [28] investigated the binary sorption of Cu^{+2} and Hg^{+2} metal ions using natural and crosslinked chitosan membranes. The influence of metal concentration and the crosslinking agent in the mixture (i.e., glutaraldehyde and epichlorohydrin) were evaluated. Porous membranes of chitosan were prepared and the raw chitosan membranes were crosslinked using aqueous glutaraldehyde and epichlorohydrin solutions. Batch sorption experiments were conducted using a sorbent dosage of 12 mg/mL at pH 5 and 20 °C. For natural chitosan membranes, the Hg^{+2} ions were more sorbed than the Cu^{+2} ions, indicating a stronger interaction between the first metallic specie and the sorbent. The sorbed amount of Cu^{+2} ions in binary solutions was significantly reduced in comparison with the single system, which was attributed to the competition of Hg^{+2} ions. On the other hand, the results for glutaraldehyde-crosslinked and epichlorohydrin-crosslinked chitosan membranes indicated that, in some cases, the sorbed amount in binary systems was higher than those reported for monometallic systems, suggesting a synergy of electrostatic and chelation mechanisms. Different versions of Langmuir-based model were used for data correlation obtaining a well fit of experimental data. Literature suggested that amino and hydroxyl groups of chitosan may participate in sorption of heavy metals [27,29]. It appears that the interaction of these groups with metallic ions can depend of the pH and also of the main solution components. Finally, the sorption behavior of chitosan is also related to its deacetylation degree where the sorption capacity improves as the deacetylation degree increases [29].

2.6. Crab Shell

Recently, Kim [30] reported the application of crab shells as sorbent for multicomponent heavy metal removal. Most crab products are used for food processing and the crab shells can be obtained cheaply from process wastes. Shell of Chinonecetes was obtained as waste from a crabmeat processing plant. A particle size of 420 – 841 μm with a specific surface area of 13.35 m^2/g was considered for the sorption experiments. The chemical composition analysis indicated that this waste contained protein, ash, lipid, and chitin. Experimental tests were done with binary and ternary mixtures of Cd^{+2}, Pb^{+2} and Cr^{+3} using a sorbent dosage of 1 mg/mL and an equimolar concentration of 0.5 mmol/L for each metallic specie at pH 5 and 30 °C. Sorption data suggested that the presence of Cd^{+2} did not significantly affect the removal of both Pb^{+2} and Cr^{+3} in both binary and ternary solutions. It appears that Cr^{+3} and Pb^{+2} ions had severe inhibition effect on the removal of Cd^{+2} especially in ternary mixtures. This study concluded that Pb^{+2} and Cr^{+3} can be easily removed in mixed metal ions systems using this sorbent. Finally, the data modeling was not performed in this study.

2.7. Natural Minerals and Sediments

In recent years, the study of different types of natural low-cost sorbents such as minerals and sediments has received more attention. These natural sorbents are abundant in nature and are considered suitable for the removal of trace heavy metals. In this context, natural zeolites have gained a significant interest in sorption field due to their valuable sorption characteristics provided by combination of ion-exchange and molecular-sieve properties, their nontoxic nature, and wide availability [31]. Clinoptilolite is one of the most common natural zeolites and its large industrial deposits are connected with volcanic sedimentary high-silica rocks. Several studies have investigated various aspects of heavy metal removal from aqueous solutions by clinoptilolite, including the chemical modification of this zeolite to improve its sorption behavior. However, in few works the influence of other ions on heavy metal removal from mixed solutions has been studied. For instance, the sorption behavior of clinoptilolite rock was tested in multicomponent solutions of Ni^{+2}, Cu^{+2}, Pb^{+2} and Cd^{+2} ions [31]. These studies were performed at pH 6.2 using an initial metal concentration of 20 mg/L for each metallic ion. For this zeolite, Ni^{+2} sorption decreased significantly due to competition with other ions. Unfortunately, multicomponent isotherms were not performed and the competitive effects of all metal ions can not be clearly identified. It is convenient to mention that the sorption behavior of zeolites is affected by several factors such as metal concentration, temperature, pH, and crystalline structure of the zeolites.

Alternatively, other low-cost mineral sorbents have been successfully utilized for the removal of heavy metal ions from water. For example, Prasad et al. [32] reported the application of low-grade phosphate rock on multicomponent sorption of Pb^{+2}, Cu^{+2} and Zn^{+2} ions. This mineral is considered as waste for fertilizer industries due to its very low phosphate value and its use in sorption process is a viable alternative for its disposal. Samples of low-grade rock phosphate from India were collected. X-ray diffraction analysis of this mineral indicated the presence of calcite, fluorapatite, quartz, dolomite and iron oxide. Samples of rock phosphate with a surface area of 7.29 m^2/g were used in the sorption experiments, where the sorbent dosage was 5 mg/mL. Ternary solutions of Pb^{+2}-Cu^{+2}-Zn^{+2} were employed to obtain kinetic and equilibrium sorption data at 30 °C. Results indicated that the removal of each ion was suppressed by the presence of other competing metal ions. In fact, the sorption capacity of low-grade phosphate rock decreased in multimetallic system in comparison with a single component solution. Kinetic and equilibrium data were correlated using classical monocomponent pseudo-first and second order models, while Langmuir and Freundlich models were used for isotherm fitting. It appears that ion exchange coupled with complexation mechanism is the most probable mechanism responsible for metal uptake by low-grade rock phosphate.

On the other hand, Boujelben et al. [33] studied the feasibility of using natural iron oxide-coated sediment as sorbent for the removal of Cu^{+2} and Ni^{+2}. The selection of this material was based on its low cost and abundance in Tunisian ores. The surface area of this solid was 6.97 m^2/g and it was characterized by some techniques as FTIR spectroscopy, energy dispersive of X-ray and X-ray diffraction. The results of elemental analysis indicated the presence of silica, iron oxides and other minerals. Binary sorption experiments were performed at pH 5 and 20 °C using different metal concentrations (0.5 – 1.9 mmol/L) and a sorbent dosage of 20 mg/mL. The sorbed amount of metal ions in the mixed solutions was less than those for single-component solutions showing an antagonistic competitive effect between these metallic species. In fact, the removal of Cu^{+2} was greater than Ni^{+2}, suggesting that the functional groups on the surface of this sediment had a relatively stronger affinity for Cu^{+2} than Ni^{+2}. This study concluded that the natural iron oxide-coated sediment may be used for the simultaneous removal of Cu^{+2} and Ni^{+2} ions from metal-containing effluents.

2.8. Lignin

The use of Kraft lignin as an alternative low-cost sorbent for heavy metal removal has been considered to solve the disposal problem associated to this industrial waste [12]. Lignin is recognized as the second most abundant natural polymer after cellulose and comprises from 17 to 30% of plant biomass. In particular, lignin isolated from wastes of Kraft pulping has a high surface area ($\cong 1260$ m^2/g) and presents polyhydric phenols and sulfur-containing groups that may act for the removal of heavy metals. Mohan et al. [12] have reported the removal of Cu^{+2}, Cd^{+2} and Zn^{+2} in binary and ternary metal solutions using Kraft lignin at pH 4.5 and 25 °C. It is convenient to mention that authors only reported and analyzed the sorption behavior for Cd^{+2} and Cu^{+2} ions, and the sorption capacities for Zn^{+2} were not provided. Besides, the sorption tests were performed at different metal concentrations (0.01 – 5 mmol/L) using a Cu^{+2} to Cd^{+2} ratio of 1:1. Results of this study shown that metal sorption capacity for both Cd^{+2} and Cu^{+2} decreased more in ternary mixtures in contrast with the binary systems. For all studied systems, there was sorption suppression by the presence of other metallic species. The sorption capacity of lignin for Cu^{+2} ions in the binary and ternary systems was always significantly greater than the other metal ions. It appears that the presence of Zn^{+2} affects the removal of both Cd^{+2} and Cu^{+2} ions, being more significant the competitive effect for Cd^{+2}. Besides, in the binary system Cd^{+2}-Cu^{+2}, lignin preferred Cu^{+2} to Cd^{+2} ions. These relative sorption preferences were related to the relative ionic property orders (e.g. hydrated ionic radius, electronegativity and standard reduction potential). The correlation of multicomponent sorption data was performed using the classical (i.e., monocomponent) Langmuir and Freundlich models where the Langmuir isotherm provided the best fit. Authors suggested that several mechanisms are involved in the multicomponent heavy metal removal using lignin, which may include sorption, surface deposition and ion exchange.

2.9. Olive Wastes

The production of olive oil generates large volumes of wastes that vary in composition depending on the production system [34-36]. Current studies have proposed the waste of olive oil production as sorbent of heavy metals. For example, Pagnanelli et al. [34] studied the simultaneous removal of Cu^{+2} and Cd^{+2} ions using olive pomace, which is a solid waste from olive oil production. These authors noted that the oil production yields a solid residue (olive pomace) (30%), which may be used as fertilizer, nutritive additive for animal food, source of heat energy, soil stabilizer, and also as low-cost sorbent. Olive pomace consists of cellulose, lignin and uronic acids along with oily wastes and polyphenolic compounds. This complex matrix contains numerous functional groups useful for metal binding. The behavior of this sorbent was tested using binary solutions of Cu^{+2} and Cd^{+2} ions with different metal concentrations (0.3 – 1.8 mmol/L) at different pH levels. Overall, the sorption of each metal decreased as the initial concentration of the antagonist metal in solution increased. This effect was more evident for Cd^{+2} sorption while little effect can be noticed for Cu^{+2} at tested conditions. The competition effect was more evident at pH 5 than 4 for both Cd^{+2} and Cu^{+2} ions. A statistical analysis indicated that Cu^{+2} ions significantly influence Cd^{+2} removal at both pH levels. Olive pomace may bind metallic species by different mechanism such as complexation, chelation, physical sorption, ion exchange and electrostatic interactions.

On the other hand, Martinez-Garcia et al. [35] reported the application of olive mill waste for the sorption of heavy metals from aqueous solution. This waste has a high moisture content (55 – 60%) and contains polyphenolic compounds, which limit disposal alternatives. Multicomponent sorption experiments were performed using binary and ternary metallic solutions of Pb^{+2}, Cd^{+2} and Cu^{+2} ions at 20 °C and different conditions of pH. This study noted that when Cu^{+2} was in solution with other metal ions, its uptake was considerably reduced. Also, Pb^{+2} sorption presented the same adverse effect when it was mixed with other metallic species. Authors concluded that the uptake ability of olive mill waste was seriously compromised resulting in low sorption capacities for tested heavy metals.

Finally, another study reported the reuse of olive stone waste in its native form without further treatment as sorbent material for the removal of Cu^{+2}, Cd^{+2}, Ni^{+2} and Pb^{+2} from binary mixtures [36]. An olive stone waste with a specific surface area of 0.187 m^2/g and obtained from pulp generated in the oil production industry was used in the sorption studies. Batch experiments were carried out at 20 °C, initial pH of 5.5 and using binary metal mixtures in equimolar concentrations. Authors noted that metals in binary mixtures showed an antagonistic competitive effect; however, multicomponent sorption isotherms were not reported with exception of Cd^{+2}-Pb^{+2} system. They suggested that sorption-complexation in addition to ion-exchange may be involved in the case of sorption of the Cu^{+2}, Cd^{+2} and Pb^{+2} ions, while ion-exchange appears to be the most important mechanism for Ni^{+2} sorption.

2.10. Orange Wastes

Pérez-Marín et al. [37] reported the sorption of Cd^{+2}, Zn^{+2} and Pb^{+2} ions in binary mixtures using orange wastes as sorbent. Orange waste consists of cellulose, hemicellulose, pectin, and limonene. FTIR analysis indicated the presence of metal binding groups such as carboxyl and hydroxyl. This waste was collected from an orange juice manufacturer, washed with tap water and finally dried. Binary sorption experiments were performed at pH 4 using the subsequent addition method with initial metal concentrations from 0.07 to 1.5 mmol/L. For each binary system studied (Cd^{+2}-Zn^{+2}, Cd^{+2}-Pb^{+2}, Pb^{+2}-Zn^{+2}), an antagonistic sorption behavior was determined where the sorbed amount of one ion decreased when the concentration of the co-ion increased. Specifically, the removal of Cd^{+2} and Zn^{+2} was moderately affected by the presence of the other metal. For binary mixtures with Pb^{+2}, the uptake of Cd^{+2} and Zn^{+2} decreased significantly, especially at high Pb^{+2} concentrations. However, the presence of Cd^{+2} and Zn^{+2} ions in solution has a small effect on the capacity of orange waste to remove Pb^{+2} ions. The affinity of orange wastes for these heavy metals was related to the physicochemical parameters of metallic species: atomic weight, ionic radius, possible coordination number, and electronegativity. Finally, the extended Langmuir model was successfully used for data regression.

2.11. Peat

Peat has been recognized as a low-cost sorbent for removal of heavy metal ions from wastewaters [38]. It is a naturally abundant and inexpensive material, which is constituted by lignin, cellulose, humic and fulvic acids. Studies reported in literature indicate that peat contains polar functional groups such as aldehydes, ketones, carboxylic, hydroxylic and phenolic groups, that can be involved in the heavy metal uptake via sorption. Besides, peat is also known by its ion exchange properties [13,39,40]. In particular, the presence of humic acid in the peat is considered as the responsible of the metal ion sorption. Probably, peat is the most studied low-cost sorbent for removal of heavy metals in multicomponent systems and the sorption behavior of peat has been tested especially in binary and ternary systems [13,38-43].

For example, McKay and Porter [39] reported the results for multicomponent equilibrium studies of Cd^{+2}-Cu^{+2}, Cd^{+2}-Zn^{+2}, Cu^{+2}-Zn^{+2} and Cd^{+2}-Cu^{+2}-Zn^{+2} mixtures on peat. Sorption experiments were determined at 20 °C and pH 4.5, using metal solutions with different initial concentrations. By comparing the single and multimetallic sorption capacities, competition effects can be observed between the different metal species in solution. In fact, the sorption capacity of Cu^{+2} in the binary and ternary systems was always significantly greater than the other metal ions. This study showed that Cu^{+2} has a significant impact on sorption behavior of both Zn^{+2} and Cd^{+2}. This study suggested that the sorption mechanism for Cu^{+2} is different from that of Cd^{+2}, Zn^{+2} and other divalent metals.

On the other hand, Ho et al. [41] and Ho and McKay [42] studied the competitive sorption of Cu^{+2} and Ni^{+2} onto peat. Specifically, Ho et al. [41] reported the effect that a competing ion has on the rates of removal of Cu^{+2} and Ni^{+2} ions at pH 5 and 25 °C, while Ho and McKay [42] studied the effects of competitive sorption in batch systems at various metal ion concentrations of Cu^{+2}-Ni^{+2} at pH 4.5 and 25 °C. In bi-solute kinetic studies, the presence of secondary metal affects the sorption of both Cu^{+2} and Ni^{+2}, and the equilibrium concentrations of both metals were lower than in their respective mono-solute systems. It appears that Cu^{+2} has a greater effect on the Ni^{+2} uptake in the bi-solute systems causing a decrease in the diffusion rate. Ho et al. [41] established that a pseudo-second order model provides a more appropriate description of the bi-solute binding of Cu^{+2} and Ni^{+2} ions to peat. The results of equilibrium sorption studies of Ho and McKay [42] also indicated that competition occurred in Cu^{+2}-Ni^{+2} system and Cu^{+2} is removed more extensively than Ni^{+2}. The predicted equilibrium data using Langmuir-based models were found to be in agreement with experimental values.

Peat has also been used for simultaneous removal of Cr^{+3}, Cd^{+2} and Cu^{+2} ions in binary metal solutions at pH 4 and 22 – 25 °C [38]. As expected, the presence of co-ions decreased the metal uptake and this competitive effect increased as co-ion content was increased. This study indicated that the percentage reduction in metal uptakes ranged from 50 to 70% at the highest co-ion concentrations. However, Cd^{+2} as a co-ion diminished Cr^{+3} uptake by a maximum of 30%, whereas Cu^{+2} uptake was reduced by approximately 50% in the presence of the same Cd^{+2} concentration. Both Cr^{+3} and Cu^{+2} caused large and similar reductions in Cd^{+2} uptakes. This study concluded that the similarity of the uptake competition effects of Cr^{+3} and Cu^{+2} is noteworthy and is likely to result from the likeness of their ionic radii.

Qin et al. [13] and Qin and Wen [44] studied the competitive sorption of Pb^{+2}, Cu^{+2} and Cd^{+2} in binary and ternary systems. Both studies concluded that Pb^{+2} was always favorably sorbed on peat over Cu^{+2} and Cd^{+2}, and Cu^{+2} over Cd^{+2} in the multisolute systems. The individual sorption capacities of the three metallic species decreased in binary and ternary systems, where the decrease in sorption capacity was greater in ternary solute system as compared to binary systems. In fact, Cd^{+2} sorption decrease was more significant in binary and ternary systems than Pb^{+2} and Cu^{+2}. Pb^{+2} ions significantly inhibited the removal of Cu^{+2} and Cd^{+2}, and Cd^{+2} was more affected in the competitive sorption. Hence, the sorption capacity of Pb^{+2} was reduced to a less extent than that of Cu^{+2} and Cd^{+2}. These studies indicated that as the metal concentrations increased further, metals with higher affinity competed with metal with lower affinity for the sorption sites of peat. When metal competes for the same sorption sites of a sorbent, metal with a greater affinity could displace others with a lower affinity. Multicomponent kinetic studies showed typical biphasic kinetics with a rapid sorption of Pb^{+2}, Cu^{+2} and Cd^{+2} on peat at the initial stage followed by a slower one. The second-order model fitted the kinetics of these ions in multicomponent systems obtaining satisfactory correlation coefficients. Finally, Qin et al. [13] reported the application of X-ray absorption spectroscopy for studying the mechanisms of competitive removal of heavy metals on peat. Their results showed that both Cu^{+2} and Pb^{+2} were bonded primarily to carboxylic ligands of peat without excluding hydroxylic groups, providing an evidence for the competitive behavior of these metallic species.

Recently, Balasubramanian et al. [40] reported the multicomponent sorption of Pb^{+2}, Zn^{+2} and Cd^{+2} ions onto Indonesian peat at 23 °C and pH 6. From results obtained using binary and ternary metallic solutions, it was observed that Pb^{+2} was favorably sorbed onto peat over Cd^{+2} and Zn^{+2}, and Cd^{+2} over Zn^{+2}. The sorption capacities for three metallic species showed decreases in both binary and ternary systems, and the decrease was greater in the ternary systems as compared to the binary system. This decrement in sorption capacity was associated to the metal interactions and sorption antagonistic behavior. These authors concluded that in addition to ion exchange, a surface sorption–complexation mechanism may be involved in heavy metal removal using peat. In general, carbon-oxygen surface function groups were considered to be responsible for the sorption of heavy metal ions. It is convenient to note that the possible differences in competitive effects and sorption preferences may be related to the great variety of peat types.

2.12. Pine Bark

Pine bark, another agricultural waste, has been used for multicomponent removal of Cd^{+2}, Ni^{+2}, Cu^{+2} and Pb^{+2} ions in binary, ternary and quaternary metallic solutions [45]. Sorption capacities of bark and other agricultural materials are generally attributed to their protein, carbohydrates and phenolic compounds, which have metal-binding functional groups such as carboxyl and amino groups. Pine bark from Ottawa region was used for the sorption tests without treatment and the experiments were performed at pH 4, in which each metal had an initial concentration of 100 mg/L. The interaction effects in multicomponent sorption experiments using bark were identified and the authors reported that in most cases the sorption capacity for one ion was significantly affected by the presence of the others. It appears that Pb^{+2} ions suppressed the sorption of both Cu^{+2} and Cd^{+2} ions in ternary and binary systems. On the other hand, Ni^{+2} sorption was strongly inhibited by Cu^{+2} ions in the ternary and quaternary systems that contained these metals. However, Ni^{+2} inhibited the removal of both Cu^{+2} and Pb^{+2} ions in binary solutions. It is interesting to note that synergism effect was reported for Ni^{+2} ions in several binary mixtures at tested conditions. As expected, the competitive effect in quaternary mixture is higher than those reported for ternary and binary mixtures. These results suggest a complex interaction of heavy metal ions on pine bark under competitive conditions. Overall, this study concluded that the following affinity series may be established using binary selectivity indexes: $Pb^{+2} > Cu^{+2} > Cd^{+2} > Ni^{+2}$. The principal mechanisms for heavy metal removal using pine bark may be due to the sorption on surface and pores, and complexation [45].

2.13. Sewage Sludge

Sewage sludge is a natural carbonaceous material with volatile components in their structure. By this reason, this material has been considered as potential precursor for the production of sorbents. For example, Otero et al. [46] have reported the study of two different sewage sludge-based sorbents for the removal of heavy metals under competitive conditions. Sewage sludge from an urban treatment plant using activated sludge biological treatment was used for the production of sorbents by pyrolysis. This sludge was pyrolized with and without previous chemical activation. These carbonized sewage sludges were used for multicomponent sorption experiments. Authors indicated that surface area of the chemically activated carbon (472 m^2/g) was higher than the carbon prepared without activation (60 m^2/g). Sorption experiments were performed in binary solutions of Hg^{+2}-Pb^{+2}, Hg^{+2}-Cu^{+2}, Hg^{+2}-Cr^{+3}, Pb^{+2}-Cu^{+2}, Pb^{+2}-Cr^{+3}, and Cu^{+2}-Cr^{+3} at 25 °C and pH 3 − 5. Results indicated that the carbonized sewage sludge with chemical activation has a higher capacity to remove these metal ions. In all cases, the presence of a competitive metal in solution caused a reduction of the sorption capacity compared with the obtained in single sorption. The presence of Cr^{+3} affects less the sorption of Pb^{+2} and Hg^{+2} than any other metal ion. The sorption of Pb^{+2} was remarkably reduced by Hg^{+2}. The Cr^{+3} is the less competitive metal for Pb^{+2} removal. Note that Cu^{+2} sorption was strongly inhibited by Hg^{+2} ions while the presence of Pb^{+2} ions in solution had a small effect on Cr^{+3} and Cu^{+2} sorption. Conventional Langmuir isotherm was used for data modeling in these binary metallic solutions. The sorption capacity in competition onto carbonized sewage sludge was $Hg^{+2} > Pb^{+2} > Cu^{+2} > Cr^{+3}$.

3. COMPARISON OF MULTICOMPONENT SORPTION CAPACITIES OF LOW-COST SORBENTS UNDER COMPETITIVE CONDITIONS AND THE SORBENT REGENERATION

3.1. Sorption Capacities

The review indicates that a wide variety of sorbents has been studied for removal of metallic species in multicomponent systems. Many of these materials have not cost, are abundant, easily available and may be biodegradable. Their use as sorbents for water treatment provides an aggregated value. They are usually used without any treatment but it is feasible to modify their morphology, texture, surface groups, and chemical composition for enhancing the sorption capacity. It is convenient to remark that the improvement of sorption capacity in these sorbents using a proper treatment may not imply a significant increase of its final cost.

With illustrative purposes, Figures 1 − 3 and Table 3 show the highest sorption capacities of metals in aqueous solutions (q_e) for several sorbents. These capacities have been standardized and are reported in molar basis for a direct comparison because the analysis of sorption behavior may be misinterpreted when they are on weight basis [12]. Literature may fail to provide the detailed experimental conditions where the sorbent behavior has been tested, and these conditions may vary significantly from one study to another. Therefore, these sorption capacities should be considered as a reference of values that can be achieved under a specific set of conditions rather than a maximum sorption behavior.

As expected, the competitive effect in sorption process is more noticeable with the increase in the number of metal ions in solution and the sorbent behavior may vary significantly for different co-ions (see results reported in Figures 1 – 3 and Table 3). Overall, antagonistic competitive effects occur for various sorbents and different metallic systems. Note that the majority of sorption data is focused on equilibrium studies in binary solutions. In fact, Tables 2 and 3 indicate that there is a lack of sorption studies employing solutions with three or more co-ions. Binary solutions with Cd^{+2} and Cu^{+2} as co-ion have been widely used to assess competitive effects on the sorption behavior of several materials. The sorption capacities of Cd^{+2} and Cu^{+2} metal ions in aqueous solution using some low-cost sorbents are given in Figures 1 and 3, respectively. The industrial use and pollutant potential of these metals is perhaps an explanation of their selection as benchmark in sorption studies. It appears that the presence of Cu^{+2} in multicomponent solutions has a significant effect on sorption of other co-ions. Although there are significant differences in the sorbent behavior, chitosan and alginate have demonstrated outstanding sorption capacities in multimetallic systems. Peat may also offer an attractive behavior for some binary solutions (see Figures 1 – 3).

Note that several authors have attempted to use various physical and chemical properties of metal ions such as ionic radius, electronegativity, electron affinity, chemical coordination characteristics, and solvatation to explain and justify the affinity and sorption preferences in multimetallic solutions [19]. Although the trends of multimetallic sorption behavior may show qualitatively dependence on certain of these chemical properties, at present it is difficult to identify common factors because several variables affect the sorbent behavior. Specifically, the sorption preference and affinity for different heavy metals are related to the characteristics of the sorbent (e.g., functional groups, structure, textural properties, etc), the solution chemistry (e.g., pH, temperature, ionic strength), and the presence of diverse sorption mechanisms. Undoubtedly, the identification of factors affecting the selectivity and affinity of low-cost sorbents is a future research topic.

In this context, it is convenient to remark that the multicomponent isotherms are useful to characterize the sorbent capabilities when several metallic species are present. They are also important to explore systematically the effect of the concentration of one metal ion on the uptake of other metal ions and to identify the effect of pH, temperature, and ionic strength on sorbent behavior. For example, the application of three-dimensional sorption surfaces for binary systems allows the understanding of competitive effects of solutes, and the extrapolation and interpolation of metal uptakes [38].

Table 3. Sorption capacities and competitive effects reported for several low-cost sorbents in aqueous solutions of ternary, quaternary and quinary metal systems

Sorbent	Sorption capacity, mmol/g [1]							Antagonism	Synergism	Non-interaction	Ref.
	Cd^{+2}	Cu^{+2}	Cr^{+3}	Zn^{+2}	Pb^{+2}	Ni^{+2}	Hg^{+2}				
Ternary mixture											
Bone char	0.200	0.430		0.150				✓			23
Chicken feathers		0.007			0.003		0.003	NS			25
Crab shell	0.100		0.500					✓ (Cd^{+2})		✓	30
Lignin	0.143	0.152		NS				✓ (Cu^{+2},Cd^{+2})			12
Low grade phosphate rock		0.148		0.076	0.045			✓			32
Peat	0.040	0.080		0.030				✓			13,39
	0.050	0.320			0.450			✓			
	0.116			0.138	0.106			✓			
Pine bark	0.023	0.066			0.041	0.002		✓			45
	0.047	0.099			0.042	0.058		✓	✓ (Cu^{+2})		
	0.028	0.089			0.039	0.0		✓			
Rice husk ash	0.023			0.070		0.062		✓			10
Volcanic lava ash	0.007	0.009	0.005					NS		✓ (Ni^{+2})	19
Quaternary and quinary mixture											
Pine bark	0.038	0.061			0.040	0.0		✓			45
Chicken feathers	0.002	0.008		0.001	0.004	0.002		NS			25

[1] NS indicates that sorption capacity or competitive effect is not specified.

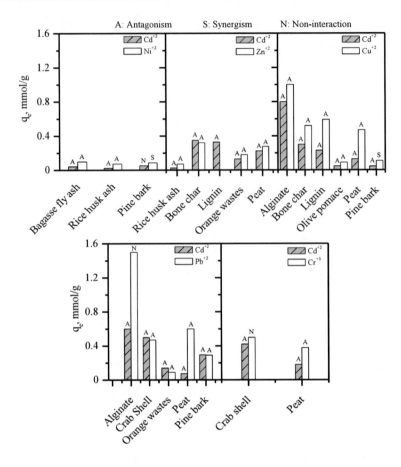

Figure 1. Sorption capacities and competitive effects reported for several low-cost sorbents in aqueous solutions of binary metal systems with Cd^{+2} as principal co-ion.

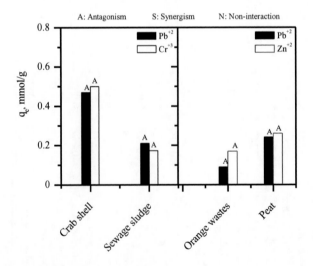

Figure 2. Sorption capacities and competitive effects reported for several low-cost sorbents in aqueous solutions of binary metal systems with Pb^{+2} as principal co-ion.

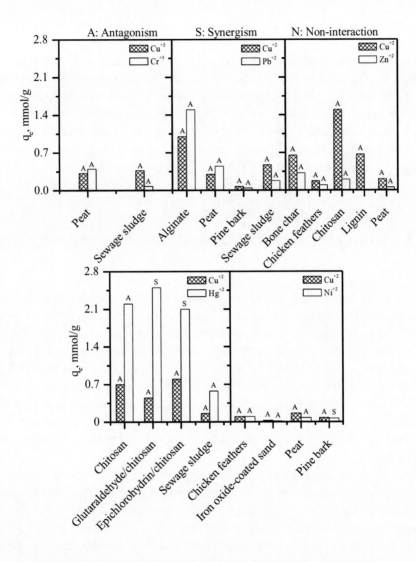

Figure 3. Sorption capacities and competitive effects reported for several low-cost sorbents in aqueous solutions of binary metal systems with Cu^{+2} as principal co-ion.

However, the obtaining of multicomponent isotherms at different operating conditions may require a long and tedious experimental procedure especially for multisolute systems. As discussed in previous section, some studies may fail to obtain the multicomponent isotherms and, as a consequence, the competitive effects of all metal ions can not be clearly identified. In these conditions, experimental designs can be used to assess the sorbent behavior in systems with various metallic species. For instance, Pérez-Marin et al. [37] introduced alternative experimental strategies based on an aggregation method and an experimental design for easily obtaining sorption data in multicomponent systems. This kind of experimental approach is very useful for characterizing the sorbent behavior under competitive conditions.

3.2. Regeneration of Low-Cost Sorbents

The sorbent regeneration is also an important issue to establish the feasibility of new materials in wastewaters treatment. Several desorbing agents have been tested for metal recovery and sorbent regeneration and they include both inorganic and organic agents such as HCl, HNO$_3$, H$_2$SO$_4$, CH$_3$COOH, EDTA, and NaOH. The behavior of these desorbing agents depends on the sorbent type, the concentration of sorbed metals, and the operating conditions (e.g., concentration of desorbing agent, temperature, and sorbent dosage). Overall, the literature indicates that aqueous solutions of HCl and HNO$_3$ are effective for metal desorption in several low-cost sorbents. However, some studies have suggested that the complete regeneration of sorbent used for heavy metal removal is not possible due to the incorporation of metal into the sorbent structure, re-sorption process and other factors [14,17].

4. MODELING OF MULTICOMPONENT SORPTION OF HEAVY METALS

As mentioned in previous sections, the sorption data generally implies experimental information obtained from equilibrium and kinetic studies. Kinetic experiments are performed to establish the equilibrium time, to study the rate of solute uptake, and to establish the rate-controlling step; while equilibrium sorption studies are necessary to provide the maximum sorption capacity of the sorbent, to calculate physico-chemical parameters of sorption process, and to determine competitive effects in multicomponent systems. The equilibrium relationships between sorbent and sorbate are described by sorption isotherms, which are usually represented by the relationship between the quantity sorbed and the sorbate concentration remaining in the solution at a fixed operating conditions (i.e., pH, temperature, ionic strength, and others).

In order to predict the sorbent behavior under competitive conditions, it is necessary to carry out modeling studies based on multicomponent equilibrium and kinetics studies. Thus, data collection in the study of sorption process is normally followed by regression of the experimental information using theoretical or empirical models with the aim of developing mathematical equations that describe satisfactorily the system under analysis. These models can be used for interpolation or extrapolation of sorption behavior, to investigate competitive mechanisms, and to calculate parameters useful for the design, optimization and control of water treatment processes.

The modeling of multicomponent equilibrium sorption has been a research topic during many years. Actually, several models have been proposed and applied to correlate multicomponent sorption data for heavy metal removal. In the literature, the modeling of multisolute sorption can be approached by using classical multicomponent equations, usually considered as empirical models, or by developing chemico-physical mechanistic models able not only to represent but also to explain and predict the experimental sorbent behavior [34,47]. Note that a major understanding of the chemical and physical aspects involved in multicomponent sorption process is possible with the use of mechanistic models instead of empirical ones. Mechanistic models suppose the presence of different types of metal binding sites on the sorbent surface and consider specific reactions between these sites and the metal species in solution, where different reaction mechanisms can be used. These models require, at least, a preliminary sorbent characterization and knowledge of the particular solution chemistry of the solutes under study [34,47]. Unfortunately, due to the complexity of sorption behavior and the potential presence of several mechanisms for heavy metal removal using low-cost sorbents, complex mechanistic models are required for a successful data modeling. In addition, the development of these models may involve wide and deep experimental studies and independent sets of data to give real consistency to the model parameters and also to avoid that a better fitting was reached only by the introduction of additional adjustable parameters [47]. By this reason, it is a common practice to use empirical models for multimetallic sorption modeling due to their flexibility and simplicity both in formulation and computer implementation, which are attractive characteristics for their application in the design of wastewaters treatment processes.

In the following sections, we briefly describe the classical multicomponent models used for competitive sorption data analysis as well as different key aspects for performing a reliable data regression.

4.1.   Description of Classical Multicomponent Sorption Models

Traditional sorption equations employed for representing single solute systems have been used to develop several multicomponent sorption models. They are simple mathematical expressions with relatively few adjustable parameters, generally two or three parameters for representing the sorption behavior of each solute. The model parameters can be fitted both on single and multicomponent experimental data with sufficient accuracy for describing the complexity of competitive sorption data for heavy metal removal.

In literature, the models for multicomponent sorption are generally considered as predictive and competitive models [34,47]. In predictive models, it is frequently assumed a hypothetical sorption behavior where the sorption behavior of solutes does not depend on other species in solution and, as a consequence, the model parameters are regressed by using only single component data. On the other hand, the concept of non-ideal competition among several solutes in solution assumes that each species may modify its sorption behavior if other competitive species are present or not. Therefore, the model parameters for competitive models are usually obtained from data fitting of multicomponent sorption experiments or by combination of both single and multicomponent data. Note that multicomponent sorption models can be made more flexible by inserting additional correction parameters that take into account the interaction between the solutes in solution and these parameters are fitted on multicomponent sorption data. These correction factors usually improve the results of data regression and are incorporated in the model by correcting the individual sorbate concentration using an interaction term, which is assumed as a characteristic of each species and depends on the concentration of the other components in the solution [14].

Table 4 describes a set of representative models used for the correlation of sorption isotherms in multicomponent systems. Several multicomponent isotherm models have been derived from the classical isotherms equations by keeping the same assumptions made in the treatment of pure component in the sorption equilibrium. These models include Langmuir-based, Sips, Freundlich, and Redlich-Peterson multicomponent equations. For example, extended, non-modified and modified Langmuir models are extensions of the basic Langmuir isotherm [17,18]. Characteristics and details of some models can be found in studies reported by Srivastava et al. [14,17,18], Pagnanelli et al. [34] and Pagnanelli et al. [47]. It is convenient to remark that the names of multicomponent sorption models are a matter of debate. Therefore, in the context of this chapter, the nomenclature adopted in Table 4 is used for discussion of the model behavior in multicomponent sorption studies. This nomenclature is consistent with the reported by Srivastava et al. [14,17,18] and Ahmadpour et al. [48]. In general, the derivatives of Langmuir and Freundlich models have been widely used in several studies because they can be easily incorporated in a complete process model and may offer a good fit using few adjustable parameters (see results reported in Table 5). Specifically, Langmuir and Freundlich-based models have been applied for data fitting of multicomponent sorption using bagasse fly ash, rice husk ash, chicken feathers and other sorbents. However, it is convenient to remark that there is no general model applicable to all sorbate/sorbent systems due to the wide range of systems leading to a wide variety of equilibrium behavior.

On the other hand, few attempts have been performed for modeling multicomponent kinetic sorption data in comparison with those studies related to equilibrium behavior. Typically, multicomponent kinetics studies are performed to determine the equilibrium time and the modeling, if any, is carried out using a predictive approach where the classical kinetic equations and their parameters used for single component systems are applied in multicomponent systems, e.g. Prasad et al. [32] and Ho et al. [41].

4.2.   Determination of Adjustable Parameters of Multicomponent Sorption Models

In general, the adjustable parameters of multicomponent sorption models can be obtained using the following approaches: a) all parameters are determined from single sorption experiments and the data fitting in multisolute systems is not required, b) some parameters are derived from mono-component data but also there are adjustable parameters that take into account the interaction between the solutes in solution and that are fitted on multicomponent sorption data, and c) all model parameters are fitted using sets of multicomponent experimental data.

The first approach is the most used for modeling the heavy metal removal using low-cost sorbents and employs multicomponent models containing only parameter values obtained from single metal experiments. This approach avoids any fitting on multicomponent experimental data. However, several studies indicated that this approach may fail to describe the competitive effects between metal ions and usually provides poor estimations for multicomponent sorption equilibria [16].

Table 4. Multicomponent isotherm models used for the sorption data regression with low-cost sorbents

Isotherm name	Model	Description	Ref.
Extended Langmuir	$$q_{e,i} = \dfrac{q_{max} K_i C_{e,i}}{1 + \sum\limits_{j=1}^{c} K_j C_{e,j}}$$	This model assumes that the surface sites are uniform and that all the sorbate molecules in solution are competing for the same surface sites (i.e., a unique q_{max} for the different species in competition). The model parameters are q_{max} and K_i.	14
Non-modified Langmuir	$$q_{e,i} = \dfrac{q_{m,i} K_{L,i} C_{e,i}}{1 + \sum\limits_{j=1}^{c} K_{L,i} C_{e,j}}$$	This model is an extension of the basic Langmuir isotherm and is characterized by specific adjustable parameters ($q_{m,i}$ and $K_{L,i}$) for each species in competition.	14
Modified Langmuir	$$q_{e,i} = \dfrac{q_{m,i} K_{L,i} (C_{e,i}/n_{L,i})}{1 + \sum\limits_{j=1}^{c} K_{L,i} (C_{e,j}/n_{L,j})}$$	In this model, the interactive effect between different sorbates is incorporated by correcting the individual sorbate concentration by an interaction term $n_{L,i}$.	14
Non-modified Sips	$$q_{e,i} = \dfrac{a_{s,i} C_{e,i}^{1/n_{s,i}}}{1 + \sum\limits_{j=1}^{c} b_{s,j} C_{e,j}^{1/n_{s,j}}}$$	This model is also an extension of the conventional Sips isotherm and is characterized by specific adjustable parameters ($a_{s,i}$, $b_{s,i}$ and $n_{s,i}$) for each species in competition. This equation corresponds to a special case of surface energetic heterogeneity.	48
IAST-Sips	$$q_{e,i} = \dfrac{K_{s,i} b_i C_{e,i} \left(\sum\limits_{j=1}^{c} b_j C_{e,j} \right)^{1/n_i - 1}}{\left(1 + \left(\sum\limits_{j=1}^{c} b_j C_{e,j} \right)^{1/n_i} \right)}$$	This model is obtained by applying the ideal adsorption solution theory (IAST). The adjustable parameters are $K_{s,i}$, b_i and n_i for each species in solution.	48
Sheindorf-Rebuhn-Sheintuch (Freundlich-type)	$$q_{e,i} = K_{F,i} C_{e,i} \left(\sum\limits_{j=1}^{c} a_{ij} C_{e,j} \right)^{n_{Fi} - 1}$$	This model assumes that each component individually obeys the Freundlich isotherm where an exponential distribution of site sorption energies exists. The adjustable parameters are a_{ij}, $K_{F,i}$ and n_{Fi} where competition coefficients a_{ij} account for the inhibition to the sorption of the component i by the component j.	54
Non-modified Redlich-Peterson	$$q_{e,i} = \dfrac{K_{R,i} C_{e,i}}{1 + \sum\limits_{j=1}^{c} a_{R,j} C_{e,j}^{\beta_j}}$$	This model is an extension of the Redlich-Peterson isotherm and is characterized by specific adjustable parameters ($K_{R,i}$, $a_{R,i}$ and β_i) for each species in competition.	17
Modified Redlich-Peterson	$$q_{e,i} = \dfrac{K_{R,i} (C_{e,i}/n_{R,i})}{1 + \sum\limits_{j=1}^{c} a_{R,i} (C_{e,j}/n_{R,j})^{\beta_j}}$$	This model is a modification of multicomponent Redlich-Peterson isotherm, which is obtained by introducing an interaction term $n_{R,i}$.	17

Table 5. Summary of data modeling using multicomponent sorption equations and several low-cost sorbents

Sorbent	Heavy metals	Isotherms and trends in the best model for sorption data fit	Modeling approach	Ref.
Alginate	Cu^{+2} - Cd^{+2} Pb^{+2} - Cd^{+2} Cu^{+2} - Pb^{+2}	Modified Langmuir > Non-modified Langmuir > IAST-Sips	Predictive and competitive	16
Bagasse fly ash	Cd^{+2} - Ni^{+2}	Extended Freundlich > Sheindorf-Rebuhn-Sheintuch > Extended Langmuir > Modified Langmuir > Non-modified Langmuir Extended Freudlich > Sheindorf-Rebuhn-Sheintuch > Modified	Predictive and competitive	14
Rice husk ash	Cd^{+2} - Ni^{+2}	Langmuir > Non-modified Langmuir > Modified Redlich-Peterson > Extended Langmuir > Non-modified Redlich-Peterson Extended Freudlich > Sheindorf-Rebuhn-Sheintuch > Modified	Predictive and competitive	17,18
	Cd^{+2} - Zn^{+2}	Langmuir > Modified Redlich-Peterson > Extended Langmuir > Non-modified Langmuir > Non-modified Redlich-Peterson Sheindorf-Rebuhn-Sheintuch > Modified Langmuir > Extended	Predictive and competitive	
	Cd^{+2}-Ni^{+2}-Zn^{+2}	Langmuir > Non-modified Langmuir > Modified Redlich-Peterson > Non-modified Redlich-Peterson	Predictive and competitive	
Chicken feathers	Cu^{+2} - Zn^{+2} Cu^{+2} - Ni^{+2} Zn^{+2} - Ni^{+2} Cd^{+2} - Zn^{+2}	Freundlich-type > Non-modified Langmuir > IAST-Sips	Predictive	24
Orange wastes	Cd^{+2} - Pb^{+2} Zn^{+2} - Pb^{+2}	Extended Langmuir	Competitive	37

This behavior is generally associated to the fact that the non-ideal interactions occur in multimetallic sorption process. For the case of b) and c), the data regression for determining adjustable parameters is more flexible in modeling the sorption behavior than the simple prediction by inserting parameters regressed from separate sets of data.

The determination of model parameters is based on the minimization of the differences between experimental and calculated data for each sorbate. Therefore, it is necessary to establish the parameters of multicomponent models that provide the best fit to measured data using a proper objective function. Several objective functions, which are generally called *error functions*, can be used for sorption data fitting and the values of model parameters may be significantly affected by the choice of this objective function [49,50]. The classical objective functions used in the modeling of multimetallic sorption data are given below

$$F_{obj} = \sum_{i=1}^{c} \sum_{j=1}^{ndat} w_i \left(q_{ij}^{calc} - q_{ij}^{exp} \right)^2 \tag{1}$$

$$F_{obj} = \sum_{i=1}^{c} \sum_{j=1}^{ndat} w_i \left| q_{ij}^{calc} - q_{ij}^{exp} \right| \tag{2}$$

$$F_{obj} = \sum_{i=1}^{c} \sum_{j=1}^{ndat} w_i \left(\frac{q_{ij}^{calc} - q_{ij}^{exp}}{q_{ij}^{exp}} \right)^2 \tag{3}$$

$$F_{obj} = \sum_{i=1}^{c} \sum_{j=1}^{ndat} w_i \left| \frac{q_{ij}^{calc} - q_{ij}^{exp}}{q_{ij}^{exp}} \right| \tag{4}$$

where $q_{i,exp}$ and $q_{i,calc}$ are the experimental and predicted metal uptakes for metal i, c is the number of metallic species present in solution, $ndat$ is the overall number of experimental data used for data correlation, and w_i is a weight factor. The metal uptakes for each component q_i are calculated by a mass balance

$$q_i = \frac{(C_{0,i} - C_{f,i})V}{m} \tag{5}$$

where $C_{0,i}$ and $C_{f,i}$ are the initial and final concentration of metal i in the multicomponent solution, V is the solution volume used for sorption experiments, and m is the sorbent amount, respectively.

The objective functions involving fractional errors (e.g., Eqs. 3 and 4) are preferred for data fitting because they weigh errors in small and large quantities equally. For all objective functions, the introduction of weight factors (w_i) leads to the bias of data fitting towards a specific sorbate. It is worth noting that several studies may fail to report the objective function and numerical strategy for finding the adjustable parameters of sorption models. This aspect is crucial considering that the values of adjustable parameters depend on these aspects.

The sorption data modeling is usually performed by linear and non-linear regression procedures with the local optimization methods available in commercial software such as Matlab, Mathematica, Origin, Excel (MS-Solver), Statistica, SPSS, and others. Linear regression has been the classical approach to determine parameter values of sorption models [50,51]. Unfortunately, the linear regression is not useful and feasible for data fitting of multicomponent models. In this context, a non-linear regression approach should be applied to determine the parameter values for multicomponent models. Data correlation can be performed either by direct optimization of the objective function or by solving an equivalent system of non-linear equations obtained from the stationary conditions of the optimization problem. Although isotherm and kinetics models have a simple mathematical structure and relatively few adjustable parameters, the parameter estimation problems in sorption data fitting usually have non-linear and non-convex solution spaces [52]. In fact, we have to face a global optimization problem for sorption data regression, which may be difficult to solve using traditional local optimization methods (e.g., gradient-based methods or simplex optimization method) due to: a) the presence of several local minima for the objective function used as optimization criterion, b) the number of adjustable model parameters can be large especially for systems with more than three heavy metals, and c) the model parameters may vary over a wide range of the solution domain. Note that the global minimum of *error function* (i.e. objective function) is the best solution to the parameter estimation problem. The failure to find the globally optimal parameters for a specific model, and using locally optimal parameters instead, can have significant consequences in subsequent calculations, and may cause errors, uncertainties in equipment design and erroneous conclusions about model behavior. Moreover, fair comparisons between different models can only occur if the global optimum parameters of all models have been identified. As can be expected, finding the global minimum is more difficult that finding a local optimum and the behavior of classical optimization strategies used for non-linear regressions can be impeded by the presence of local minima [53]. In this regard, the models with higher number of parameters (e.g., models with interaction terms) are expected to be more difficult to solve than those with lower dimension due to the increase in the complexity of solution space of parameter estimation problem. Therefore, the use of reliable methods for solving parameter estimation problems in heavy metal sorption modeling is very important.

Extensive research effort has been dedicated to improve the modeling of sorption isotherm and kinetics especially for single mono-component systems [49,50]. Most of the studies has reported the effect of model type and the method (i.e., linear or non-linear regression) used in deriving the model parameters. However, there is a lack of studies concerning with the application of global optimization strategies for sorption data fitting especially for multicomponent systems [52,53].

In particular, stochastic global optimization methods, also known as meta-heuristics, have shown some promise for solving parameter estimation problems [52,53]. Their features offer several advantages for solving parameter estimation problems such as generality, reliable and robust performance, little information requirement for the optimization problem to be solved, easy implementation, and reasonable computational requirements. Evidently, the global search capabilities of these solvers become more important when data modeling is performed using multiparameter models (e.g., modified Langmuir or Redlich-Peterson isotherms). Different meta-heuristic methods can be used for sorption parameter estimation and they include: simulated annealing, differential evolution, harmony search, genetic algorithms and particle swarm optimization. To the best of our knowledge, ISOFIT software [53] is the only free available tool for fitting sorption data in monocomponent systems that employs a stochastic global optimization method, specifically, the particle swarm optimization. Based on the authors' experience, stochastic optimization methods may offer the best compromise between reliability and efficiency for multivariable parameter estimation problems. However, further studies are necessary to identify the relative strengths of available stochastic optimization methods for multicomponent sorption data modeling of heavy metals. Additionally, other numerical strategies such as neural networks may be used to calculate multimetallic sorption isotherms [29].

4.3. Statistical Criterions for Evaluating the Goodness of Multicomponent Sorption Data Fitting

A variety of statistics must be used to quantify the overall quality of the data fitting and to compare the behavior of kinetic and isotherm equations used in data regression. The most common statistic measures for evaluating the overall goodness of the fit include the mean average deviation between calculated and experimental sorption capacities, the standard deviation, and the coefficient of determination R^2. These statistics should be accompanied by a study of the behavior of the relative residuals $e_i = (q_{i,\exp} - q_{i,\text{calc}})/\, q_{i,\exp}$ to identify obvious patterns (i.e., the residuals should be structureless or have a defined tendency) and to perform model comparison. Plots of residuals can be used to perform this analysis. Finally, details of alternative statistics criterions useful for data fitting of sorption models are described by Matott and Rabideau [53].

5. CONCLUSION

A wide variety of low-cost sorbents has been studied for heavy metal removal from aqueous solution under competitive conditions. The use of these sorbents is recommended since they are relatively cheap or have no cost, easily available, renewable and may show high affinity for several heavy metals. Besides, the treatment of these sorbents may increase significantly their sorption behavior.

Multicomponent sorption studies for heavy metal removal are important to establish the interference of one metal on the uptake of the other metal ions. In general, the literature of low-cost sorbents indicates that the competitive effects for heavy metal ions become more marked with the increase in the number of solutes in solution where the sorption of one metal ion generally interferes with that of another. However, the comparison of their sorption capacities is difficult due to the inconsistencies and discrepancies in experimental data conditions and representation. From the literature reviewed, alginate, chitosan and peat are sorbents that stand out for their sorption behavior in multimetallic systems.

The modeling of multicomponent sorption process requires further investigation especially in the application of robust numerical strategies for the determination of adjustable parameters in kinetic and isotherm models. Besides, it is necessary to perform more studies for improving the sorbent regeneration and recovery of metal ions.

REFERENCES

[1] Bailey, S.E., Olin, T.J., Bricka, R.M., Adrian, D.D. A review of potentially low-cost sorbents for heavy metals. *Water Research* 33 (1999) 2469-2479.

[2] Wan Ngah, W.S., Hanafiah, M.A.K.M. Removal of heavy metal ions from wastewater by chemically modified plant wastes as adsorbents: A review. *Bioresource Technology* 99 (2008) 3935-3948.

[3] Volesky, B. Detoxification of metal-bearing effluents: biosorption for the next century. *Hydrometallurgy* 59 (2001) 203-216.

[4] Sud, D., Mahajan, G., Kaur, M.P. Agricultural waste material as potential adsorbent for sequestering heavy metal ions from aqueous solutions – A review. *Bioresource Technology* 99 (2008) 6017 – 6027.

[5] Wang, J., Chen, C. Biosorbents for heavy metals removal and their future. *Biotechnology Advances* 27 (2009) 195-226.

[6] Doyurum, S., Celik, A. Pb(II) and Cd(II) removal from aqueous solutions by olive cake. *Journal of Hazardous Materials* B138 (2006) 22-28.

[7] Demirbas, A. Heavy metal adsorption onto agro-based waste materials: A review. *Journal of Hazardous Materials* 157 (2008) 220-229.

[8] Babel, S., Kurniawan, T.A. Low-cost adsorbents for heavy metals uptake from contaminated water: a review. *Journal of Hazardous Materials* B97 (2003) 219-243.

[9] Hanzlik, J., Jehlicka, J., Sebek, O., Weishauptova, Z., Machovic, V. Multi-component adsorption of Ag(I), Cd(II) and Cu(II) by natural carbonaceous materials. *Water Research* 38 (2004) 2178 – 2184.

[10] Srivastava, V.M., Mall, I.D., Mishra, I.M. Equilibrium modeling of ternary adsorption of metal ions onto rice husk ash. *Journal of Chemical and Engineering Data* 54 (2009) 705-711.

[11] Sheng, P.X., Ting, Y.P., Chen, J.P. Biosorption of heavy metals ions (Pb, Cu and Cd) from aqueous solutions by the marine alga *sargassum s.p.* in single- and multiple-metal systems. *Industrial and Engineering Chemistry Research* 46 (2007) 2438-2444.

[12] Mohan, D., Pittman Jr., C.U., Steele, P.H. Single, binary and multi-component adsorption of copper and cadmium from aqueous solutions on Kraft lignin-a biosorbent. *Journal of Colloid and Interface Science* 297 (2006) 489-504.

[13] Qin, F., Wen, B., Shan, X.Q., Xie, Y.N., Liu, T., Zhang, S.Z., Khan, S.U. Mechanisms of competitive adsorption of Pb, Cu and Cd on peat. *Environmental Pollution* 144 (2006) 669-680.

[14] Srivastava, V.C., Mall, I.D., Mishra, I.M. Equilibrium modeling of single and binary adsorption of cadmium and nickel onto bagasse fly ash. *Chemical Engineering Journal* 117 (2006) 79-91.

[15] Papageorgiou, S.K., Kouvelos, E.P., Katsaros, F.K. Calcium alginate beads from *Laminaria digitata* for the removal of Cu^{+2} and Cd^{+2} from dilute aqueous metal solutions. *Desalination* 224 (2008) 293-306.

[16] Papageorgiou, S.K., Katsaros, F.K., Kouvelos, E.P., Kanellopoulos, N.K. Prediction of binary adsorption isotherms of Cu^{+2}, Cd^{+2} and Pb^{+2} on calcium alginate beads from single adsorption data. *Journal of Hazardous Materials* 162 (2009) 1347-1354.

[17] Srivastava, V.C., Mall, I.D., Mishra, I.M. Removal of cadmium (II) and zinc (II) metal ions from binary aqueous solution by rice husk ash. *Colloids and Surfaces A: Physicochemical and Engineering Aspects* 312 (2008) 172-184.

[18] Srivastava, V.C., Mall, I.D., Mishra, I.M. Competitive adsorption of cadmium(II) and nickel(II) metal ions from aqueous solution onto rice husk ash. *Chemical Engineering and Processing: Process Intensification* 48 (2009) 370-379.

[19] Toscano, G., Caristi, C., Cimino, G. Sorption of heavy metal from aqueous solution by volcanic ash. *Comptes Rendus Chimie* 11 (2008) 765-771.

[20] Ko, D.C.K., Cheung, C.W., Choy, K.K.H., Porter, J.F., McKay, G. Sorption equilibria of metal ions on bone char. *Chemosphere* 54 (2004) 273-281.

[21] Ko, D.C.K., Porter, J.F., McKay, G. Application of the concentration-dependent surface diffusion model on the multicomponent fixed-bed adsorption systems. *Chemical Engineering Science* 60 (2005) 5472-5479.

[22] Cheung, C.W., Ko, D.C.K., Porter, J.F., McKay, G. Binary metal sorption on bone char mass transport model using IAST. *Langmuir* 19 (2003) 4144-4153.

[23] Cheung, C.W., Choy, K.K.H., Porter, J.F., G. McKay, G. Empirical multicomponent equilibrium and film-pore model for the sorption of copper, cadmium and zinc onto bone char. *Adsorption* 11 (2005) 15-29.

[24] Al-Asheh, S., Banat, F., Al-Rousan, D. Adsorption of copper, zinc and nickel ions from single and binary metal ion mixtures on to chicken feathers. *Adsorption Science and Technology* 20 (2002) 849-864.

[25] Kar, P., Misra, M. Use of keratin fiber for separation of heavy metals from water. *Journal of Chemical Technology and Biotechnology* 79 (2004) 1313-1319.

[26] de la Rosa, G., Reynel-Avila, H.E., Bonilla-Petriciolet, A., Cano-Rodríguez, I., Velasco-Santos, C., Martínez-Hernández, A. Recycling poultry feathers for Pb removal from wastewater: kinetic and equilibrium studies. *International Journal of Chemical and Biomolecular Engineering* 1 (2008) 185-193.

[27] Juang, R.S., Shao, H.J. A simplified equilibrium model for sorption of heavy metal ions from aqueous solutions on chitosan. *Water Research* 36 (2002) 2999-3008.

[28] Vieira, R.S., Guibal, E., Silva, E.A., Beppu, M.M. Adsorption and desorption of binary mixtures of copper and mercury ions on natural and crosslinked chitosan membranes. *Adsorption* 13 (2007) 603-611.

[29] Kaminski, W., Tomczak, E., Jaros, K. Interactions of metal ions sorbed on chitosan beads. *Desalination* 218 (2008) 281-286.

[30] Kim, D.S. The removal by crab shell of mixed heavy metal ions in aqueous solution. *Bioresource Technology* 87 (2003) 355-357.

[31] Sprynskyy, M., Buszewski, B., Terzyk, A.P., Namiesnik, J. Study of the selection mechanism of heavy metal (Pb^{+2}, Cu^{+2}, Ni^{+2} and Cd^{+2}) adsorption on clinoptilolite. *Journal of Colloid and Interface Science* 304 (2006) 21-28.

[32] Prasad, M., Xu, H., Saxena, S. Multi-component sorption of Pb(II), Cu(II) and Zn(II) onto low-cost mineral adsorbent. *Journal of Hazardous Materials* 154 (2008) 221-229.

[33] Boujelben, N., Bouzid, J., Elouear, Z. Adsorption of nickel and copper onto natural iron oxide-coated sand from aqueous solutions: study in single and binary systems. *Journal of Hazardous Materials* 163 (2009) 376-382.

[34] Pagnanelli, F., Mainelli, S., De Angelis, S., Toro, L. Biosorption of protons and heavy metals onto olive pomace: modelling of competition effects. *Water Research* 39 (2005) 1639-1651.

[35] Martinez-Garcia, G., Bachmann, R.T., Williams, C.J., Burgoyne, A., Edyvean, R.G.J. Olive oil waste as a biosorbent for heavy metals. *International Biodeterioration and Biodegradation* 58 (2006) 231-238.

[36] Fiol, N., Villaescusa, I., Martínez, M., Miralles, N., Poch, J., Serarols, J. Sorption of Pb(II), Ni(II), Cu(II) and Cd(II) from aqueous solution by olive stone waste. *Separation and Purification Technology* 50 (2006) 132-140.

[37] Pérez-Marín, A.B., Ballester, A., González, F., Blázquez, M.L., Muñoz, J.A., Sáez, J., Meseguer-Zapata, V. Study of cadmium, zinc and lead biosorption by orange wastes using the subsequent addition method. *Bioresource Technology* 99 (2008) 8101-8106.

[38] Ma, W., Tobin, J.M. Development of multimetal binding model and application to binary metal biosorption onto peat biomass. *Water Research* 37 (2003) 3967-3977.

[39] McKay, G., Porter, J.F. Equilibrium parameters for the sorption of copper, cadmium and zinc ions onto peat. *Journal of Chemical Technology and Biotechnology* 69 (1997) 309-320.

[40] Balasubramanian, R., Perumal, S.V., Vijayaraghavan, K. Equilibrium isotherm studies for the multicomponent adsorption of lead, zinc, and cadmium onto indonesian peat. *Industrial and Engineering Chemistry Research* 48 (2009) 2093-2099.

[41] Ho, Y.S., Wase, D.A.J., Forster, C.F. Kinetic studies of competitive heavy metal adsorption by sphagnum moss peat. *Environmental Technology* 17 (1996) 71-77.

[42] Ho, Y.S., McKay, G. Competitive sorption of copper and nickel ions from aqueous solution using peat. *Adsorption* 5 (1999) 409-417.

[43] Liu, Z., Zhou, L., Wei, P., Zeng, K., Wen, C., Lan, H. Competitive adsorption of heavy metal ions on peat. *Journal of China University of Mining and Technology* 18 (2008) 255-260.

[44] Qin, F., Wen, B. Single- and multi-component adsorption of Pb, Cu and Cd on peat. *Bulletin of Environmental Contamination and Toxicology* 78 (2007) 265-269.

[45] Al-Asheh, S., Duvnjak, Z. Sorption of cadmium and other heavy metals by pine bark. *Journal of Hazardous Materials* 56 (1997) 35-51.

[46] Otero, M., Rozada, F., Morán, A., Calvo, L.F., García, A.I. Removal of heavy metals from aqueous solution by sewage sludge based sorbents: competitive effects. *Desalination* 239 (2009) 46-57.

[47] Pagnanelli, F., Esposito, A., Veglio, F. Multi-metallic modelling of biosorption of binary systems. *Water Research* 36 (2002) 4095-4105.

[48] Ahmadpour, A., Wang, K., Do, D.D. Comparison of models on the prediction of binary equilibrium data of activated carbons. AIChE Journal 44 (1998) 740-752.

[49] Kundu, S., Gupta, A.K. Arsenic adsorption onto iron oxide-coated cement (IOCC): regression analysis of equilibrium data with several isotherm models and their optimization. *Chemical Engineering Journal* 122 (2006) 93-106.

[50] Foo, K.Y., Hameed, B.H. Insights into the modeling of adsorption isotherm systems. *Chemical Engineering Journal* 156 (2010) 2-10.

[51] Kumar, K.V., Sivanesan, S. Comparison of linear and non-linear model in estimating the sorption isotherm parameters for safranin onto activated carbon. *Journal of Hazardous Materials* B123 (2005) 288-292.

[52] Bonilla-Petriciolet, A., Lira-Padilla, M.G., Soto-Becerra, C. Aplicación del método de recocido simulado en la regresión de isotermas de adsorción. *Revista Internacional de Contaminación Ambiental* 21 (2005) 201-206.

[53] Matott, L.S., Rabideau, A.J. ISOFIT – A program for fitting sorption isotherms to experimental data. *Environmental Modelling and Software* 23 (2008) 670 – 676.

[54] Sheindorf, C., Rebhum, M., Sheintuch, M. A Freundlich-type multicomponent isotherm. *Journal of Colloid Interface Science* 79 (1981) 136-142.

In: Water Production and Wastewater Treatment
Editor: B. Antizar-Ladislao et al.

ISBN 978-1-61728-503-5
© 2011 Nova Science Publishers, Inc.

Chapter 6

THE ADSORPTION OF DYES ON WASTE TYRE DERIVED ACTIVATED CARBON

O.S. Chan, C.W. Wong and G. McKay

Department of Chemical and Biomolecular Engineering,
Hong Kong University of Science and Technology,
Clear Water Bay, Kowloon, Hong Kong

ABSTRACT

In this chapter, waste tyre was used as a raw material for the production of activated carbons through pyrolysis. Tyre char (TC) and two tyre derived activated carbons (TAC1 and TAC2) were produced. The TAC1 was activated at 950°C for 4 hr in 85% CO_2 and 15% N_2 atmosphere while TAC2 was firstly treated with 3M HCl for 18 hr and then pyrolysed at 950°C in steam generated by heating water at 0.45mL/min and 150mL/min of N_2 for 4hr. The tyre char and tyre derived activated carbon were characterised with regard to their physical and chemical properties. The adsorption of acid (Acid Blue 25) and basic (Methylene Blue) dyes in aqueous solution were studied. Equilibrium data were fitted to various adsorption isotherms including Langmuir, Freundlich, Redlich-Peterson and Langmuir-Freundlich. It was found that the adsorption capacity of MB was higher than of AB25 for all the adsorbents prepared from tyre. It also showed that the adsorption capacity increased after higher temperature activation and more significantly after acid demineralization treatment. This was due to the fact that tyre char was practically a non-porous material, with a higher temperature treatment, a mesoporous structure was developed. With acid demineralisation, activated carbon with a higher micro- and meso-porosity and an increase in the surface area was further developed.

1. INTRODUCTION

It is estimated that the total number of waste tyres in China already reached more than 112 million pieces in 2004 and the amount projected to 2010 will be well over 200 million(Anon, 2005). The disposal of the scrap tyre will be a severe global environmental problem that needs to be solved in the near future as the waste tyres do not decompose easily, this is due to chemically cross-linked rubber molecules that neither melt nor dissolve. The main hazard of having piles of tyres packing together is the possibility of fire or become a mosquito breeding ground. Therefore, reuse or recycling of waste tyres becomes an important social concern. As a result, the "Regulations on the Management of the Recovery and Reuse of Scrap Tyres" in collaboration with the Environment and Resources Committee of the National People's Congress has been drafted in 2005. The most commonly adopted disposal method for used tyre is to landfill especially since the method of landfilling has been improved continuously due to granulation (Warith and Rao, 2006), but it is still an uneconomical and non-environmental friendly method of disposal as the landfill space become more scarce.

It will be a significant improvement if the waste tyres can be recycled and reprocessed into more valuable materials. Pyrolysis of scrap tyre is widely accepted as an alternative process for recovering the value in scrap tyres. However, the process is very energy intensive, even though the tyre derived fuel from pyrolysis of tyre produces same amount of energy as oil and 25-80% more than coal. There will be 30-40weight percent solid tyre char produced during pyrolysis; hence the process economy depends strongly on its application and market value, for example the light oil(Cunliffe and Williams, 1998), tyre char hydrocarbon, reusable adsorbent(Lin et al., 2008)

On the other hand, activated carbon has been widely used for the adsorption process in wastewater treatment. With high adsorption surface and pore development, it is capable to adsorb the toxic materials in discharged effluents, for instance, dyestuffs and heavy metals. However, this high value added product is relatively expensive, recently, many researches have been focused on the production of activated carbon like material by using low cost precursors, such as sawdust (Hamadi et al., 2001), cherry stones (Olivares-Marin et al., 2008), peanut shell (Xu and Liu, 2008), bagasse (Valix et al., 2009) and bamboo (Chan et al., 2008).

Some studies had showed that the activation of the tyre char could result in a product with reasonable desirable properties such as surface area and porosity similar to the commercially available activated carbon. For example, tyre derived activated carbon have been used in the adsorption of methane and SO_2 (Brady et al., 1996), heavy metals, Pb and Hg, adsorption by using tyre derived activated carbon (Alexandre-Franco et al., 2008; Manchon-Vizuete et al., 2005). These recycled materials could achieve an acceptable adsorption capacity since the raw material was relatively inexpensive, so the cost of the whole adsorption process could be greatly reduced.

Usually, when preparing the tyre char from the raw material, it will follow two basic steps: raw material preparation and low-temperature carbonisation. For the preparation of tyre derived activated carbon, firstly, it will start with shredding the tyre into the desired size and removal of the steel threads with a magnet. Then, it will undergo low temperature pyrolysis at 450-650°C in a nitrogen environment to break down the cross-linkage between carbon atoms and eliminate the bulk of the volatile matter to produce tyre char with carbon content of around 30-45% weight percent (Bansal et al., 1988). From the literature, the tyre char itself without further activation can be utilised directly for adsorption processes. However, further improvement of their adsorption potential, i.e. surface area, porosity and surface functional groups, can be obtained through further activation.

The methods for producing activated carbons are generally divided into physical and chemical activation. Chemical activation is an activation process that comprises heat treatment of the precursor impregnated with chemical agent such as dehydrating and oxidants, followed by activating the mixture at a temperature between 400-700 °C in a single step(Bansal et al., 1988). There are a wide variety of activating agents such as potassium hydroxide, nitric acid, zinc chloride, ferric iron and sodium carbonate commonly used in commercial production. However, using potassium hydroxide in producing the tyre activated carbons is comparatively the most popular method after some preliminary tests (Teng et al., 2000). Physical activation is another popular activation method for tyre char activation. Usually, it includes two main steps, the carbonisation or pyrolysis of the carbonaceous precursor in an inert atmosphere with nitrogen or helium and then activation by steam, carbon dioxide, air or a mixture of these gases at an elevated temperature above 750°C. Tyre char is further activated for developing the internal porous structure in the carbonised precursor by reacting with the oxidising agents to obtain larger specific surface area and porosity. More recently, some researchers work on the demineralisation and found out that this process can decrease the inorganic impurities as well as to reduce the amount of undesired ash content. Typically, acid was used to remove minerals, in the form of mineral ions. It is generally carried out prior to the physical activation, the most commonly used pre-treatment agents are HCl, H_2SO_4, HNO_3 and HF. The effect of demineralisation is highly dependent on the agent used, the concentration of pre-treatment agent, demineralisation time and char to acid ratio and especially the starting precursor. Shah et al used both HCl and H_2SO_4 to do the demineralization. After the application of acid treatment of samples, the carbon concentration was significantly increased, indicating the removal of non-carbon phases with acid. Higher carbon concentration was achieved with HCl treatment 93% than H_2SO_4 around 87%(Shah et al., 2006). This may indicate that the HCl has a better potential for the production of low ash activated carbon. Overall, the chemical and physical natures of physically activated carbons are very dependent on the activation parameters, such as activating agent, activation temperature, time, and demineralisation.

In this chapter, two activated carbons from tyre char were prepared; one by physical activation with CO_2 only while the other one was first demineralised with acid then physical activated with a mixture of steam and N_2. The adsorption of dyes (Acid Blue25, AB25 and Methylene Blue, MB) was also conducted on the produced carbons to determine the dye adsorption capacity of the produced carbon. In additional, the experimental adsorption data were modelled using the conventional isotherm equations include Langmuir, Freundlich, Redlich- Peterson and Langmuir-Freundlich isotherms.

2. MATERIALS AND METHODS

2.1. Materials

The starting material was the pyrolysed tyre char, TC, from a local waste tyre processing plant. The tyre char would undergo a series of pre-treatment prior to the activation to ensure all the tyre chars were treated in the same way to give the quality consistence of the tyre char. First, the tyre char would be crushed and sieved to a particle size smaller than 2mm, then the steel would be removed by the magnet. Finally, the tyre char would be pyrolysed once again at 550°C for 2 hour to ensure the volatile compounds in the char was removed.

2.2. Preparation of Adsorbents

TAC1 preparation: Approximately 30g of tyre char was placed onto the ceramic holder and placed into the tube furnace. The activation set up is shown in Figure 1. Nitrogen was used as a purge gas at 500mL/min for 1 hour. The tyre char was heated at 15 ^{0}C /min until 950^{0}C. The sample was then activated at the same temperature for 4 hr using 425mL/min of CO_2 and 75mL/min of N_2. When activation was completed, the sample was cooled to room temperature in the furnace under nitrogen flow. The activated carbon was washed thoroughly with DI water until the pH is close to neutral , then it was dried in an oven at 110 °C for 24hr before use.

TAC2 preparation: Approximately 30g of tyre char was put into the glass beaker with 3M HCl at 1:3 char to acid mass ratio for acid demineralisation to remove ash and impurities. The tyre char was demineralised for 18 hr and filtered thoroughly and rinsed with deionised water to remove the residual acid until neutral pH. After drying in an oven at 110 °C for 24hr, the demineralised sample was then placed onto the ceramic holder and heated in the horizontal tube furnace. The activation set up is shown in Figure 1. Nitrogen was used as a purge gas at 500mL/min for 1 hour. The demineralised tyre char was heated at 15 ^{0}C /min until 950^{0}C. The sample was then activated at the same temperature for 4 hr with steam generated by heating water at 0.45mL/min, and 150mL/min of N_2. When activation was completed, the sample was cooled to room temperature in the furnace under nitrogen flow. The activated carbon was washed thoroughly with DI water until the pH is close to neutral. After drying in an oven at 110 °C for 24hr the sample was ready for use.

The carbon yield was calculated from:

$$Yield = W_{ac}/ W_{tyre\ char} \times 100 \tag{1}$$

where W_{ac} is the weight of activated carbon and $W_{tyre\ char}$ is the weight of total tyre char input to produce activated carbon.

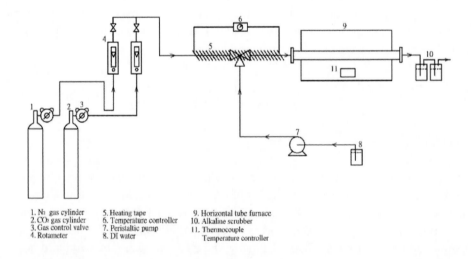

1. N_2 gas cylinder   5. Heating tape   9. Horizontal tube furnace
2. CO_2 gas cylinder   6. Temperature controller   10. Alkaline scrubber
3. Gas control valve   7. Peristaltic pump   11. Thermocouple
4. Rotameter   8. DI water   Temperature controller

Figure1. Schematic diagram of the activation furnace.

2.3. Characterisation of Adsorbents

The total surface area of the activated carbon was determined from N_2 adsorption isotherm at 77K in a Quantachrome Autosorb 1 CLP. The samples were degassed at 200˚C in vacuum for 12 hours prior to the adsorption measurements. Total surface areas were calculated using the BET equation (Brunauer et al., 1938). The molecular area of the nitrogen adsorbate was taken as 16.2 Å^2. The total pore volumes were calculated by converting the nitrogen gas adsorbed at a relative pressure of 0.98 to the volume of liquid adsorbate. The micropore volume and micropore surface area were estimated using the t-plot method(Lippens and de Boer, 1965). The pore size distribution was determined by the application of BJH equation (Barrett et al., 1951).

An elemental analyser, model ELEMENTAR VARIO EL III, was used to determine the mass fractions of the carbon, hydrogen, nitrogen and sulphur content (in weight percent) of the waste tyre, tyre char and activated carbon. For each sample, at least three determinations were conducted until the confidence level was within 5%. The average of the data was used as the results.

2.4. Adsorption of Dyes from Solution

Adsorbates: Acid Blue 25 (AB25) and Methylene Blue (MB) were supplied from Aldrich Chemical Company, Inc. and used directly without further treatment. Their properties are listed in Table 1:

In this chapter, Acid Blue 25 and Methylene Blue were used, this is because typically acid dye is more difficult to biodegraded and Methylene Blue number is widely used as an indicator of the adsorptive capacity of activated carbon. This parameter is related to the macro- and mesopore capacity of activated carbon(Lussier et al., 1994).

Equilibrium time determination: The time required to reach equilibrium was determined by using 8 jars containing 50mL of 2mmol/L dye solution and in contact with 0.05g of activated carbon. The bottles were sealed and placed in a shaker at 120 rpm. Every 3 days, one of the bottle was removed from the shaker and samples were then withdrawn by a syringe, filtered through a 0.22 µm syringe filter and diluted to the appropriate level and liquid-phase dye concentration,C_t, was then determined by measuring the absorbance of the samples at maximum absorbance (λ_{max}) which is 601 nm for Acid Blue 25 (AB 25) and 661 nm for Methylene Blue (MB) with a Varian Cary 1E UV/Vis spectrophotometer.

Table 1. Dye properties

	Acid Blue 25	Methylene Blue
Abbreviation	AB25	MB
Molecular weight (g/mol)	416.4	319.9
Dye content (%)	45	95
Maximum wavelength (nm)	601	664
Charge	-1	1
Molecular size (Å) (WxLxT)	12.45x10.17x2.53	7x13.1x2.12

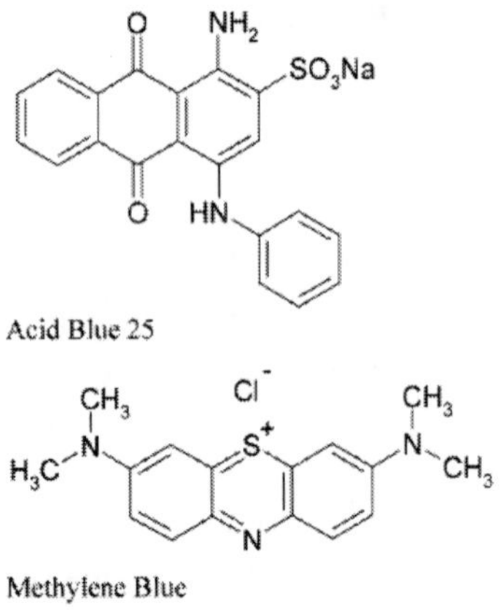

Acid Blue 25

Methylene Blue

Figure2. Structure of Acid Blue 25 and Methylene blue.

The liquid-phase dye concentration was measured at different time intervals and equilibrium was reached when the adsorption capacity of the adsorbent remains constant.

Equilibrium adsorption tests: A constant mass of adsorbent (0.05 g) was weighed into 75 mL glass bottles and in contacted with 50 mL of dye solutions of different initial concentration. The bottles were sealed and placed in a shaker at 120 rpm until equilibrium was reached. Samples were then withdrawn by a syringe, filtered through 0.22 μm syringe filter and diluted to the appropriate level and analysed using a Varian Cary 1E UV/Vis spectrophotometer to determine the residual equilibrium liquid-phase dye concentration, C_e. The equilibrium adsorption capacity, q_e (mmol/g), at different dye concentrations was determined by a mass balance on the dye:

$$q_e = (C_o - C_e)\frac{V}{m} \tag{2}$$

where C_0 (mmol/l) is the initial concentration, C_e (mmol/l) is the equilibrium concentration in the liquid phase, V is the volume of liquid phase (L), and m is the mass of the absorbent (g). The plot of equilibrium adsorption capacity against equilibrium concentration in the liquid phase graphically depicts the equilibrium isotherm.

3. RESULTS AND DISCUSSION

3.1. Activated Carbon Characterization

Table 2 shows the properties of the tyre char and two tyre derived activated carbons. The yield of the carbon dioxide activated carbon was a lot higher than the steam activated carbon. This is possibly due to the differences of activation energy between the steam and carbon dioxide. The activation reactions are as follows:

For carbon dioxide as an activating agent,

$C + CO_2 \rightarrow 2CO \; \Delta H = +159 kJ/mol$

For steam as an activating agent,

$C + H_2O \rightarrow CO + H_2 \; \Delta H = +117 kJ/mol$

$CO + H_2O \rightarrow CO_2 + H_2 \; \Delta H = -41 kJ/mol$

The activation energies of the reactions between char and carbon dioxide or steam are 159 kJ/mol and 117kJ/mol that the reaction of carbon dioxide requires higher activated energy(Marsh and Rodriguez-Reinoso, 2006) . Also, carbon dioxide has a greater molecular size which diffuses slower and with more difficulty into the narrow pores than steam. Another reason may due to the greater stability of activated char produced by carbon dioxide and remained longer on the char surface, and results in a slower reaction rate. As a result, the burnoff will be significantly decreased for the carbon dioxide activated carbon. Another possible reason will be that for the steam activation, the reaction of first equation will give out carbon monoxide, which will then react with H_2O to form CO_2, the the CO_2 will react with carbon and consume more carbon. In this case, the carbon will go through double activation and hence higher burn-off. It is also observed by other researchers that the carbon dioxide activated carbon with a burnoff 75% of that produced by steam(Li et al., 2005). Another group of researchers found out that the tyre chars possess higher reactivity with steam activation than carbon dioxide and found that the burnoff by carbon dioxide was 69.5% of that produced by steam on average while steam activated carbon had a higher BET surface area than carbon dioxide activation (Gonzaez et al., 2006).

The BET surface area and pore volumes are also shown in the Table 2 for the tyre char and two produced carbon, TC, TAC1 and TAC2, respectively. For the starting material, tyre char, there were no micropores and only limited amount of mesopores was observed. There was no micropores development in TAC1 as well, however, the carbon dioxide activation allowed mesopores to develop and the pore volume was three times higher compared to the original tyre char. Micropores and a significant amount of mesopores were developed with acid demineralisation and steam activation. TAC2 has shown a relatively high surface area that is comparable to the commercial activated carbon (Calgon F400 with BET surface area around $800 m^2/g$).

Table 2. Properties of the adsorbents

Name	Yield (%)	Surface Area (m^2/g)	Vmic (cm^3/g)	Vmes (cm^3/g)	Vtot (cm^3/g)	C (%)	H (%)	N (%)	S (%)	O(%)
TC	--	41.92	0	0.11	0.11	81.9	1.39	2.4	3.16	11.15
TAC1	59.2	186.8	0	0.32	0.32	74.6	1.82	0.28	3.85	19.45
TAC2	28.6	970	0.118	1.122	1.24	69.3	1.57	0.07	0.39	28.67

The influence of the two activating agents on the pore structure development of the activated carbon is different. Generally, the carbon activated by steam at high burn off resulted in a wider pore size distribution for both meso- and macropores (Arriagada et al.,

1994; Bansal et al., 1988). It supported the results in this chapter, with a greater burnoff of the TAC2 and with significant amount of mesopores development.

Some researchers found that activation with carbon dioxide at a temperature higher than 1000°C resulted in the rapid burn off of the exterior of the particles and opened and widened microporosity (Rodriguez-Reinoso et al., 1995). Increased porosity was accompanied by a parallel increase in surface area. Most of the studies showed that steam was more effective than carbon dioxide as an activation agent. Steam activation not only produced a slightly narrower microporous activated carbon but also could develop the same porosity as carbon dioxide activation with a 50°C less in activation temperature. Some researchers agreed that steam activated carbon gave a better BET surface area than carbon dioxide activated carbon and having a BET surface area in excess of 1000m^2/g(Ariyadejwanich et al., 2003; Brady et al., 1996; Gonzalez et al., 2006; San Miguel et al., 2002; San Miguel et al., 2003). Other researchers suggested that the mild oxidation of char with superheated steam resulted in a BET surface area enhancement and microporosity development (Merchant and Petrich, 1992).

It was been suggested that the activated carbons obtained by steam activation process were mainly mesoporous with limited microporosity (Lopez et al., 2009). Demineralisation is another possible cause in the significant increase of surface area of TAC2. Although there is limited research on the demineralisation of tyre char activated carbon, possibly because of the high cost in the preparation and intensive washing required after the demineralisation. All of the studies indicated that there were significant improvements of textural properties in the tyre char activated carbon. After acid demineralisation, there was a decrease in burn off, lowering of the ash content and an increased in surface area and porosity. It was found that the demineralised tyre chars had a lower reactivity when activated; this might be due to the catalytic effect of the inorganic compounds such as Ca, Zn, P, etc on the activation. It was also found that the removal of undesired inorganic impurities that blocked the pore structure of the pyrolysed char occurred, leading to an increase of surface area, micro- and mesopore volumes(Ariyadejwanich et al., 2003; Cunliffe and Williams, 1999; Galvagno et al., 2009; Mui et al., 2009; Shah et al., 2006; Ucar et al., 2005; Zhu et al., 2009). This result was extremely positive, since the impurities in the tyre char, such as inorganic oxides and sulphur content might cause a pollution problem and limit its applications could be reduced.

Table 2 also shows the elemental analysis results of the prepared carbons. The carbon content of the tyre char is reasonably high with around 82 wt% with small amounts of hydrogen, nitrogen and sulphur. Carbon levels decreased during the activation for both carbon dioxide activation and steam activation. The hydrogen content remained at similar level, while most of the nitrogen was eliminated during the activation. The sulphur seemed remain the same level with the carbon dioxide activation but was almost eliminated in the steam activated carbon with demineralisation. This is because the acid demineralisation will remove the ash-forming minerals, sulphate, pyritic sulfur, and organic sulfur (Mukherjee and Borthakur, 2003).

There was significant increase in the oxygen content (by difference method). This might be caused by the oxygen in the steam or CO_2 reacting with parts of the carbonised materials to produce CO and CO_2, which opened up blocked pores and creating new pores in the carbon (Bansal et al., 1988). As well as this, the reaction of the CO_2, steam, air and diluted oxygen formed chemisorbed oxygen, called surface oxygen complexes which possed a broad range of chemical functionality surface group including carboxylic, phenolic and etc, those functional group will be particularly good for adsorbing positive charge molecules.

3.2. Dye Adsorption

The adsorption capacity was directly affected by: Firstly, the physical and chemical nature of the adsorbent, such as pore structure, chemical functional groups; Secondly, the nature of the adsorbate, its pKa, functional groups present, polarity, molecular dimension; and finally the experimental conditions such as pH, temperature and the adsorbate concentration (Haghseresht et al., 2002).

As shown in Figures 3 and 4, the experimental adsorption capacity of the TAC2 was the highest among the three carbons with around 1.15mmol/g of AB25 and around 1.25mmol/g of MB, followed by the TAC1 and with very little adsorption was observed for the TC. This was because the higher surface area and porosity of the TAC2 providing more active sites to adsorb the dye molecules. As both dyes were relatively small molecules (Table 1), the adsorption was mainly taken place in both meso and micropores. As the total pore volume for TAC2 was the highest, nearly 4 times higher than TAC1 and 10 times of TC, hence, it would be able to adsorb more of both dyes. Its adsorption capacity for AB25 was higher than the commercial activated carbon, F400, with only 0.7mmol/g(Chan et al., 2008). Similarly, the adsorption capacity for the basic dye was slightly higher than the acid dye for all the carbon. This might be due to two causes, firstly, the dimension of Methylene Blue was smaller than the Acid Blue 25, so it could diffuse faster and into the smaller pore of the inner area and volume of the activated carbon particle. Secondly, as there was an increase in oxygen context of the activated carbon, the surface oxygen complexes that would be more favourable to adsorb the positively charged molecules, i.e. the basic dye.

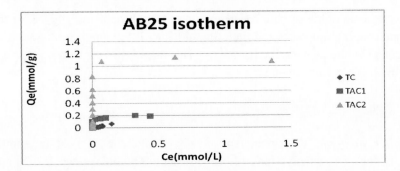

Figure 3. The AB25 adsorption isotherm on tyre char and tyre derived activated carbon..

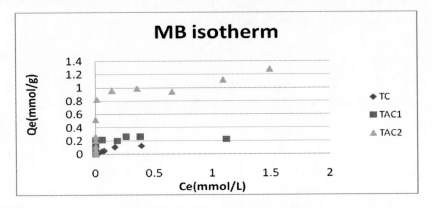

Figure 4. The MB adsorption isotherm on tyre char and tyre derived activated carbon.

However, many researchers used the monolayer capacity that calculated from Langmuir isotherm to compare the adsorption capacity in Table 2, in this case the adsorption of AB25 is more than the MB, this shown that the TAC2 has heterogeneous surface, This indicated that with different degrees of activation, there were some changes in the surface chemistry and functional groups, hence further studies should be carried out to determine the effect of the activation conditions on the surface properties and its effect on dye adsorption.

3.3. Equilibrium Isotherm Modelling

The experimental data were fitted into Langmuir, Freundlich, Redlich-Peterson (RP) and Langmuir-Freundlich (LF) equations to determine which isotherm gave the best correlation to the experimental data shown in Figures5, 6and 7.

Langmuir isotherm: The Langmuir adsorption isotherm is most widely used for modelling the adsorption behaviour of the adsorbates from a liquid solution(Langmuir, 1916). It has several critical assumptions, which include monolayer adsorption, all sites are identical and energetically equivalent, one adsorbate occupies one site, and the adsorption energy is constant throughout the adsorption process, no interaction between adsorbates in the adjacent sites and finally it has a saturation or equilibrium value, where no more adsorption can take place. Its equilibrium capacity can be represented by the expression:

$$q_e = K_L C_e / (1 + a_L C_e) \qquad (3)$$

where q_e is the solid phase sorbate concentration at equilibrium (mmol/g), C_e is the aqueous phase sorbate concentration at equilibrium (mmol/L), K_L is Langmuir isotherm constant (L/g), a_L is Langmuir isotherm constant (L/mmol). The monolayer capacity, q_{mono}, can then be calculated by the following equation:

$$q_{mono} = K_L / a_L \qquad (4)$$

Freundlich isotherm: The Freundlich model (Freundlich, 1906) is an empirical model incorporating the heterogeneity of the adsorption energies on the surface. It is commonly used for the description of multilayer adsorption with interaction between adsorbed molecules. The model predicts that the dye concentrations on the material will increase when there is an increase in concentration of the dye in solution.

$$q_e = K_F C_e^{\frac{1}{n}} \qquad (5)$$

where q_e is the solid phase sorbate concentration in equilibrium (mmol/g), C_e is liquid phase sorbate concentration in equilibrium (mmol/L), K_F is Freundlich constant (L/g) and $1/n$ is the heterogeneity factor.

Redlich–Peterson isotherm: Redlich and Peterson have proposed an empirical equation incorporating three parameters. It can be used to represent adsorption equilibria over a wide concentration range, and can be applied to both homogeneous and heterogeneous systems (Redlich and Peterson, 1959). This isotherm combines elements from both the Langmuir and

Freundlich equations, and the adsorption mechanism does not follow ideal monolayer adsorption. It reduces to Henry's equation when $b_R = 0$ and to Langmuir isotherm when $b_R = 1$.

$$q_e = K_R C_e / (1 + a_R C_e^{bR})$$ (6)

where q_e is solid phase sorbate concentration in equilibrium (mmol/g), C_e is liquid phase sorbate concentration in equilibrium (mmol/l), K_R is Redlich– Peterson isotherm constant (L/g), a_R is Redlich– Peterson isotherm constant and b_R is the exponent which lies between 1 and 0.

Langmuir-Freundlich isotherm: The Langmuir-Freundlich or Sips isotherm combines the Langmuir and Freundlich equations with three parameters K_{LF}, a_{LF} and b_{LF}. At low sorbate concentrations it effectively reduces to the Freundlich isotherm and thus does not obey Henry's law. At high sorbate concentrations, it predicts a monolayer sorption capacity characteristic of the Langmuir isotherm(Sips, 1948) .

$$q_e = K_{LF} C_e^{1/b}{}_{LF} / (1 + a_{LF} C_e^{1/b}{}_{LF})$$ (7)

where q_e is the adsorbed amount at equilibrium (mmol/g), where a_{LF} is the LF model isotherm constant (L/g); K_{LF} the LF constant (L/mmolg) and 1/b the LF model exponent.

Modelling comparison: Three sets of modelling data of the individual adsorbents are plotted in Figures 3 to 5 and the individual dye adsorption model parameters are shown in Table 3. The sum of the squares of the errors (SSE) is used to identify the best fit model. SSE is chosen as the error anaylysis method is because we are more interested in the monolayer capacity, so the bias toward the data obtained at high end of concentration is desired.

$$\text{SSE} = (q_{e,calc} - q_{e,exp})^2$$ (8)

From Table 3, lowest SSE values were obtained using the Freundlich model for the adsorption of AB25 on TC and TAC1 and for TAC2, the Freundlich model provide thesecond best correlation. The Freundlich model fitted the experimental data of MB better than the other models since it provided the smallest SSE for TC and TAC1, for TAC2 the Langmuir-Freundlich model was best followed by Freundlich. Freundlich isotherm could be used to described the adsorption of the dyes onto the tyre carbons, since in this case as less than 5% difference. A two parameter model is better than three parameter.

Table 3. Modelling parameters for the dye –carbon system

AB 25	Langmuir			Q_{mono}^{o}	Freundlich			Redlich-Peterson				Langmuir-Freundlich			
	KL	aL	SSE	o	KF	1/n	SSE	KR	aR	bR	SSE	KLF	bLF	aLF	SSE
TC	4.12E-01	5.73E+00	1.56E-04	7.19E-02	7.24E-01	1.24E+00	6.24E-05	2.92E+02	7.09E+02	1.00E-03	1.56E-04	2.74E-02	1.00E+00	1.33E+00	3.04E-03
TA C1	1.13E+03	6.98E+03	1.30E-02	1.62E-01	2.14E-01	1.11E-01	3.65E-04	4.59E+04	2.16E+05	8.91E-01	7.72E-03	2.14E-01	9.00E+00	1.00E-02	7.74E-03
TA C2	2.11E+03	1.91E+03	1.00E+00	1.10E+00	1.13E+00	3.99E-02	1.01E+00	2.23E+03	2.01E+03	9.97E-01	1.00E+00	1.62E+02	1.64E+00	1.44E+02	1.00E+00

MB	Langmuir			Q_{mono}^{o}	Freundlich			Redlich-Peterson				Langmuir-Freundlich			
	KL	aL	SSE	o	KF	1/n	SSE	KR	aR	bR	SSE	KLF	bLF	aLF	SSE
TC	1.13E+00	6.02E+00	5.38E-04	1.88E-01	2.27E-01	5.51E-01	9.62E-04	1.13E+00	6.02E+00	1.00E+00	5.38E-04	2.82E+00	7.66E-01	1.83E+01	4.70E-04
TA C1	1.75E+03	7.70E+03	3.65E-02	2.27E-01	2.61E-01	9.38E-02	2.39E-02	1.35E+03	5.51E+03	9.70E-01	3.63E-02	3.72E-01	8.48E+00	4.42E-01	2.39E-02
TA C2	2.97E+03	2.90E+03	3.76E-01	1.02E+00	1.16E+00	1.52E-01	2.60E-01	1.54E+04	1.36E+04	8.81E-01	2.43E-01	5.67E+00	3.23E+00	4.08E+00	2.24E-01

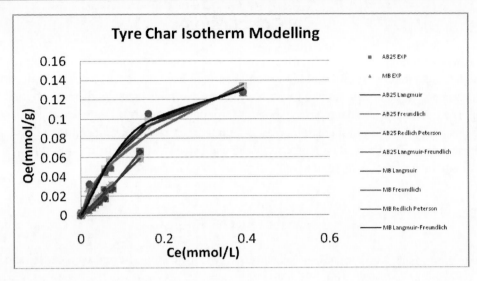

Figure.5. Plot of sorption of dyes on TC with modelling.

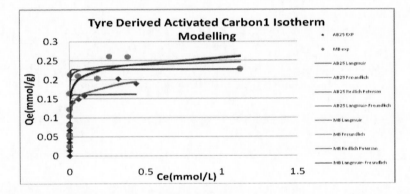

Figure.6. Plot of sorption of dyes on TAC1 with modelling.

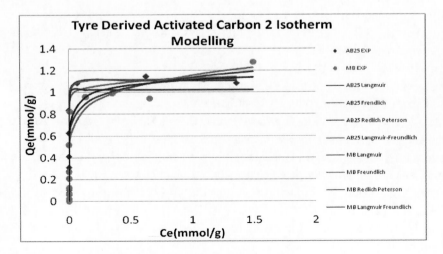

Figure.7. Plot of sorption of dyes on TAC2 with modelling.

4. Conclusions

The preparation of high BET surface area activated carbons from waste tyre by pyrolysis at high temperature with different activating agent had been demonstrated. The high surface area carbon showed nearly three to five times higher adsorption capacity than the original tyre char. The tyre char showed a relatively poor adsorption for both dyes. Both textural properties and chemical properties of the carbon played an important role in the adsorption of both acid and basic dyes. The Freundlich isotherm model can be used to describe the adsorption of the dyes onto the tyre char and tyre derived activated carbon reasonably well.

References

Alexandre-Franco, M., Fernandez-Gonzalez, C., MacIas-Garcia, A. and Gomez-Serrano, V., *Adsorption* 2008, *14*, (4-5), 591-600.

Anon, China *Chemical Reporter* 2005, (23).

Ariyadejwanich, P., Tanthapanichakoon, W., Nakagawa, K., Mukai, S. R. and Tamon, H., *Carbon* 2003, *41*, (1), 157-164.

Arriagada, R., Garcia, R. and Reyes, P., *J. Chem. Technol. Biotechnol.* 1994, *60*, (4), 427-435.

Bansal, R. P., Donnet, J. and Stoeckli, F., *Active Carbon.* (Marcel Dekker, New York, 1988).

Barrett, E. P., Joyner, L. G. and Halenda, P. P., *Journal of the American Chemical Society* 1951, *73*, (1), 373-380.

Brady, T. A., Rostam-Abadi, M. and Rood, M. J., *Gas Separation and Purification* 1996, *10*, (2), 97-102.

Brunauer, S., Emmett, P. H. and Teller, E., *Journal of the American Chemical Society* 1938, *60*, (2), 309-319.

Chan, L. S., Cheung, W. H. and McKay, G., Desalination 2008, *218*, (1-3), 304-312.

Cunliffe, A. M. and Williams, P. T., Journal of Analytical and Applied Pyrolysis 1998, *44*, (2), 131-152.

Cunliffe, A. M. and Williams, P. T., *Energy and Fuels* 1999, *13*, (1), 166-175.

Freundlich, H. M. F., *Zeitschrift Fur Physikalische Chemie Stochiometrie und Verwandtschaftslehre* 1906,
57, (4), 385–471.

Galvagno, S., Casciaro, G., Casu, S., Martino, M., Mingazzini, C., Russo, A. and Portofino, S., *Waste Management* 2009, *29*, (2), 678-689.

Gonzaez, J. F., Encinar, J. M., Gonzaez-Garcia, C. M., Sabio, E., Ramiro, A., Canito, J. L. and Ga簸an, J., *Applied Surface Science* 2006, *252*, (17), 5999-6004.

Gonzalez, J. F., Encinar, J. M., Gonzalez-Garcia, C. M., Sabio, E., Ramiro, A., Canito, J. L. and Ganan, J., *Applied Surface Science* 2006, *252*, (17), 5999-6004.

Haghseresht, F., Nouri, S., Finnerty, J. J. and Lu, G. Q., *Journal of Physical Chemistry B* 2002, *106*, (42), 10935-10943.

Hamadi, N. K., Xiao Dong, C., Farid, M. M. and Lu, M. G. Q., *Chemical Engineering Journal* 2001, *84*, (2), 95-105.

Langmuir, I., *The Journal of the American Chemical Society* 1916, *38*, (2), 2221-2295.

Li, S. Q., Yao, Q., Wen, S. E., Chi, Y. and Yan, J. H., *Journal of the Air and Waste Management Association* 2005, *55*, (9), 1315-1326.

Lin, C., Huang, C. L. and Shern, C. C., *Resources, Conservation and Recycling* 2008, *52*, (10), 1162-1166.

Lippens, B. C. and de Boer, J. H., *Journal of Catalysis* 1965, *4*, (3), 319-323.

Lopez, G., Olazar, M., Artetxe, M., Amutio, M., Elordi, G. and Bilbao, J., *Journal of Analytical and Applied Pyrolysis* 2009, *85*, (1-2), 539-543.

Lussier, M. G., Shull, J. C. and Miller, D. J., *Carbon* 1994, *32*, (8), 1493-1498.

Manchon-Vizuete, E., MacIas-Garcia, A., Nadal Gisbert, A., Fernandez-Gonzalez, C. and Gomez-Serrano, V., *J. Hazard. Mater.* 2005, *119*, (1-3), 231-238.

Marsh, H. and Rodriguez-Reinoso, F., *Activated Carbon* 2006.

Merchant, A. A. and Petrich, M. A., *Chemical Engineering Communications* 1992, *118*, 251-263.

Mui, E. L. K., Cheung, W. H., Valix, M. and McKay, G., *Microporous and Mesoporous Materials* 2009.

Mukherjee, S. and Borthakur, P. C., *Fuel* 2003, *82*, (7), 783-788.

Olivares-Marin, M., Fernandez, J. A., Lazaro, M. J., Fernandez-Gonzalez, C., Macias-Garcia, A., Gomez-Serrano, V., Stoeckli, F. and Centeno, T. A., *Materials Chemistry and Physics* 2008.

Redlich, O. and Peterson, D. L., *Journal of Physical Chemistry* 1959, *63*, (6), 1024.

Rodriguez-Reinoso, F., Molina-Sabio, M. and Gonzalez, M. T., *Carbon* 1995, *33*, (1), 15-23.

San Miguel, G., Fowler, G. D., Dall'Orso, M. and Sollars, C. J., *Journal of Chemical Technology and Biotechnology* 2002, *77*, (1), 1-8.

San Miguel, G., Fowler, G. D. and Sollars, C. J., *Carbon* 2003, *41*, (5), 1009-1016.

Shah, J., Jan, M. R., Mabood, F. and Shahid, M., *Journal of the Chinese Chemical Society* 2006, *53*, (5), 1085-1089.

Sips, R., *The Journal of Chemical Physics* 1948, *16*, (5), 490-495.

Teng, H., Lin, Y. C. and Hsu, L. Y., *Journal of the Air and Waste Management Association* 2000, *50*, (11), 1940-1946.

Ucar, S., Karagoz, S., Ozkan, A. R. and Yanik, J., *Fuel* 2005, *84*, (14-15), 1884-1892.

Valix, M., Cheung, W. H. and McKay, G., *Adsorption* 2009, *15*, (5-6), 453-459.

Warith, M. A. and Rao, S. M., *Waste Management* 2006, *26*, (3), 268-276.

Xu, T. and Liu, X., Chinese *Journal of Chemical Engineering* 2008, *16*, (3), 401-406.

Zhu, J., Shi, B., Chen, L., Liu, D. and Liang, H., *Waste Management and Research* 2009, *27*, (6), 553-560.

In: Water Production and Wastewater Treatment
Editor: B. Antizar-Ladislao et al.

ISBN 978-1-61728-503-5
© 2011 Nova Science Publishers, Inc.

Chapter 7

ADSORPTION OF BASIC DYES BY ACTIVATED CARBON FROM WASTE BAMBOO

L.S. Chan[1,2], W.H. Cheung[2], S. J. Allen[1] and G. McKay[2]

[1]School of Chemistry and Chemical Engineering, Queen's University Belfast,
Belfast, Northern Ireland, UK
[2]Department of Chemical and Biomolecular Engineering, Hong Kong University of
Science and Technology, Clear Water Bay, Kowloon, Hong Kong

ABSTRACT

Bamboo, indigenous to Hong Kong and China, is widely used as scaffolding in local construction and building projects. Over 50,000 tonnes of bamboo scaffolding waste is disposed as landfill waste each year. These wastes can be used as a sustainable raw material for the production of a range of high value added activated carbons for various applications e.g. adsorbents, catalysts or catalyst supports. Super-high surface area activated carbons were produced by thermal activation of waste bamboo scaffolding with phosphoric acid. Surface areas up to $2500 m^2/g$ were produced. In order to evaluate the adsorption capacity of the produced carbons, dye adsorption was conducted on the carbons produced and compared with a commercially available carbon. Two basic dyes, namely, Basic Yellow 11 (BY11) and Maxilon Red GRL 200% (MR) were used. It was found that both basic dyes were readily adsorbed onto the produced carbon and were up to three times higher than the commercial carbon. In addition, experimental results were fitted to equilibrium isotherm models including Langmuir, Freundlich, and Redlich-Peterson.

INTRODUCTION

In the textile industry, dyestuff is used to provide garments with different colour and shade. A consumption rate of approximately one billion kg of dye was reported in 1994 (Marc, 1996). An estimated 10-20% of dyes (active substance) used is lost in residual liquors through exhaustion and washing operations. Reverse osmosis, ion exchange, coagulation, precipitation, catalytic reduction, herbal filtration, electrodialysis and adsorption, all have been used to treat textile effluents. However, available effluent treatment processes for dye containing effluents are currently only capable of removing about half the dyes lost in residual liquors to the environment. Adsorption is the most widely use and effective treatment process for textile effluent. Numerous adsorbents including inorganic, agricultural and shell-fish by-products have been considered for adsorption (Juang, et al., 1996, Namasivayam, et al., 2001, Garg, et al., 2003, Walker, et al., 2003, Ramesh, et al., 2005, Crini, 2006). The use of activated carbons however, has been widely favoured because of their high adsorption capacities and amphoteric properties, which enable their adsorption of both cationic and anionic pollutants in effluents (Corapcioglu and Huang, 1987, Chern and Wu, 1999, Al-Degs, et al., 2000, Annadurai, et al., 2000). The relatively high cost of activated carbon and its regeneration problems hindered its usage, especially in third world countries. A challenge in the field of activated carbon production is to produce specific materials with given properties including pore size distribution and surface area from low cost precursors and at low temperature. In recent years, considerable interest has been focused on low cost alternative materials for the production of active carbons from wastes and agricultural by-products such as waste tyres, fruit stones, oil-palm shell and bagasse (Tsai, et al., 1998, Ahmedna, et al., 2000, Marshall, et al., 2000, Valix, et al., 2004) with no need of regeneration.

In Hong Kong and South-East China, with the booming in the construction and building industry, a large quantity of construction wastes is generated each year. One of these wastes is bamboo, which is uniquely used in this region as scaffolding for building projects. Over 50,000 tonnes of bamboo scaffolding each year is dumped as construction waste in Hong Kong. With limiting landfilling space available, alternative usages of this sustainable material are being sought. Bamboo is a tropical plant and is indigenous to Southern Asia, including China, Hong Kong, Thailand and Vietnam. It has a rapid growth rate and consumes little energy (0.5MJ/kg). Bamboo waste can be used as the precursor for the production of a range of activated carbons and carbon chars due to its high carbon content (44%). The chars can be further treated using various chemicals and over a range of temperatures to produce a selection of activated carbons for various uses (Wu, et al., 1999, Ohe, et al., 2003). Bamboo-based activated carbon has the potential to be a sustainable and commercially available for the treatment of 1) gaseous pollutants, 2) liquid pollutants in industrial effluents, 3) in drinking water filtration applications and 4) fuel cell and electronic applications.

Phosphoric acid activation is a conventional method for the preparation of active carbon from lignocellulosic materials (Laine, et al., 1989). The precursor is impregnated with a solution of phosphoric acid, heat treated to 600°C and washed with water to remove excess acid. Phosphoric acid induces important changes in the pyrolytic decomposition of the lignocellulosic materials as it promotes depolymerisation, dehydration and redistribution of constituent biopolymers (Jagtoyen and Derbyshire, 1993, 1998). So far, only limited research has been carried out on bamboo as precursor utilizing the high temperature physical activation. BET-nitrogen surface area ranges from 491 to 1038 m^2/g have been obtained (Wu, Tseng and Juang, 1999, Abe, et al., 2001, Kannan and Sundaram, 2001, Asada, et al., 2002).

In this chapter, the feasibility of producing activated carbon from waste bamboo scaffolding by low temperature chemical activation with phosphoric acid will be investigated. In addition, the adsorption capacities of basic dyes, namely, Basic Yellow 11 (BY11) and Maxilon Red GRL 200% (MR), is conducted on the produced carbon and compared with a commercially available carbon, Calgon F400.

MATERIALS AND METHODOLOGY

Materials

The received waste bamboo scaffolding was washed with water and reduced to size by hammer milling prior to experiment. Particle size of 500 – 710 μm was used. The average chemical composition of bamboo is measured by an elemental analysis and is shown in Figure 1. The major elements are carbon (47.6%) and oxygen (43.9%) accounting for around 91% of bamboo. Other elements include hydrogen (6.5%), nitrogen (0.3%), sulphur (0.3%) and ash (1.4%). This raw material has been pre-treated by transfer into alumina containers, soaking and saturating with ortho-phosphoric acid (H_3PO_4) at different acid to bamboo ratio (Xp). The mixture has been stirred thoroughly to ensure homogenous mixing of the bamboo and H3PO4. Then, the samples were subjected to a two-step heating process at 150°C for two hours and then at 600°C in a furnace under flowing nitrogen for a range of time. After heating, samples were cooled, washed and dried for further analysis and characterisation.

Carbon Characterisation Test

Chemical activated carbons were characterised by BET surface area, pore size distribution, elemental analysis and dye adsorption equilibrium capacity. The apparent surface area of the activated carbon was determined from N2 adsorption at 77K in a Coulter 3100 analyzer using the Brunauer, Emmett and Teller (BET) equation ((Brunauer, et al., 1938). The molecular area of the nitrogen adsorbate was taken as 16.2 Å^2.

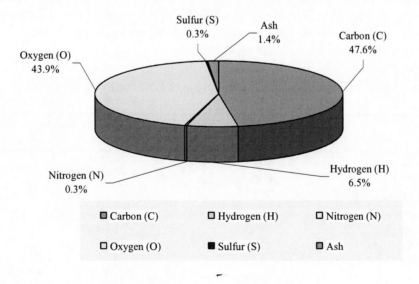

Figure 1. Elemental composition of bamboo.

The micropore volume was estimated by applying the Horvath Kawazoe (HK) method (Horvath and Kawazoe, 1983) which assumes slit pore shapes on the nitrogen adsorption isotherms. Mesopore volume was estimated using the Kelvin equation (Bansal, et al., 1988).

The total pore volumes were calculated by converting the nitrogen gas adsorbed at a relative pressure 0.98 to the volume of liquid adsorbate.

Dye Adsorption Equilibrium Capacity Test

The basic dye adsorption test was used to determine the adsorption capacity of the produced carbons using two basic dyes; Basic Yellow 11 (BY11) was supplied by Sigma-Aldrich Chemical Company while Maxilon Red GRL 200% (MR) was supplied by Hong Kong Polytechnic University. Table 1 and Figure 2 show the properties and structure of the dyes, respectively. The dimensions of dye molecules were estimated using the software, ChemSketch by ACD, Inc.

A fixed mass of activated carbon, 0.020g was weighed into 80 mL glass bottles and brought into contact with 50mL of dye solution with predetermined initial dye concentrations. The bottles were sealed and agitated continuously at 200 rpm in the thermostatic shaker bath and maintained at a temperature of 25 °C ± 1 °C until equilibrium was reached. At time t = 0 and equilibrium, the dye concentrations of the solutions were measured by Varian Cary 1E UV-Vis Spectrophotometer. These data were used to calculate the adsorption capacity, q_e, of the adsorbent. The adsorption capacities (q_e) of the each activated carbon were determined by:

$$q_e = \frac{V}{m}(C_0 - C_e)$$

(1)

where q_e = the dye concentration on the adsorbent at equilibrium (mmol/g) C_0 = the initial dye concentration in the liquid phase (mmol of dye / L), C_e = the liquid-phase dye concentration at equilibrium (mmol of dye / L), V = the total volume of dye-activated carbon mixture (L), m = mass of activated carbon used (g). Finally, the adsorption capacity, q_e, was plotted against the equilibrium concentration, C_e.

Table 1. Physical and chemical properties of the basic dyes

	Basic Yellow 11 (BY11)	Maxilon Red GRL 200% (MR)
Colour Index	48055	110825
Abbreviation	BY11	BR46
Molecular Weight (g/mol)	372.9	501
Dye Content (%)	20	73
Chromophore	Methine	Monoazo
Maximum Wavelength, λ_{max} (nm)	412	530
Charge	+1	+1
Width (Å)	15.293	13.325
Depth (Å)	14.918	14.569
Thickness (Å)	4.148	6.063

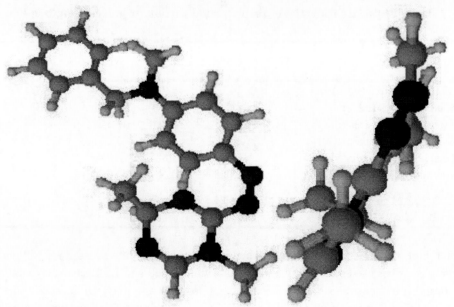

Maxilon Red GRL 200%, (MR).

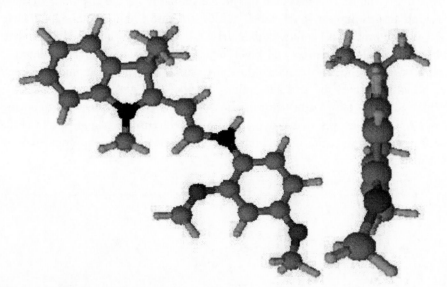

Basic Yellow 11, (BY11).

Figure 2. Molecular structure of the basic dyes.

RESULTS AND DISCUSSION

Basic Dyes Adsorption Capacities

Three bamboo carbons, namely, two carbons with high surface area (HSA1 and HSA2) and one with low surface area (LSA) were prepared for the study of basic dyes adsorption capacities, their properties are shown in Table 2.

Table 2. Physical Properties of the activated carbon produced from bamboo

Properties	HSA1	HSA2	LSA	F400
BET surface area (m^2/g)	2471	2200	758	747
Micropore area (m^2/g)	2172	1398	724	673
External surface area (m^2/g)	245	802	34	74
Average pore diameter (Å)	22.20	34.31	22.33	25.18
Total pore volume (cc/g)	1.341	1.887	0.423	0.470
Micropore volume (cc/g)	1.023	0.651	0.377	0.348
$\dfrac{\text{Micropore Volume}}{\text{Total Pore Volume}}$	0.763	0.345	0.891	0.740

Both high surface area carbons adsorbed over three times more than the F400 and LSA for both basic dyes as shown in Figures 3 and 4 while F400 and LSA have very similar low capacities, this demonstrates that surface area and porosity also plays an important role in the adsorption of basic dyes. Both HSA1 and HSA2 have similar high adsorption capacities for both basic dye systems. This may also link to the similar molecule size of the basic dyes that can penetrate further into activated carbon porous structure with little steric hindrance.

Overall, the produced bamboo carbons (HSA1 and HSA2) adsorbed basic dyes, BY11 and MR, with similar capacities and much better than their commercial counterpart. From previous works (Pereira, et al., 2003, Moreno-Castilla, 2004), for anionic dyes (acid dyes), surface basicity affected the dye adsorption directly. This was caused by the oxygen-free Lewis base sites related to the delocalised π-electrons of the defective grapheme layers. Similarly, for cationic dyes (basic dyes) the carboxylic groups of the carbon surface were more effective. However, the interactions with the π-electrons of the grapheme layers still played a major role.

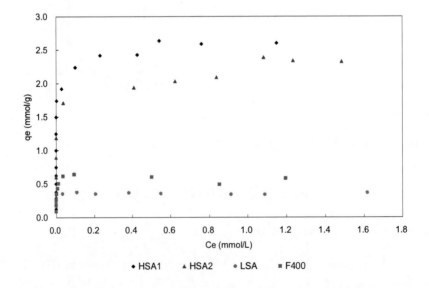

Figure 3. Plot of q_e against C_e for the adsorption of MR onto bamboo produced carbons.

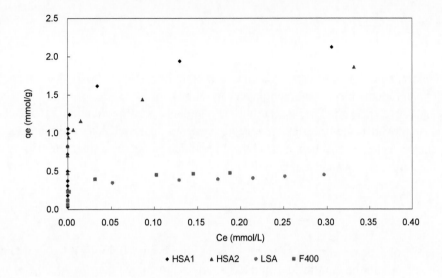

Figure 4. Plot of q_e against C_e for the adsorption of BY11 onto bamboo produced carbons.

Equilibrium Adsorption Isotherm Modelling

In order to optimise the design of a sorption system to remove the dyes, it is important to establish the most appropriate correlation for the equilibrium curves. The experimental data of the amount of sorbate adsorbed on the sorbent are substituted into an equilibrium isotherm model to determine the best-fit model for the sorption system. Using this relationship, any variation in the concentration of dye on the adsorbent with the concentration of dye in solution is correlated. Three widely used models are Langmuir (Langmuir, 1918), Freundlich (Freundlich, 1906) and Redlich-Peterson (Redlich and Peterson, 1959).

Langmuir Isotherm: Langmuir (Langmuir, 1918) proposed a theory to describe the adsorption of gas molecules onto metal surfaces. Langmuir's model of adsorption depends on the assumption that intermolecular forces decrease rapidly with distance and consequently predicts the existence of monolayer coverage of the adsorbate at the outer surface of the adsorbent. The saturated or monolayer (as $C_t \rightarrow \infty$) capacity can be represented by the expression:

$$q_e = \frac{K_L C_e}{1 + a_L C_e} \qquad (2)$$

where q_e is solid phase sorbate concentration at equilibrium (mmol/g), C_e is aqueous phase sorbate concentration at equilibrium (mmol/L), K_L is Langmuir isotherm constant (L/g), a_L is Langmuir isotherm constant (L/mmol) and K_L/a_L gives the theoretical monolayer saturation capacity, Q_0. The Langmuir equation is applicable to homogeneous sorption where the sorption of each sorbate molecule onto the surface has equal sorption activation energy. The Langmuir equation obeys Henry's Law at low concentration; when the concentration is very low, $a_L C_e$ is far smaller than unity, it implies $q_e = K_L C_e$, hence, it is analogous to Henry's Law. Therefore, a linear expression of the Langmuir equation is:

$$\frac{C_e}{q_e} = \frac{1}{K_L} + \frac{a_L}{K_L} C_e \qquad (3)$$

Therefore, a plot of C_e/q_e versus C_e gives a straight line of slope a_L/K_L and intercept $1/K_L$, where K_L/a_L gives the theoretical monolayer saturation capacity, Q_0.

Freundlich Isotherm: The Freundlich (Freundlich, 1906) equation is an empirical equation employed to describe heterogeneous systems, in which it is characterised by the heterogeneity factor 1/n. When n=1/n, the Freundlich equation reduces to Henry's Law. Hence, the empirical equation can be written:

$$q_e = K_F C_e^{\frac{1}{n}} \qquad (4)$$

where qe is solid phase sorbate concentration in equilibrium (mmol/g), Ce is liquid phase sorbate concentration in equilibrium (mmol/L), KF is Freundlich constant (L/mg1-1/n/g) and 1/n is the heterogeneity factor. This isotherm is another form of the Langmuir approach for adsorption on an "amorphous" surface. The amount adsorbed material is the summation of adsorption on all sites. The Freundlich isotherm is derived by assuming an exponential decay energy distribution function inserted in to the Langmuir equation. It describes reversible adsorption and is not restricted to the formation of the monolayer. A linear form of the Freundlich expression can be obtained by taking logarithms of Equation (4),

$$\ln q_e = \ln K_F + \frac{1}{n} \ln C_e \qquad (5)$$

Therefore, a plot of $\ln q_e$ versus $\ln C_e$ enables the constant K_F and exponent 1/n to be determined.

Redlich-Peterson Isotherm: Redlich and Peterson (Redlich and Peterson, 1959) incorporate three parameters into an empirical isotherm. The Redlich-Peterson isotherm model combines elements from both the Langmuir and Freundlich equation and the mechanism of adsorption is a hybrid one and does not follow ideal monolayer adsorption. The Redlich-Peterson equation is widely used as a compromise between Langmuir and Freundlich systems.

$$q_e = \frac{K_R C_e}{1 + a_R C_e^{\beta}} \qquad (6)$$

where q_e is solid phase sorbate concentration in equilibrium (mmol/g), C_e is liquid phase sorbate concentration in equilibrium (mmol/L), K_R is Redlich-Peterson isotherm constant (L/g), a_R is Redlich-Peterson isotherm constant (L/mg$^{1-1/\beta}$) and β is the exponent which lies between 1 and 0.

Linear Approach

Langmuir Isotherm

Langmuir's model of adsorption depends on the assumption that intermolecular forces decrease rapidly with distance and consequently predicts the existence of monolayer coverage of the adsorbate at the outer surface of the adsorbent. The adsorption data were analysed according to the linear form of the Langmuir isotherm equation. (Equation 3).

The plots of the specific sorption (C_e/q_e) against the equilibrium concentration for the four dye-carbons system are shown in Figures 5 to 6, respectively. All the isotherms were found to be linear over the whole range of the concentration studied and their respective isotherm constants and the correlation coefficients, R^2, are shown in the Table 3. The extremely high R^2 values reflect that the adsorption data follows the Langmuir model very closely. The Langmuir monolayer capacity Q_o represents the saturation capacity of acid dyes in each of the systems and the values for the adsorption system studied are also shown in Table 3.

Freundlich Isotherm

The Freundlich equation predicts that the dye concentrations on the adsorbent will increase so long as there is an increase in the dye concentration in the liquid. However, the experimental data in the present systems indicate that there is a limiting value of the solid phase concentration. By plotting ln q_e versus ln C_e yields the following graphs from the linear transformation of the Freundlich equation. Figures 7 to 8 show the logarithmic plots of the Freundlich expression for the selected dye-carbon adsorption system. The figures exhibit deviation from linearity on the Freundlich linear plot for the whole concentration range. However, for the system of MR adsorbed onto HSA1, the linear Freundlich plots can be divided into regions, i.e. region 1 and region 2, and this interpretation results in better fits to the experimental data at the higher concentration region 2 as shown in Figure 9. The two may be characteristic of two different surfaces and indicative of a wide variation in the two binding site energies. In the initial stage of adsorption the dyes will find their strongest orientation for strong binding on the extensively available carbon surface.

Table 3. Langmuir sorption isotherm constant for different dye systems

Dye	Carbon	K_L (L/g)	a_L (L/mmol)	Q_o (mmol/g)	R2
MR	HSA1	6.667E+02	3.525E+02	1.891	0.999
	HSA2	9.091E+01	5.308E+01	1.713	0.996
	LSA	9.709E+01	2.756E+02	0.352	0.998
	F400	-1.250E+03	-2.271E+03	0.551	0.990
BY11	HSA1	1.667E+03	7.952E+02	2.099	0.998
	HSA2	5.263E+02	2.850E+02	1.848	0.994
	LSA	6.711E+01	1.538E+02	0.436	0.992
	F400	2.128E+02	4.497E+02	0.473	0.999

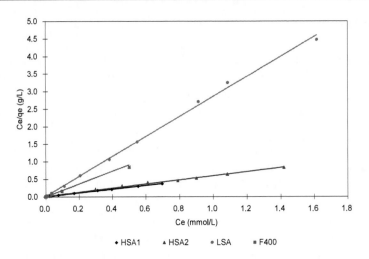

Figure 5. Langmuir Isotherm Linear Plots for MR single component system.

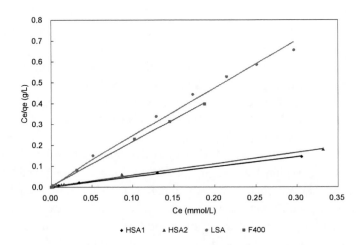

Figure 6. Langmuir Isotherm Linear Plots for BY11 single component system.

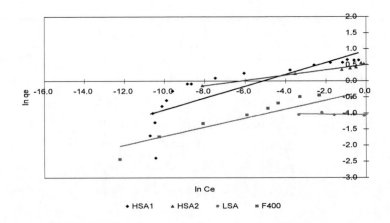

Figure 7. Freundlich Isotherm Linear Plots for MR single component system.

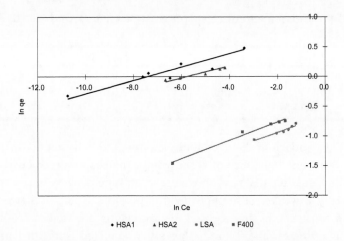

Figure 8. Freundlich Isotherm Linear Plots for BY11 single component system.

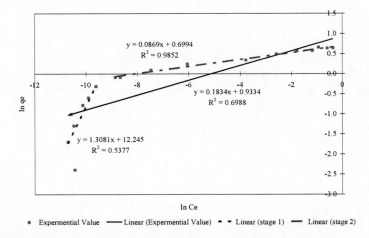

Figure 9. Freundlich multi-stage model for MR and HSA1 adsorption system.

Table 4. Freundlich sorption isotherm constants for different dye systems

Dye	Carbon	b_F	K_F (L/mg$^{1-1/n}$/g)	R^2
MR	HSA1	1.834E-01	2.543E+00	0.699
	HSA2	8.150E-02	1.654E+00	0.965
	LSA	-8.000E-03	3.497E-01	0.081
	F400	1.402E-01	7.267E-01	0.845
BY11	HSA1	2.413E+00	1.130E-01	0.998
	HSA2	2.012E+00	1.232E-01	0.961
	LSA	5.215E-01	1.454E-01	0.934
	F400	6.335E-01	1.543E-01	0.986

Table 5. Multi region Freundlich sorption isotherm constants for dye systems

System	Region	b_F	K_F (L/mg$^{1-1/n}$/g)	R^2
	(1)	1.308E+00	2.079E+05	0.538
MR + HSA1	(2)	8.690E-02	2.013E+00	0.985
	Whole	2.543E+00	1.834E-01	0.699

Eventually, the approach of the dye molecules from the bulk solution will become more restrictive due to the steric hindrance of adsorbed dye molecules already occupying much of the surface sites. It is possible that now only an "end-on" approach by the dye molecule might be feasible and only a weaker adsorption bond is possible. Table 4 shows the Freundlich sorption isotherm constants, b_F and K_F, and the correlation coefficients, R^2 for all the dye-carbon adsorption systems while Table 5 shows the predicted isotherm parameters for the Freundlich multi-stage models for the MR with HSA1 systems.

Non-Linear Approach

Due to the inherent bias resulting from the linear transformation of the two parameter equilibrium isotherms, it was decided that a nonlinear approach of the two and three parameter isotherm models by minimising the sum of squares of the error (SSE) function.

$$SSE = \sum_{i=1}^{n} \left(q_{e,cal} - q_{e,\exp}\right)_i^2 \tag{7}$$

where $q_{e,calc}$ are the theoretical adsorbed solid phase concentrations of sorbate on sorbent, which have been calculated from one of the isotherm equations and $q_{e,meas}$ are the experimentally determined adsorbed sorbate concentrations obtained from equation (1) using the experimentally measured equilibrium sorbate liquid phase concentrations, C_e. A trial and error procedure was used to determine the isotherm parameters by minimising the error values through the application of the Solver add-in from the spreadsheet software, Microsoft Excel.

Although this is the most common error function in use, it has one major drawback. Isotherm parameters derived using this error function will provide a better fit as the magnitude of the errors and thus the squares of the errors increase – biasing the fit towards the data obtained at the high end of the concentration range.

The experimental data were fitted into Langmuir, Freundlich, Redlich-Peterson equations to determine which isotherm gives the best correlation to experimental data. Tables 6 and 7 show the values of the parameters for the three isotherm equations. By comparing the SSE of three isotherm equations for BY11, the Langmuir equation fits reasonably well for all carbons. The Freundlich equation provides the best fit of the bamboo carbons. This indicates the possibility of reversible adsorption and is not restricted to the formation of the monolayer. It predicts that the dye concentrations on the adsorbent will increase so long as there is an increase in the dye concentration in the liquid. However, the Redlich-Peterson equation provides the best correlation for the F400.

Table 6. Equilibrium isotherm models' parameters for BY11- Carbon system

	HSA1	HSA2	LSA	F400
Langmuir Isotherm				
K_L (L/g)	3899.367	1191.034	24.546	259.715
a_L (L/mmol)	2120.589	791.663	54.027	567.896
Q_o (mmol/g)	1.839	1.504	0.454	0.457
SSE	1.931	1.755	0.075	0.020
Freundlich Isotherm				
K_F (L/mg$^{1-1/n}$/g)	2.423	2.086	0.527	0.620
1/n	0.114	0.134	0.151	0.146
SSE	1.292	1.501	0.074	0.019
Redlich-Peterson Isotherm				
K_R (L/g)	5390.515	4585.060	56.419	570.0003
a_R (L/mg$^{1-1/\beta}$)	2366.185	2248.169	111.499	1013.323
β	0.920	0.880	0.899	0.903
SSE	1.731	1.522	0.074	0.018

This suggests a reasonable fixed value for the sorption activation energy, which could correspond to the chelation bond energy between the dye ion and surface of the carbon, most likely with a lone pair of electrons on the carbon surface.

For MR – carbon systems, similar to the BY11 system, the Langmuir equation provides reasonable correlation for all carbons. The Redlich-Peterson equation provides the best fit for all carbons except HSA2 in which Freundlich is the best fit model.

Table 7. Equilibrium isotherm models' parameters for MR - Carbon system

	HSA1	HSA2	LSA	F400
Langmuir Isotherm				
K_L (L/g)	11852.972	6206.817	18091.685	1279.597
a_L (L/mmol)	6994.135	3958.791	51278.851	2338.480
Q_o (mmol/g)	1.695	1.568	0.353	0.547
SSE	0.514	0.878	0.050	0.073
Freundlich Isotherm				
K_F (L/mg$^{1-1/n}$/g)	2.144	1.661	0.353	0.684
1/n	0.132	0.085	0.000	0.105
SSE	0.794	0.701	0.050	0.063
Redlich-Peterson Isotherm				
K_R (L/g)	17813.518	17331.201	9141.207	7952.733
a_R (L/mg$^{1-1/\beta}$)	9199.995	10464.509	25907.075	13226.475
β	0.940	0.927	1.000	0.945
SSE	0.166	0.714	0.050	0.054

CONCLUSION

The preparation and investigation of high BET surface area activated carbons from scrap construction bamboo by low temperature chemical activation has been demonstrated. The high surface area carbon shows nearly three times higher adsorption capacities for both dyes than the commercial carbon, F400. Due to its smaller molecule size, both high surface area carbons have higher adsorption capacities for BY11. However, the low surface area carbon shows poor adsorption for both dyes. The surface area of the carbon plays an important role in the adsorption of the dyes while the porosity has little effect. For BY11, the Freundlich equation provides the best fit for the bamboo carbon while the Redlich-Peterson is the best model to describe the F400 system. For MR, the Redlich-Peterson provides the best isotherm equation for all the carbons except for HSA2 in which the Freundlich equation provides the best correlation. For both basic dyes, the adsorption mechanisms are heterogeneous in nature. It is possible more than one mechanism is involved in the adsorption process.

ACKNOWLEDGMENT

The authors would like to acknowledge the support of the Research Grant Council of Hong Kong SAR, the Innovation and Technology Fund of Hong Kong SAR, Hong Kong University of Science and Technology and Green Island International Ltd.

REFERENCES

Abe, I.; Fukuhara, T.; Iwasaki, S.; Yasuda, K.; Nakagawa, K.; Iwata, Y.; Kominami, H.; Kera, Y., Development of a high density carbonaceous adsorbent from compressed wood. *Carbon* 2001, *39* (10), 1485-1490.

Ahmedna, M.; Marshall, W. E.; Rao, R. M., Production of granular activated carbons from select agricultural by-products and evaluation of their physical, chemical and adsorption properties. *Bioresour. Technol.* 2000, *71* (2), 113-123.

Al-Degs, Y.; Khraisheh, M. A. M.; Allen, S. J.; Ahmad, M. N., Effect of carbon surface chemistry on the removal of reactive dyes from textile effluent. *Water Res.* 2000, *34* (3), 927-935.

Annadurai, G.; Lee, D. J.; Juang, R. S., Box-Behnken studies on dye removal from water using chitosan and activated carbon adsorbents. *J. Chin. Inst. Chem. Eng.* 2000, *31* (6), 609-615.

Asada, T.; Ishihara, S.; Yamane, T.; Toba, A.; Yamada, A.; Oikawa, K., Science of bamboo charcoal: Study on carbonizing temperature of bamboo charcoal and removal capability of harmful gases. *J. Health Sci.* 2002, *48* (6), 473-479.

Bansal, R. P.; Donnet, J.; Stoeckli, F., *Active Carbon*. Marcel Dekker: New York, 1988.

Brunauer, S.; Emmett, P. H.; Teller, E., Adsorption of gases in multimolecular layers. *J. Am. Chem. Soc.* 1938, *60*, 309-319.

Chern, J. M.; Wu, C. Y., Adsorption of binary dye solution onto activated carbon: Isotherm and breakthrough curves. *J. Chin. Inst. Chem. Eng.* 1999, *30* (6), 507-514.

Corapcioglu, M. O.; Huang, C. P., The Adsorption of Heavy-Metals onto Hydrous Activated Carbon. *Water Res.* 1987, *21* (9), 1031-1044.

Crini, G., Non-conventional low-cost adsorbents for dye removal: A review. *Bioresour. Technol.* 2006, *97* (9), 1061-1085.

Freundlich, H., Concerning adsorption in solutions. *Z. Physik. Chem. A* 1906, *57* (4), 385-470.

Garg, V. K.; Gupta, R.; Yadav, A. B.; Kumar, R., Dye removal from aqueous solution by adsorption on treated sawdust. *Bioresour. Technol.* 2003, *89* (2), 121-124.

Horvath, G.; Kawazoe, K., Method for the Calculation of Effective Pore-Size Distribution in Molecular-Sieve Carbon. *J. Chem. Eng. Jpn.* 1983, *16* (6), 470-475.

Jagtoyen, M.; Derbyshire, F., Some Considerations of the Origins of Porosity in Carbons from Chemically Activated Wood. *Carbon* 1993, *31* (7), 1185-1192.

Jagtoyen, M.; Derbyshire, F., Activated carbons from yellow poplar and white oak by H3PO4 activation. *Carbon* 1998, *36* (7-8), 1085-1097.

Juang, R. S.; Tseng, R. L.; Wu, F. C.; Lin, S. J., Use of chitin and chitosan in lobster shell wastes for color removal from aqueous solutions. *J. Environ. Sci. Health Part A-Environ. Sci. Eng. Toxic Hazard. Subst. Control* 1996, *31* (2), 325-338.

Kannan, N.; Sundaram, M. M., Kinetics and mechanism of removal of methylene blue by adsorption on various carbons - a comparative study. *Dyes Pigment.* 2001, *51* (1), 25-40.

Laine, J.; Calafat, A.; Labady, M., Preparation and Characterization of Activated Carbons from Coconut Shell Impregnated with Phosphoric-Acid. *Carbon* 1989, *27* (2), 191-195.

Langmuir, I., The adsorption of gases on plane surfaces of glass, mica and platinum. *J. Am. Chem. Soc.* 1918, *40* (9), 1361 - 1403.

Marc, R., Asian texile dye makers are a growing power in changing market. *CandEN* 1996, *73*, 10-12.

Marshall, W. E.; Ahmedna, M.; Rao, R. M.; Johns, M. M., Granular activated carbons from sugarcane bagasse: production and uses. *Int. Sugar J.* 2000, *102* (1215), 147-151.

Moreno-Castilla, C., Adsorption of organic molecules from aqueous solutions on carbon materials. *Carbon* 2004, *42*, 83-93.

Namasivayam, C.; Radhika, R.; Suba, S., Uptake of dyes by a promising locally available agricultural solid waste: coir pith. *Waste Manage.* 2001, *21* (4), 381-387.

Ohe, K.; Nagae, Y.; Nakamura, S.; Baba, Y., Removal of nitrate anion by carbonaceous materials prepared from bamboo and coconut shell. *J. Chem. Eng. Jpn.* 2003, *36* (4), 511-515.

Pereira, M. F. R.; Soares, S. F.; Orfao, J. J. M.; Figueiredo, J. L., Adsorption of dyes on activated carbons: influence of surface chemical groups. *Carbon* 2003, *41* (4), 811-821.

Ramesh, A.; Lee, D. J.; Wong, J. W. C., Adsorption equilibrium of heavy metals and dyes from wastewater with low-cost adsorbents: A review. *J. Chin. Inst. Chem. Eng.* 2005, *36* (3), 203-222.

Redlich, O.; Peterson, D. L., A Useful Adsorption Isotherm. *J. Phys. Chem.* 1959, *63* (6), 1024.

Tsai, W. T.; Chang, C. Y.; Lee, S. L., A low cost adsorbent from agricultural waste corn cob by zinc chloride activation. *Bioresour. Technol.* 1998, *64* (3), 211-217.

Valix, M.; Cheung, W. H.; McKay, G., Preparation of activated carbon using low temperature carbonisation and physical activation of high ash raw bagasse for acid dye adsorption. *Chemosphere* 2004, *56* (5), 493-501.

Walker, G. M.; Hansen, L.; Hanna, J. A.; Allen, S. J., Kinetics of a reactive dye adsorption onto dolomitic sorbents. *Water Res.* 2003, *37* (9), 2081-2089.

Wu, F. C.; Tseng, R. L.; Juang, R. S., Preparation of activated carbons from bamboo and their adsorption abilities for dyes and phenol. *J. Environ. Sci. Health Part A-Toxic/Hazard. Subst. Environ. Eng.* 1999, *34* (9), 1753-1775.

In: Water Production and Wastewater Treatment
Editor: B. Antizar-Ladislao et al.

ISBN 978-1-61728-503-5
© 2011 Nova Science Publishers, Inc.

Chapter 8

INVESTIGATIONS ON ARSENIC ADSORPTION ONTO DOLOMITIC SORBENTS

Y. Salameh[1], M.N.M. Ahmad,
S.J. Allen, and G.M. Walker

School of Chemistry and Chemical Engineering, Queen's University Belfast,
Belfast BT9 5AG, Northern Ireland, UK

ABSTRACT

Arsenic is present in potable water in many areas in the world as a result of both natural impacts and anthropogenic discharge, with arsenic bearing waters requiring proper treatment before use. At present, there is a considerable interest in studying new sorbent materials for the removal of arsenic from aqueous solutions. This work discusses the feasibility of arsenic uptake onto raw dolomite which is considered to be a potential inexpensive adsorbent. Experimental investigations were undertaken in equilibrium isotherm and kinetic systems in order to evaluate the adsorption capacity by taking into consideration the experimental parameters such as: pH; initial solute concentration; mass-volume ratio; particle size of adsorbent; contact time, the effect of various ions present and the effect of changing the temperature. The equilibrium time was determined to be 5 days for dolomite. Desorption studies were also undertaken. The data for the dolomite-As were compared with granular activated carbon in an identical set of experiments. The data were mathematically described using empirical equilibrium isotherm models, namely Langmuir and Freundlich models. The maximum arsenic removal with dolomite was found at pH 2 and was dependent on the dosage of dolomite, adsorbent particle size and the presence of various anions. For the kinetic Experiments the data were mathematically described using adsorption kinetic models, namely pseudo first-order and pseudo second-order models. Thermodynamic results indicate that the adsorption follows an exothermic chemisorption process. The experimental data indicate successful removal of As(V) ion from aqueous solution indicating that dolomite may be an alternative low cost adsorbent for As(V).

1Tel. +44 (0) 2890 974253, Fax. +44 (0)2890 974627 e-mail ysalameh01@qub.ac.uk.

1. Introduction

1.1. Arsenic in Groundwater

Arsenic bearing compounds are toxic to all living organisms. The presence of arsenic is a worldwide environmental problem with regard to drinking water (Guan *et al.*, 2008). Significant problems occur when arsenic is widespread but undetected because its long-term health effects are caused by chronic as opposed to acute exposure. Arsenic has been linked to cancer of the bladder, lungs, skin, kidney, nasal passages, liver, and prostate (Roy, 2008; Biswas *et al.*, 2008). Non-cancer effects include gangrene, limb loss, cardiovascular and pulmonary disease, endocrine and haematological disorders, and reproductive/developmental problems. In addition, arsenic is considered an accumulative enabler, meaning people who are predisposed to various cancers, diabetes, high blood pressure and other ailments are more likely to contract these illnesses (Nguyen *et al.*, 2007).

Arsenic occurs in various mineral forms, of which 60% are arsenates, 20% are sulphides and sulphosalts, 10% are oxides and the remainder are arsenides, native elements and metal alloys (Mkandawire and Dudel, 2005). Several toxicological studies have demonstrated that the toxicity of arsenic is dependent on its chemical forms, oxidation state, physical state (gas or solution), rate of absorption into cells, rate of elimination and its chemical nature. Arsenic exists in several states of oxidation: As(0) or as ion forms like As(V) arsenate, As(III) arsenite and As(III) arsine. It is generally recognized that the soluble inorganic arsenicals are more toxic than the organic ones, and the inorganic As(III) species are more toxic than the inorganic As(V) (Sanchez de la Campa *et al.*, 2008). At moderate or high redox potentials, arsenic can be stabilized as a series of pentavalent (arsenate) oxyanions, H_3AsO_4, $H_2AsO_4^-$, $HAsO_4^{2-}$ and AsO_4^{3-}. Thus, to eliminate these toxic metals from water, a potential adsorbent must have the anion exchange properties (Yusof and Malek, 2008).

Increased concentrations of arsenic in natural waters have been reported in many areas of the world such as, in South East Asia (Bangladesh, Vietnam, West Bengal-India, Nepal, Cambodia, Mongolia, China, Thailand, Pakistan and Taiwan), in Central and South America (Mexico, Chile and Argentina) and in North America (USA and Canada) and in Australia. Elevated concentrations of arsenic have been also found in various European countries, i.e., Finland, Hungary, Germany, Croatia, Romania, Italy, Spain and Greece (Biterna *et al.*, 2007). Arsenic is introduced into water by natural processes such as weathering reactions, biological activity and volcanic emission; it also enters the water cycle through discharges of various industries such as smelting, petroleum refinery, fertilizers, insecticides, herbicides, glass and ceramic manufacturing industries (Shao *et al.*, 2008). Arsenic is mainly ingested through contaminated water supplies where it generally occurs as As(V) and As(III), depending on pH and redox conditions.

Due to the high toxicity and the widespread occurrence of arsenic, it is strictly controlled by environmental regulations in most areas of the world. The World Health Organization has defined a restrictive limit of 10 ppb for drinking water (WHO, 2006). To help achieve this consent limit, various treatment technologies to remove arsenic from drinking water have been designed such as: coagulation; ion exchange; reverse osmosis; liquid-liquid extraction; ultra-filtration; and adsorption (Guan *et al.*, 2008; Biswas *et al.*, 2008*)*. However, in many areas of the world there is still in a necessity for appropriate technology, which is inexpensive, simple to use and easily applied.

1.2. The Dolomite Group of Minerals

The Dolomite is considered a promising low cost adsorbent. It is composed of minerals with an unusual trigonal bar 3 symmetry. The general formula of this group is $AB(CO_3)_2$, where A can be either calcium, barium and/or strontium and the B can be either iron, magnesium, zinc and/or manganese. The structure of the Dolomite Group is taken from the Calcite Group structure. The Calcite Group structure is layered with alternating carbonate layers and metal ion layers. The structure of the Dolomite Group minerals is layered in such a way that the A metal ions occupy one layer which is followed by a carbonate layer which is followed by the B metal ion layer followed by another carbonate ($CO3$) layer, etc. The layering is of the form: $|A|CO_3|B|CO_3|A|CO_3|B|CO_3|A|$... This ordered layering of different or non-equivalent ions causes a loss of the two fold rotational axes and mirror planes that are present in the Calcite Group structure (Walker *et al.*, 2004; Walker *et al.*, 2005). The amount of calcium and magnesium in most specimens is equal, but occasionally one element may have a slightly greater presence than the other. Small amounts of iron and manganese are sometimes also present (Duffy *et al.*, 2005).

1.3. Analysis of Adsorption Equilibrium Isotherms

Two of the most commonly used isotherm models have been used in this work, namely, the Langmuir and Freundlich models. The form of the Langmuir equation can be represented as follows:

$$q_e = \frac{Q_{max} K_L C_e}{1 + K_L C_e} \tag{1}$$

Or in the linear from:

$$\frac{C_e}{q_e} = \frac{1}{K_L Q_{max}} + \frac{Ce}{Q_{max}} \tag{2}$$

where: C_e is the equilibrium concentration of As(V) in solution (mg/L); q_e is the solid phase solute concentration (mg g^{-1}); Q_{max} is the maximum arsenic uptake capacity (mg g^{-1}); K_L is the equilibrium constant.

The Freundlich model has the following form

$$q_e = k_F C_e{}^n \tag{3}$$

Or in the linear from:

$$\log q_e = \log k_F + n \log C_e \tag{4}$$

where: K_F is the constant indicative of the relative adsorption capacity of the adsorbent (mg g^{-1}); n is the constant indicative of the intensity of the adsorption and it is dimensionless.

Percentage solute removal was then calculated as follows:

$$\text{Removal}(100\%) = \frac{Co - Ce}{Co} * 100\% \tag{5}$$

where: Co and Ce are the initial and equilibrium solute concentrations respectively.

1.4. Kinetic Modelling

The batch experimental data were applied to selected adsorption kinetic models, namely pseudo first-order and pseudo second-order models. The pseudo first-order (Lagergren first-order) rate equation is as follows:

$$\ln(q_e - q_t) = \ln q_e - K_{1ads} t \tag{6}$$

where: q_e and q_t are the amount of adsorbate adsorbed (μg/g) at equilibrium and at time t (min), K_{1ads} is the adsorption rate constant. The values of K_{1ads} and q_e were calculated from the intercept and slope of the plots of $\ln(q_e - q_t)$ versus t.

The pseudo second-order equation is also based on the sorption capacity of the solid phase and is expressed as;

$$\frac{dq}{dt} = K_{2ad}(q_e - q_t)^2 \tag{7}$$

where K_{2ad} is the rate constant of second-order adsorption. For the same boundary conditions the integrated form becomes:

$$\frac{t}{q_t} = \frac{1}{K_{2ad} q_e^2} + \left(\frac{1}{q_e}\right)t \tag{8}$$

If second-order kinetics is applicable, the plot of t/q against t of should give a linear relationship, from which q_e and K_{2ad} can be determined from the slope and intercept of plot.

1.5. Thermodynamic Modelling

To calculate the thermodynamic activation parameters such as enthalpy of activation, ΔH°, entropy of activation, ΔS°, and free energy of activation, ΔG°, the Eyring equation was applied (Al-Ghouti et al., 2005),

$$\ln\left(\frac{K_{2ads}}{T}\right) = \left[\ln\left(\frac{k_B}{h_p}\right) + \frac{\Delta S^o}{R}\right] - \frac{\Delta H^o}{R}\left(\frac{1}{T}\right), \tag{9}$$

where: $\Delta G^\circ = \Delta H^\circ - T\Delta S^\circ$ (10)
where k_B is the Boltzmann constant (1.3807×10^{-23} J/K), h_P is the Planck constant (6.6261×10^{-34} J s), R is the ideal gas constant (8.314 J g^{-1} K^{-1}), K_{2ad} is the pseudo-second-order constant (k_2) for arsenic adsorption.

The activation energy of arsenic adsorption onto the dolomite can be calculated by the relationship :

$$\ln(K_{2ad}) = \ln(K_o) - \frac{E}{R}\left(\frac{1}{T}\right) \tag{11}$$

where K_o is the rate constant of adsorption (g/mg min). Plotting the pseudo-second-order constant against the reciprocal temperature gives a reasonably straight line, the gradient of which is $-E/R$.

2. EXPERIMENTAL MATERIALS AND METHODS

2.1. Adsorbent Characterisation

The dolomite used in this study was mined from a deposit in County Fermanagh, Northern Ireland. The typical chemical composition of the dolomite in the deposit was 44% $MgCO_3$ and 53% $CaCO_3$.

Table 1. General properties of activated carbon used in this study

specification	value
BET surface area, m2/g	941
External surface area, m2/g	396
Micropore surface area, m2/g	541

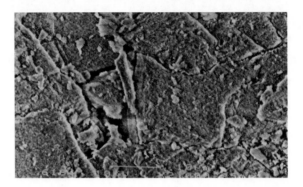

Figure 1. SEM of surface of raw dolomite sample at a magnitude of 2000mm×25 mm.

The dolomite was ground and sieved on a series of test sieves. A sample of dolomite was analysed for specific surface area using BET nitrogen adsorption employing a Nova 4200e, surface area and pore size analyser (Quantachrome Instruments), the surface area was found to be $17.36(m^2g^{-1})$ for particle size 1.0-1.2 mm. Figure 1 shows a SEM image for a raw dolomite sample. It can be observed that the dolomite structure consists of a crystalline structure with inter-special voids. Activated carbon used in the studies was commercially available having specification as given in Table 1.

2.2. Adsorbate Characterisation

A 2000ppb stock arsenic solution was prepared in a 1L volumetric flask using deionized water. The stock solution was made from sodium arsenic dibasic heptahydrate $(Na_2HAsO_4.7H_2O)$, Aldrich Chemical Co. Inc, USA. In addition 0.1g $NaHCO_3$ was added to buffer pH fluctuations during the experiment. Most groundwaters have some alkalinity present, which tends to be in the order of 250-600 mg/L HCO_3. The addition of bicarbonate is therefore not seen to comprise the experiment.

A simple picture of arsenic chemical speciation calculated based on their stability constants has been outlined in Figure 2 (Shao *et al.*, 2008). The monovalent anionic species of arsenate were dominant at pH ranging from 2 to 6, while in the case of arsenite were significant at alkaline region of pH 9–12.

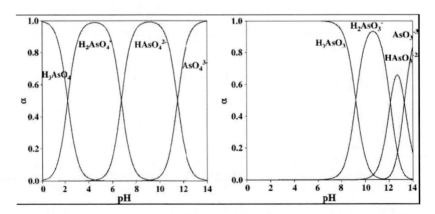

Figure 2. Distribution of arsenate and arsenite as a function of pH (after Shao et al., 2008).

2.3. Experimental Methods

Preliminary experiments were conducted to evaluate the impact of using dolomite as an adsorbent for As(III). However, the results indicated very low removal (<10%). Therefore, oxidation of the arsenite to arsenate using ozone or chloride may be required before dolomite adsorption; surface modification of the dolomite could also enhance the removal of As(III).

Equilibrium experiments were carried out using 0.05 ± 0.0005g of the dolomite which was contacted with 50 ml of arsenic solution. Appropriate dilutions were made to give a range of arsenic concentrations. The pH was adjusted by using (1 mol/dm^3) HCl or (1 mol/dm^3) NaOH. The samples were placed in glass jars and subsequently capped and shaken in a mechanical shaker (Gerhardt Bonn type 655) for 5 days at 80 rpm. Samples of the aqueous phase were taken at regular intervals, filtered through a 0.45 μm cellulose nitrate membrane filter (Swinnex-25 Millipore) and prepared for analyses using ICP-AES. The samples were made up to 10 ml to give a 2% nitric acid solution. All experiments were conducted at the room temperature which was 22°C. Duplicate samples were measured and standard error in the readings was less than 3%. Blank samples were also used. The adsorption of As(V) into filter paper was studied and found to be 73 ppb maximum. An identical procedure was applied to a series of experiments using activated carbon.

Kinetic experiments were carried out using a standard ratio of 1.0 ± 0.0005g of the dolomite which was contacted with 500 ml of arsenic solution for eight hours on hot plate stirrers to adjust the temperature if required (standard temperature 22°C). Magnetic stirrer was used for the agitation purpose. The agitation speed was set at 150 rpm. Appropriate dilutions were made to give a range of arsenic concentrations. The pH was adjusted by using (1 mol/dm^3) HCl or (1 mol/dm^3) NaOH. Samples of the aqueous phase were taken at regular intervals by using needles and then were filtered through a 0.45 μm cellulose nitrate membrane filter (Swinnex-25 Millipore) and prepared for analyses using ICP-AES. The samples were made up to 10 ml to give a 2% nitric acid solution. Duplicate samples were measured and standard error in the readings was less than 3%. Blank samples were also used.

A desorption study was undertaken using H$_2$O, HCl (1 mol/dm^3) and NaOH (1 mol/dm^3) as eluent solutions. These experiments were performed immersing raw dolomite in 50 cm^3 of eluent solution for 120 h with stirring at 80 rpm. The bulk solute concentration in solution was measured as previously described. The extent of desorption was calculated from Eq. (6).

$$Desorption(\%) = \frac{desorbed \cdot amount \cdot of \cdot solute}{absorbed \cdot amount \cdot of \cdot solute} \times 100 \qquad (12)$$

3. RESULTS AND DISCUSSION

3.1. Equilibrium Investigations

3.1.1. Effect of Ph

The effect of pH on the percentage of As(V) removal from aqueous solution using dolomite and activated carbon is illustrated in Figure 3.

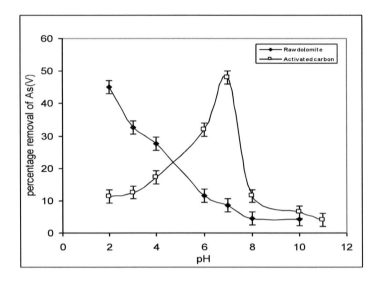

Figure 3. The pH dependence of As(V) adsorption on raw dolomite and activated carbon. Adsorbent dose: 1g/L; Adsorbent particle size: 0.7-2.0 mm; Initial arsenic concentration: 500 ppb; contact time: 5 days.

The figure shows the maximum percentage removal onto raw dolomite ($\approx$45%) occurs at pH 2 and onto activated carbon ($\approx$48%) occurs at pH 7. The removal rate onto dolomite decreases with the increase in pH. Variation in pH will affect the surface charge of the adsorbent and the degree of ionisation and speciation of arsenic. This pH dependence of the binding showed that ion exchange and electrostatic interactions are involved in the binding mechanism of As(V) by raw dolomite. The adsorption of As(V) onto dolomite may be due to two effects: firstly, the rough surface of the raw dolomite gives solid contact resulting in chemisorption of As(V) at a low concentration. Secondly, regarding the chemistry of the dolomite, since it is mainly composed of $MgCO_3$ and $CaCO_3$, this may allow the formation arsenic oxide and probably arsenic carbonate, so precipitation of these compounds may be a further As(V) removal mechanism. An alternative hypothesis may be that the arsenate is adsorbed readily to the outside surface of the raw dolomite granules, and then is gradually adsorbed into internal macro-meso porous cavities at a much slower rate. However, raw/unprocessed dolomite has a limited internal pore distribution and a modest pore surface area (BET surface area = 17.36 m^2g^{-1}).

3.1.2. Effect of Initial Solute Concentration

In order to determine the adsorption capacity for arsenic on dolomite and for process design purposes, equilibrium adsorption isotherm data are of fundamental importance. Figures 4 and 5 illustrate the Langmuir and Freundlich isotherms respectively for As(V)-dolomite systems. For Langmuir the values of K_L = 3.14 (L mg^{-1}) and Q_{max} = 0.526(mg g^{-1}). For Freundlich the values of K_F = 12.3(mg g^{-1}) (mg L^{-1}) and n = 2.02. Based on (the linear regression coefficient) R^2 values the data indicate that the sorption of As(V) has been well described the Langmuir and Freundlich models, with the R^2 values of 0.967 and 0.981 for Langmuir and Freundlich respectively. The dimensionless parameter, R_L [where: R_L = $1/(1+Co.K_L)$], indicates the deviation of the adsorption isotherm from linearity. R_L = 1 indicates the adsorption is linear with homogeneous adsorption sites.

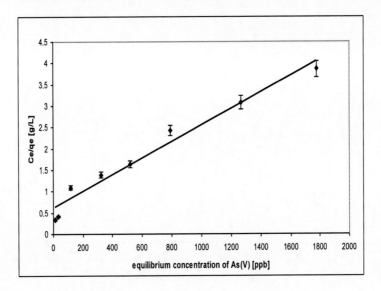

Figure 4. Langmuir plot for the adsorption of arsenic onto raw dolomite. Adsorbent dose: 1g/L; volume of test solution: 50 ml; pH 2; contact time: 5 days.

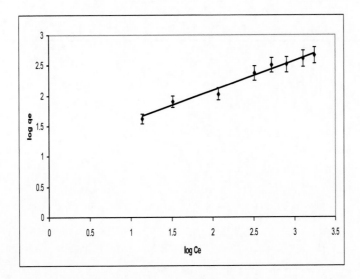

Figure 5. Freundlich plot for the adsorption of arsenic onto raw dolomite. Adsorbent dose: 1g/L; volume of test solution: 50 ml; pH 2; contact time: 5 days.

$R_L < 1$ shows that the adsorption is favourable, new adsorption sites are available and the adsorption capacity increases. $R_L > 1$ indicates that the adsorption bonds are weak, adsorption capacities decrease and unfavourable. The R_L values for the range of the arsenic concentrations under investigation have been calculated and found to lie between 0 and 1, which indicated that the sorption of As(V) by raw dolomite is favourable at pH 2 and temperature 22°C.

Figures 5 and 6 show the Langmuir and Freundlich isotherms respectively for As(V)-activated carbon systems. For Langmuir the value of $K_L = 3.12 \times 10^{-3}$(L mg^{-1}) and $Q_{max} = 0.625$(mg g^{-1}). For Freundlich the values of $K_F = 1.622$(mg g^{-1}) and $n = 0.687$.

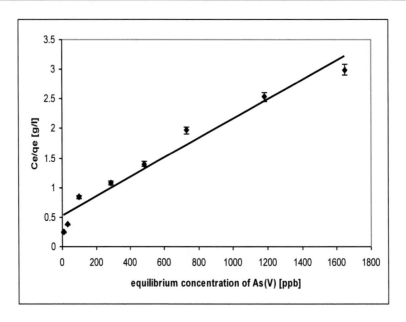

Figure 6. Langmuir plot for the adsorption of arsenic onto activated carbon. Adsorbent dose: 1g/L; volume of test solution: 50 ml; pH 7; contact time: 5 days.

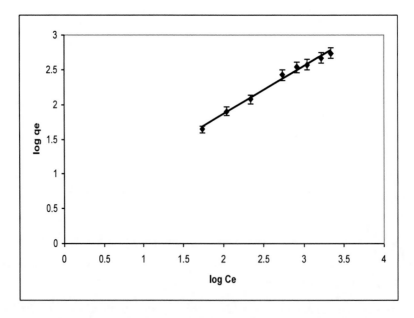

Figure 7. Freundlich plot for the adsorption of arsenic onto activated carbon. Adsorbent dose: 1g/L; volume of test solution: 50 ml; pH 7; contact time: 5 days.

3.1.3. Effect of Adsorbent Concentration

The effect of adsorbent mass to volume of solution on As(V) uptake is illustrated in Figures 8 and 9, which shows that adsorption efficiency of As(V) increased with an increase in mass of raw dolomite.

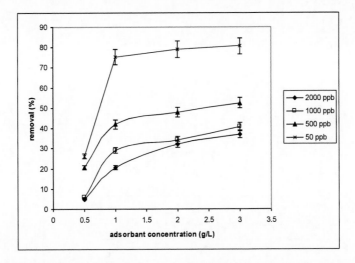

Figure 8. The dosage of adsorbent dependence for As(V) adsorption on raw dolomite. Volume of test solution: 50 ml; pH 2; contact time: 5 days.

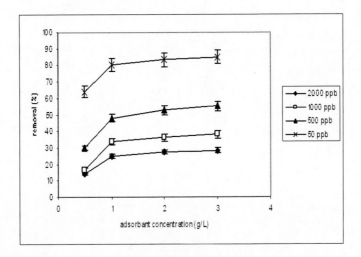

Figure 9. The dosage of adsorbent dependence for As(V) adsorption on activated carbon. Volume of test solution: 50 ml; pH 7; contact time: 5 days.

The increase in the efficiency of removal can be attributed to increased adsorbent surface area available for mass transfer, i.e., more pores and voids for As(V) chemisorption, but also higher concentrations of $MgCO_3$ and $CaCO_3$ which would increase the probability of formation of arsenic oxide and arsenic carbonate, thus increasing in the extent of precipitation as a mechanism of As(V) removal.

3.1.4. Effect of Adsorbent Particle Size

A range of particle sizes have been tested in this study in order to understand the mechanism of As(V) removal by raw dolomite. The particle size has been varied from less than 0.335 mm to (0.710-2.00) mm. Figure 10 indicates that the amount of solute adsorbed increases with the decrease in particle size of the adsorbent.

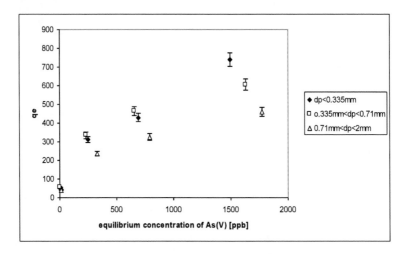

Figure 10. Adsorption isotherm of As(V) at various particle sizes (dp) of raw dolomite. Adsorbent dose: 1g/L;volume of test solution: 50 ml; pH 2; contact time: 5 days.

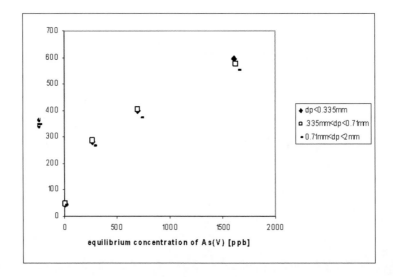

Figure 11. Adsorption isotherm of As(V) at various particle sizes (dp) of activated carbon. Adsorbent dose: 1g/L;volume of test solution: 50 ml; pH 7; contact time: 5 days.

This is probably due to an increase in the external surface area and the number of active pores per unit mass of the adsorbent found with decreasing particle size. Furthermore, the crushing of the large particles to form smaller particles facilitates crack formation, which further increases the surface area available for mass transfer. However, the data indicate that the mechanism of adsorption does not depend on the adsorbent particle size alone (i.e. surface area or channels) which may suggest As(V) removal by precipitation as arsenic oxide and probably as arsenic carbonate.

Figure 11 shows the effect of activated carbon particle size on the arsenic removal. There is a little increase with the decrease in the particle size which is indicative of a microporous/high surface area adsorbent.

3.1.5. Effect of Contact Time

The equilibrium time for the arsenate sorption on the raw dolomite and the activated carbon is illustrated in figures 12 and 13 respectively. The data indicate that equilibrium was reached in approximately 5 days on the raw dolomite, while it reached the equilibrium in approximately 2 days on the activated carbon. The initial rapid decrease in As(V) concentration using dolomite is also indicative of a precipitation process. The data also suggest that the arsenate is adsorbed readily to the outside surface of the raw dolomite granules, and then gradually adsorbed into internal macro-meso porous cavities at a much slower rate.

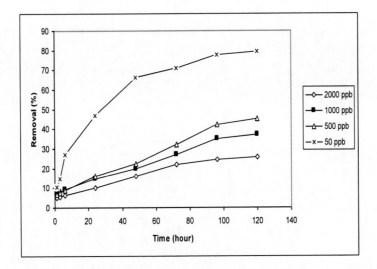

Figure 12. The contact time dependence for As(V) adsorption on raw dolomite. Volume of test solution: 250 ml; pH 2; Adsorbent dose: 1g/L.

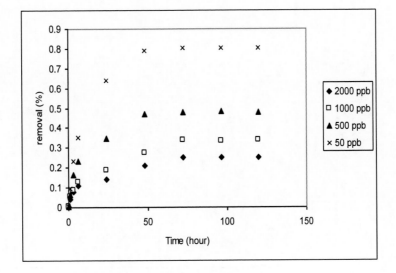

Figure 13. The contact time dependence for As(V) adsorption on activated carbon. Volume of test solution: 250 ml; pH 7; Adsorbent dose: 1g/L.

3.1.6. Effect of Presence of Various Salts

The removal of arsenate from solution in the presence of different concentrations of various anions is illustrated in Figure 14. The removal of As(V) decreased by increasing the sulphate concentration; Su and Puls (2001) reported a slight decrease of As(V) removal by zero valent iron in the presence of sulfate. The removal slightly increased by increasing the chloride concentration, this small affect may be attributed to the fact that Cl$^-$ does not compete with $H_2AsO_4^-$ (Ayoub and Mehawej, 2007), so the chloride can be considered as a non-competing element to arsenate. In the presence of the phosphate the raw dolomite shows very low efficiency in removing the As(V),

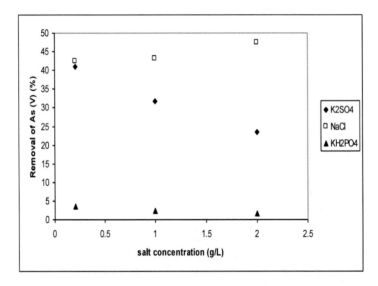

Figure 14. As(V) removal by raw dolomite in the presence of various anions. Initial arsenic concentration: 500 ppb; Volume of test solution: 50 ml; pH 2; Adsorbent dose: 1g/L.

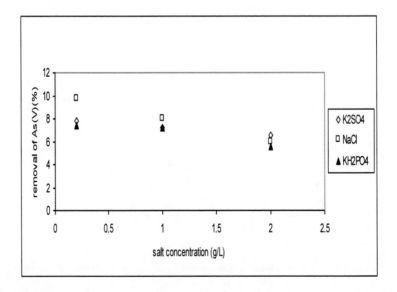

Figure 15. As(V) removal by activated carbon in the presence of various anions. Initial arsenic concentration: 500 ppb; Volume of test solution: 50 ml; pH 7; Adsorbent dose: 1g/L.

Table 2. Desorption studies of raw dolomite-As(V) loaded using various eluants

Eluant	Desorption
H2O	13%
HCl (1 M)	22.5%
NaOH (1M)	26%

This might be because AsO_4^{3-} is a sorption analog of PO_4^{3-} and competes for uptake carriers in the dolomite. Rahman *et al.* (2008) proposed the arsenate uptake in *Spirodela polyrhiza* L. might occur through the phosphate uptake pathway due to similar chemical behaviour of AsO_4^{3-} and PO_4^{3-}, other researchers reported a decrease of As(V) removal in the presence of the phosphate (Biterna *et al.*, 2007; Stachowicz *et al.*, 2008). The present findings suggest a similar mechanism for the dolomite.

Figure 15 indicates a very low removal for the arsenic onto activated carbon in the presence of sulphate, chloride and phosphate. Di Natali *et al.* (2007) reported a low removal for As(V) onto activated carbon at high salinity levels.

3.1.7. Desorption Studies

Desorption of As(V) from the raw dolomite was attempted using (1 mol/dm^3) HCl, (1 mol/dm^3) NaOH and deionized water. The experimental results showed better As(V) desorption in the basic solutions after an equilibrium time of 120 hours. This improvement in removal efficiency of the regenerated raw dolomite by the basic solution may be attributed to desorption of other chemicals or impurities that could have been present on the original raw dolomite particles, which could have interfered with the adsorption of arsenate.

3.2. Kinetic Investigations

3.2.1. Effect of Ph and Initial Solute Concentration

Previous work by our group has indicated that dolomite decreases with the increase in pH (Salameh et al., 2009). It was noted that variation in pH will affect the surface charge of the adsorbent and the degree of ionisation and speciation of arsenic. This pH dependence of the binding showed that ion exchange and electrostatic interactions are involved in the binding mechanism of As(V) by raw dolomite. The adsorption of As(V) onto dolomite may be due to two effects: firstly, the rough surface of the raw dolomite gives solid contact resulting in chemisorption of As(V) at low concentration. Secondly, regarding the chemistry of the dolomite, since it is mainly composed of $MgCO_3$ and $CaCO_3$, this may allow the formation arsenic oxide and probably arsenic carbonate, so precipitation of these compounds may be a further As(V) removal mechanism. In light of these findings, in this investigation acidic arsenic solutions were used with pH = 2.

The plots of q_t versus t at different initial Arsenic concentrations are shown in Figure 16. Two simplified mathematical analyses: pseudo first-order and pseudo second order type kinetic models were used to describe the adsorption data. The data in Figure 16 indicate that sorption is rapid during the first 60 minutes and that dynamic equilibrium is attained in approximately 360 minutes for the three concentrations investigated. Figure 18 illustrates the applicability of pseudo-second order kinetics to the adsorption data. The best fit linearization (employing the sum of square errors squared method, SSE) indicates that, although the data appear to follow first order kinetics during the initial stage of the experiment, near equilibrium the experimental data deviate significantly from the predicted data for especially at low initial concentrations. The pseudo second order rate constants, K_{2ads}, were calculated and are listed in Table 3 and show a large variation over the concentration range investigated. Moreover. the correlation coefficient ranged from $r^2 = 0.922 - 0.975$, indicating an adequate representation over the course of the experiment.

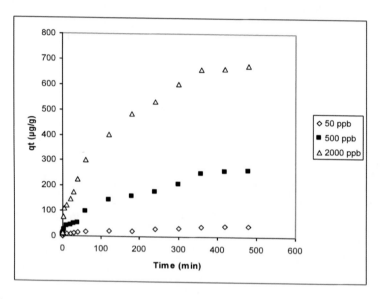

Figure 16. Adsorption curve of arsenic onto raw dolomite. Adsorbent ratio: 1g/L; pH = 2; particle size 710-2000 microns.

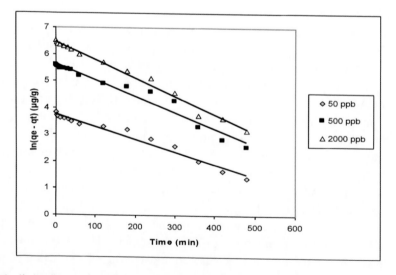

Figure 17. The linear first-order kinetic sorption isotherm for arsenic in single solute system by raw dolomite. Adsorbent ratio: 1g/L; pH = 2; particle size 710-2000 microns.

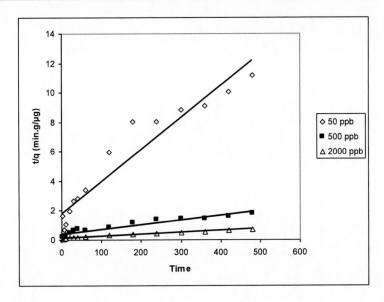

Figure 18. The linear second-order kinetic sorption isotherm for arsenic in single solute system by raw dolomite. Adsorbent ratio: 1g/L; pH = 2; particle size 710-2000 microns.

Table 3. Comparison of the first- and second-order reaction rate constants obtained at different initial arsenic concentrations

Concentration	First-order kinetic model			Second-order kinetic model	
	$K_{1ads}(\mu g /g \min)$	$q_e(\mu g/g)$	R^2	$K_{2ad}(\mu g /g \min)$	R^2
50 ppb	0.0047	43.13	0.9874	2.65×10^{-4}	0.9216
500 ppb	0.0060	280.96	0.962	2.67×10^{-5}	0.9257
2000 ppb	0.0068	652.04	0.9704	1.75×10^{-5}	0.9753

Figure 17 illustrates the applicability of pseudo-first order kinetics to the adsorption data. The best fit linearization (employing the sum of square errors squared method, SSE) indicates that, the data closely follow first order kinetics during the initial stage of the experiment. However, as with the second order kinetics, near equilibrium the experimental data deviate slightly from the predicted data for each of the concentrations investigated. The pseudo first order rate constants, K_{1ads}, were calculated and are listed in Table 3 and show only a slight increase in rate constant with increasing initial concentration. The correlation coefficient ranged from $r^2 = 0.962 - 0.987$, indicating an adequate representation of the kinetic data.

The samples were also analysed for the calcium and magnesium during the course of the kinetic experiment. The relationship between the arsenic removal from solution onto the surface of the dolomite and simultaneous dissolution of calcium and magnesium is illustrated in Figure 19. The data indicate an increase in Ca and Mg with As uptake onto the solid, which may imply the formation and precipitation of arsenic oxide and possibly arsenic carbonate on the surface of the dolomite. The graphical relationship in figure 19 between both calcium and magnesium versus arsenic removal are the same shape although the calcium is in higher concentration due to its increased solubility.

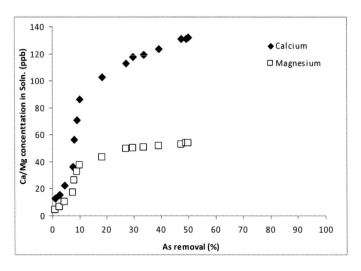

Figure 19. Ca and Mg relationship with As removal. Adsorbent ratio: 1g/L; pH = 2; particle size 710-2000 microns; Initial As concentration: 500 ppb.

The Ca/Mg versus Ca relationship shows a good deal of linearity during the early stages of the experiment however during the latter stage the system arsenic uptake appears to less dependent on Ca/Mg dissolution. This relationship may indicate a two stage arsenic removal process: (i) an initial stage involving an ion exchange type process which can be described by a pseudo-first order chemical reaction model resulting in the formation and precipitation of arsenic oxide on the surface of the dolomite; (ii) in a second process, due to the increase surface coverage of the dolomite by the precipitate, further dissolution of Ca/Mg is limited and the predicted uptake profiles of the reaction models are not achieved, although some As precipitation still occurs on the surface of the previously precipitated arsenic oxide.

3.2.2. Effect of Adsorbent Ratio

Arsenic removal at different mass of adsorbent to volume of solution ratio was studied at 22°C and at pH 2.0 by varying the adsorbent amount from 0.5 to 4 g/l at constant initial As(V) concentration. Figure 20 and 21 illustrate the applicability of pseudo-first order and pseudo-second order kinetics to the adsorption data, respectively. The kinetic models constants, K_{1ads} and K_{2ads}, were calculated and are listed in Table 5. It is noted that the percent adsorption of As(V) ions increased with time and adsorbent ratio.

Table 5. Comparison of the first- and second-order reaction rate constants obtained at different dolomite dosages

Dolomite dosage	First-order kinetic model			Second-order kinetic model	
	$K_{1ads}(\mu g /g\ min)$	$q_e(\mu g/g)$	R^2	$K_{2ad}(\mu g /g\ min)$	R^2
0.5 g dolomite	0.0058	225.13	0.949	4.51×10^{-5}	0.9422
1 g dolomite	0.0060	280.96	0.962	2.67×10^{-5}	0.9257
2 g dolomite	0.0058	303.44	0.984	2.53×10^{-5}	0.8984
4 g dolomite	0.0054	303.39	0.984	2.27×10^{-5}	0.9009

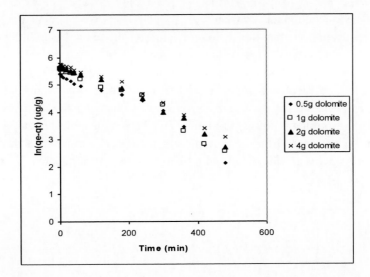

Figure 20. The linear first-order kinetic sorption isotherm for arsenic in different dolomite dosages. Arsenic concentration: 500 ppb; pH = 2; particle size 710-2000 microns.

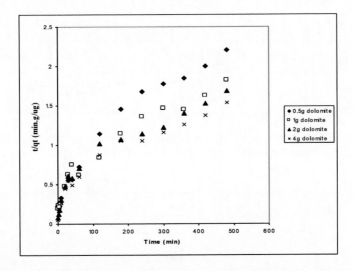

Figure 21. The linear second-order kinetic sorption isotherm for arsenic in different dolomite dosages. Arsenic concentration: 500 ppb; pH = 2; particle size 710-2000 microns.

This is obviously due to the increase in the availability of adsorption sites for complexation of As(V) ions. It is also noted that although the percentage removal of As from solution is higher with increasing adsorbent ratio, a lower ratio would maximise As solid phase concentration, q_t (mg g^{-1}) on the surface of the dolomite.

3.2.3. Effect of Adsorbent Particle Size

Different particle sizes have been tested in this study in order to understand the mechanism of As(V) removal by raw dolomite. The particle size has been changed from less than 0.335 mm to (0.710-2.00) mm. The data have been applied to the pseudo-first order and pseudo-second order kinetic models and the results are shown in figures 22 and 23, respectively. The kinetic models constants, K_{1ads} and K_{2ads}, were calculated and are listed in Table 6. The results indicate that the amount of solute adsorbed increases with the decrease in particle size of the adsorbent. This is due to an increase in the surface area and the active pores of the adsorbent found with decreasing particle size. Furthermore, the crushing of the large particles to form smaller particles facilitates crack formation, which further increases the surface area available for mass transfer. However, changing the particle size has little effect on As(V) adsorption onto raw dolomite. This behaviour indicates that the mechanism of adsorption did not depend on the particle size alone (i.e. surface area or channels), the precipitation of As(V) as arsenic oxide and probably as arsenic carbonate has a rule in arsenic removal.

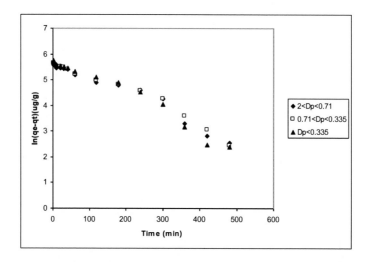

Figure 22. The linear first-order kinetic sorption isotherm for arsenic adsorption in different dolomite particle sizes. Arsenic concentration: 500 ppb; pH = 2; Adsorbent ratio: 1g/L. Dp: particle size (mm).

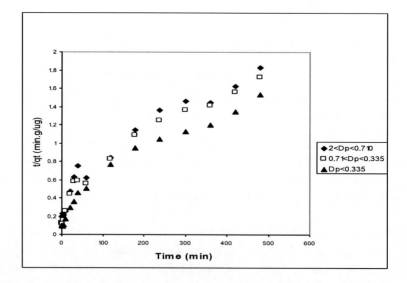

Figure 23. The linear second-order kinetic sorption isotherm for arsenic adsorption in different dolomite particle sizes. Arsenic concentration: 500 ppb; pH = 2; Adsorbent ratio: 1g/L. Dp: particle size (mm).

Table 6. Comparison of the first- and second-order reaction rate constants obtained at different dolomite particle sizes

Particle size (mm)	First-order kinetic model			Second-order kinetic model	
	$K1ads(\mu g /g\ min)$	$qe(\mu g/g)$	R2	$K2ad(\mu g /g\ min)$	R2
$0.700 - 2.000$	0.0060	280.96	0.962	$2.67 \times 10\text{-}5$	0.9257
$0.355 - 0.700$	0.0059	29041	0.966	$3.22 \times 10\text{-}5$	0.9314
Dp < 0.355	0.0069	321.57	0.965	$3.56 \times 10\text{-}5$	0.9422

3.2.4. Effect of Presence of Various Salts

The removal of arsenate from solution in the presence of different concentrations of various anions has been studied and the applicability of pseudo-first order and pseudo-second order kinetics to the adsorption data is illustrated in figures 24 and 25 respectively. The removal of As(V) decreased by increasing the sulphate concentration; Su and Puls (2001) reported a slight decrease of As(V) removal by zero valence iron in the presence of sulphate. Aresenic removal very slightly increased by increasing the chloride concentration, this non-effect may be attributed to the fact that Cl^- does not compete with $H_2AsO_4^-$ (Ayoub and Mehawej, 2007), so the chloride can be considered as a non-competing species to arsenate. In the presence of the phosphate the raw dolomite shows very low efficiency in removing the As(V). This is probably due to AsO_4^{3-} being analogous to PO_4^{3-} and therefore competes for uptake sites on the dolomite surface. Rahman *et al.* (2008) proposed the arsenate uptake in *Spirodela polyrhiza* L. might occur through the phosphate uptake pathway due to similar chemical behaviour of AsO_4^{3-} and PO_4^{3-}, other researchers reported a decrease of As(V) removal in the presence of the phosphate (Biterna *et al.*, 2007; Stachowicz *et al.*, 2008). Our present findings on the influence of phoshate correlate with these findings of previous investigators.

Arsenic concentration: 500 ppb; pH = 2; Adsorbent ratio: 1g/L; particle size 710-2000 microns.

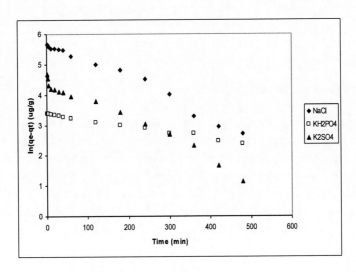

Figure 24. The linear first-order kinetic sorption isotherm for arsenic in the presence of various anions.

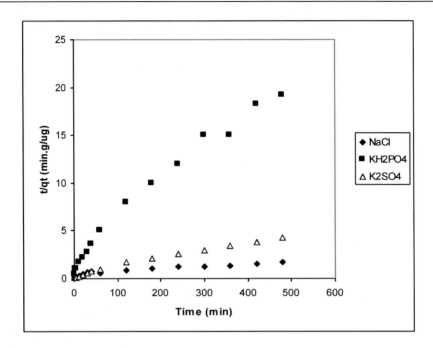

Figure 25. The linear second-order kinetic sorption isotherm for arsenic in in the presence of various anions. Arsenic concentration: 500 ppb; pH = 2; Adsorbent ratio: 1g/L; particle size 710-2000 microns.

Table 7. Comparison of the first- and second-order reaction rate constants obtained in the presence of various anions

Anion	First-order kinetic model			Second-order kinetic model	
	K1ads(µg /g min)	qe(µg/g)	R2	K2ad(µg /g min)	R2
NaCl	0.0061	294.33	0.9826	2.36 x 10-5	0.9256
K2SO4	0.0064	84.44	0.9787	2.75 x 10-4	0.9854
KH2PO4	0.0021	28.95	0.9926	9.24 x 10-4	0.978

3.3. Thermodynamic Investigations

In environmental engineering practice, both energy and entropy factors must be considered in order to determine which process will occur spontaneously (Nuhoglu and Malkoc, 2009). In order to investigate these parameters for our present As-dolomite system, adsorption kinetics were undertaken at 20, 45, 65 and 80°C, from which the equilibrium partition constant K_c, were evaluated. A plot of ln Kc as a function of 1/T is illustrated Figure 26. From this linear relationship, $\Delta H°$ and $\Delta S°$ can be calculated from the slope and intercept, respectively, with the values of $\Delta G°$, $\Delta H°$ and $\Delta S°$ (from equations 4-6) summarised in Table 8.

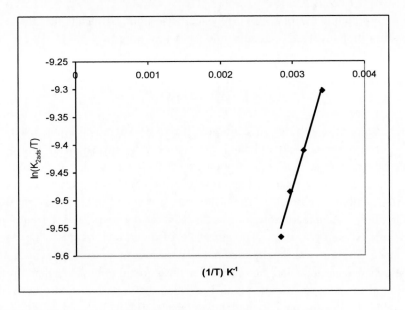

Figure 26. Ln (K2ads/T) vs 1/T for the diffusion of As(V) onto raw dolomite.

Table 8. Thermodynamic parameters for the adsorption of As(V) on raw dolomite

ΔG° (kJ/mol)				ΔH° (kJ/mol)	ΔS° (J/mol K)
T = 293	T = 318	T = 338	T = 353		
80.57	87.75	93.50	97.81	-3.67	-287.35

The free energy of the process at the temperatures investigated was positive and increased with the rise in temperature. The calculated ΔG° were positive under the temperature range studied, which indicates that the adsorption reaction is chemisorptions. The negative value of the standard entropy, ΔS°, suggests decreased randomness at the solid/solution interface during the adsorption of the arsenic ions onto the adsorbent. The change of the standard free energy increases with increasing temperatures. This indicates that an increase in the temperature is tended to decreasing the adsorption capacity.

The value of the standard enthalpy change (3.67 kJ/mol) indicates that the adsorption is physical in nature involving weak forces of attraction; also the low value of ΔH° implies that there was loose bonding between the adsorbate molecules and the adsorbent surface.

From Eq. (6), the rate parameter of arsenic adsorption, K_o, was estimated to be 17.78×10^{-3} (g/mg.min) and the activation energy, E, is -1.002 kJ/mol. Low activation energy values (<42 kJ/mol) indicate diffusion control processes and the higher activation energy values (>42 kJ/mol) indicate chemically controlled processes. This is because the temperature dependence of the pore diffusivity is relatively weak. Here, the diffusion process refers to the movement of the solute to an external surface of adsorbent and not diffusivity of material along micropore wall surfaces in a particle (Al-Ghouti *et al.*, 2005). The negative value of the activation energy suggested that the rise in the solution temperature did not favour arsenic adsorption onto dolomite. The negative value also indicates an exothermic reaction and the low value of the activation energy, E, indicates that the adsorption process of arsenic adsorption onto dolomite might be by a physical adsorption. It means that the rate-limiting step of this adsorption involved predominantly a physical process.

4. CONCLUSIONS

In order to optimize adsorption conditions for As(V) removal from aqueous solution using raw dolomite, various experimental parameters were investigated. The pH variation indicated that the maximum As(V) adsorption was achieved at pH 2 with dolomite. Isotherm studies revealed that empirical Langmuir and Freundlich mathematical models were successful in describing the process. The adsorption was found to be dependent on: the ratio of mass dolomite – volume of solution; and adsorbent particle size. The equilibrium was reached in approximately 5 days. The presence of salts was found to be an important parameter since sorption was negligible in the presence of phosphate. The extent of the competition between arsenate and the other anions was found to be dependent on the affinity of each anion to the surface. Kinetic studies revealed that a pseudo first-order rather than a pseudo second-order mathematical model was successful in describing the process. The adsorption was found to be dependent on: the ratio of mass dolomite – volume of solution and particle size of dolomite. Equilibrium was reached in approximately 6 hours. The presence of salts was found to be an important parameter since the adsorptive capacity of the raw dolomite decreased significantly in the presence of phosphate. Adsorption and precipitation as arsenic oxide and possibly as arsenic carbonate were the reaction mechanisms that contributed to the removal of As(V) by the raw dolomite. Thermodynamic results indicate that the adsorption follows an exothermic chemisorption process. In conclusion, raw dolomite may be used as a cost effective adsorbent to replace activated carbon.

Analysis of calcium and magnesium dissolution during arsenic sorption indicated a two stage arsenic removal process: (i) an initial stage involving an ion exchange type process which can be described by a pseudo-first order chemical reaction model resulting in the formation and precipitation of arsenic oxide/carbonate on the surface of the dolomite; (ii) in a second process, due to the increase surface coverage of the dolomite by the precipitate, further dissolution of Ca/Mg is limited and the predicted uptake profiles of the reaction models are not achieved, although some As precipitation still occurs on the surface of the previously precipitated arsenic oxide/carbonate.

In order to realize the full potential of dolomite as a potential adsorbent: uptake of arsenic under continuous flow conditions needs to be evaluated; moreover, surface treatment and chemical modification of dolomite may further increase capacity.

REFERENCES

Akcay, G., E. Kılınc and M. Akcay (2009). The equilibrium and kinetics studies of flurbiprofen adsorption onto tetrabutylammonium montmorillonite (TBAM). *Colloids and Surfaces A: Physicochem. Eng. Aspects* 335 (2009) 189–193.

Al-Ghouti, M. M.A.M. Khraisheh, M.N.M. Ahmad, S. Allen. Thermodynamic behaviour and the effect of temperature on the removal of dyes from aqueous solution using modified diatomite: A kinetic study. *Journal of Colloid and Interface Science* 287 (2005) 6–13.

Ayoub, G. M. and M. Mehawej (2007). Adsorption of arsenate on untreated dolomite powder. *Journal of Hazardous Materials* 148 (2007) 259–266.

Aziz, H. A., M. N. Adlan and K. S. Ariffin (2008). Heavy metals (Cd, Pb, Zn, Ni, Cu and Cr(III)) removal from water in Malaysia: Post treatment by high quality limestone. *Bioresource Technology* 99 (2008) 1578–1583.

Biswas, B. K., J. Inoue, K. Inoue, K. N. Ghimire, H. Harada, K. Ohto, H. Kawakita (2008). Adsorptive removal of As(V) and As(III) from water by a Zr(IV)-loaded orange waste gel. *Journal of Hazardous Materials* 154(2008) 1066-1074.

Biterna, M., A. Arditsoglou, E. Tsikouras and D. Voutsa(2007). Arsenate removal by zero valent iron: Batch and column tests. *Journal of Hazardous Materials* 149 (2007) 548–552.

Budinova, T., D. Savova, B. Tsyntsarski, C. O. Ania, B. Cabal, J. B. Parra, N. Petrov (2009). Biomass waste-derived activated carbon for the removal of arsenic and manganese ions from aqueous solutions. *Applied Surface Science* 255 (2009) 4650–4657.

Cano-Aguilera, I., N. Haque, G. M. Morrison, A. F. Aguilera-Alvarado, M. Gutie´rrez, J. L. Gardea-Torresdey and G. de la Rosa (2005). Use of hydride generation-atomic absorption spectrometry to determine the effects of hard ions, iron salts and humic substances on arsenic sorption to sorghum biomass. *Microchemical Journal* 81 (2005) 57– 60.

Di Natale, F., A. Erto, A. Lancia and D. Musmarra (2007). Experimental and modelling analysis of As (V) ions adsorption on granular activated carbon. *Water Research* 42 (2008) 2007 – 2016.

Duffy, A., G. Walker, S. Allen (2005). Investigations on the adsorption of acidic gases using activated dolomite. *Chemical Engineering Journal* 117 (2006) 239–244.

Gasser, M.S., H. F. Aly (2009). Kinetic and adsorption mechanism of Cu (II) and Pb(II) on prepared nanoparticle layered double hydroxide intercalated with EDTA. *Colloids and Surfaces A: Physicochem. Eng. Aspects* 336 (2009) 167–173.

Guan, X., J. Wang and C. C. Chusuei (2008). Removal of arsenic from water using granular ferric hydroxide: Macroscopic and microscopic studies. *Journal of Hazardous Materials* 156 (2008) 178-185.

Guerra, D. L., C. Airoldi and R. R. Viana (2007). Adsorption of Arsenic (V) into Modified Lamellar Kenyaite, *Journal of Hazardous Materials*. doi:10.1016/j.jhazmat.2008.06.095.

Kocaoba, S. (2007). Comparison of Amberlite IR 120 and dolomite's performances for removal of heavy metals. *Journal of Hazardous Materials* 147 (2007) 488–496.

Luxton, T. P., M. J. Eick and K. G. Scheckel (2008). Arsenate adsorption on ruthenium oxides: A spectroscopic and kinetic investigation. *Journal of Colloid and Interface Science* 325 (2008) 23–30.

Mkandawire, M., E. G. Dudel (2005). Accumulation of arsenic in Lemna gibba L. (duckweed) in tailing waters of two abandoned uranium mining sites in Saxony, Germany. *Science of the Total Environment* 336 (2005) 81– 89.

Nguyen, T. V., S. Vigenswaran, H. H. Ngo, J. Kandasamy and H. C. Choi (2007). Arsenic removal by photo-catalysis hybrid system. *Separation and purification Technology* 61 (2008) 44-50.

Nuhoglu, Y., E. Malkoc (2009). Thermodynamic and kinetic studies for environmentaly friendly Ni(II) biosorption using waste pomace of olive oil factory. *Bioresource Technology* 100 (2009) 2375–2380.

Partey, F., D. Norman, S. Ndur and R. Nartey (2008). Arsenic sorption onto laterite iron concretions: Temperature effect. *Journal of Colloid and Interface Science* 321 (2008) 493–500.

Pokhrel, D. and T. Viraraghavan (2008). Arsenic removal in an iron oxide-coated fungal biomass, column: Analysis of breakthrough curves. *Bioresource Technology* 99 (2008) 2067–2071.

Rahman, M. A., H. Hasegawa, K. Ueda, T. Maki and M. M. Rahman (2008). Arsenic uptake by aquatic macrophyte *Spirodela polyrhiza* L.: Interactions with phosphate and iron. *Journal of Hazardous Materials* 160 (2008) 356–361.

Salameh, Y., M.N.M. Ahmad, S.J. Allen and G.M. Walker, (2009) removal of arsenic from groundwater using dolomitic sorbents, submitted to Water Research

Sanchez de la Campa, A. M., J. D. de la Rosa, D. Sanchez-Rodas, V. Oliveira, A. Alastuey, X. Querol, J. L. Gomez Ariza. (2008). Arsenic speciation study of $PM_{2.5}$ in an urban area near a copper smelter. *Atmospheric Environment* 42 (2008) 6487–6495.

Shao, W., X. Li, Q. Cao, F. Luo, J. Li and Y. Du (2008). Adsorption of arsenate and arsenite anions from aqueous medium by using metal(III)-loaded amberlite resins. *Hydrometallurgy* 91 (2008) 138–143.

Stachowicz, M., T. Hiemstra and W. H. van Riemsdijk (2008). Multi-competitive interaction of As(III) and As(V) oxyanions with Ca^{2+}, Mg^{2+}, PO_3^{-4} , and CO_2^{-3} ions on goethite. *Journal of Colloid and Interface Science* 320 (2008) 400–414.

Su, C., R.W. Puls, Arsenate and arsenite removal by zerovalent iron: effects of phosphate, silicate, carbonate, borate, sulfate, chromate, molybdate and nitrate, relative to chloride, *Environ. Sci. Technol.* 35 (2001) 4562–4568.

Walker, G. M., J. A. Hanna and S. J. Allen (2005). Treatment of hazardous shipyard wastewater using dolomitic sorbents. *Water Research* 39 (2005) 2422–2428.

Walker, G. M., L. Hansen, J. A. Hanna and S. J. Allen (2003). Kinetics of a reactive dye adsorption onto dolomitic sorbents. *Water Research* 37 (2003) 2081–2089.

WHO (2006), Guidelines for drinking-water quality, third ed., Volume 1, Geneva, Switzerland.

Yusof, A. M., N. A. Malek (2008). Removal of Cr(VI) and As(V) from aqueous solutions by HDTMA-modified zeolite Y. *Journal of Hazardous Materials* 162 (2009) 1019–1024.

In: Water Production and Wastewater Treatment
Editor: B. Antizar-Ladislao et al.

ISBN 978-1-61728-503-5
© 2011 Nova Science Publishers, Inc.

Chapter 9

OZONATION AND ADSORPTION OF MTBE IN THE PRESENCE OF PERFLUOROOCTYL ALUMINA AS A CATALYST OR ADSORBENT

Amanollah Ebadi[1][1], Jafar Soltan[2][2] and Sirous Shafiei[1]

[1] Chemical Engineering Faculty, Sahand University of Technology,
P.O. Box 51335-1996, Tabriz-Iran
[2] Department of Chemical Engineering, University of Saskatchewan,
57 Campus Drive, Saskatoon, SK, S7N 5A9, Canada

ABSTRACT

Kinetics of heterogeneous ozonation of methyl *tert*-butyl ether (MTBE) in the presence of perfluorooctyl alumina (PFOAL) catalyst is reported. Because of nonpolar and hydrophobic nature of the surface of PFOAL, the reactions of ozone and MTBE on the catalyst surface proceeds mainly via direct molecular mechanism. Catalytic ozonation experiments were carried out in a batch reactor at the temperature range of 25 to 40°C. The results showed that PFOAL is an effective catalyst for enhancing the molecular mechanism of ozone reactions. With a catalyst concentration of 5 g/L contribution of rate of heterogeneous catalytic reaction in the total reaction rate was about 50%, 75%, and 85% at the reaction temperatures of 25°C, 30°C, and 40°C, respectively. The kinetic studies showed that the chemical reaction of ozone and MTBE is the controlling step in this catalytic system. Quasi-homogeneous kinetic model proved to be an appropriate approach in modeling the heterogeneous reaction of ozone with MTBE on PFOAL catalysts. This rate equation can model the kinetic data effectively (R^2=0.9644-0.9998) and has the advantage of a simpler form in comparison to Langmuir-Hinshelwood models. Activation energy of the reaction between ozone and MTBE calculated on the basis of quasi-homogeneous model was estimated as 108 kJ/mol. We also studied adsorption of MTBE from water by PFOAL and showed that PFOAL has a considerable adsorption capacity for removal of MTBE from water.

---

[1] Tabriz-Iran Tel: +98 (412) 3444356 Fax: +98(412)3444355.
2 Corresponding author, Jafar Soltan, Canada Tel: +1 (306) 966 5449 Fax: +1 (306) 966 4777.
email: j.soltan@usask.ca

Symbols Used

C_{As}	[mmol/L]	Concentration of A just adjacent to the particle surface
C_{Ab}	[mmol/L]	Concentration of A in bulk phase
C_{eq}	[mg/L]	Equilibrium concentration of adsorbate in liquid phase
D_A	[cm^2/min]	Diffusivity of the component A
D_{eA}	[cm^2/min]	Effective diffusivity of the component A
E	[--]	Weisz-Prater criterion for internal mass transfer resistances
E_{homo}	[J/mol]	Activation energy of homogeneous reactions in bulk phase
E_{hetero}	[J/mol]	Activation energy of heterogeneous reaction
f_{cat}	[mmol PFO/g]	Perfluorooctyl content of catalyst
k_{homo}	[mol/(L.min.(mol/L)$^{1+n}$)]	Apparent rate constant of homogeneous reactions in the bulk phase
$k_{hetero}.\left[\dfrac{mmol}{mmol\, PFO.\min.(mmol/L)^{m+n}}\right]$		Apparent rate constant of heterogeneous reaction
K_S	[(mg/L)$^{-1}$]	Equilibrium constant of adsorption corresponding to the first layer
K_L	[(mg/L)$^{-1}$]	Equilibrium constant of adsorption corresponding to the upper layers
L	[cm]	Dimensional parameter of the catalyst particle in Weisz-Prater Criterion, L = R/3 for a spherical particle
m_{cat}	[g/L]	Mass of the catalyst in the system per unit volume
m	[--]	Reaction order with respect to ozone (Eq. 8)
m	[--]	Total number of adsorbed layers that fill the pores (Eq. 13)
n	[--]	Reaction order with respect to MTBE (Eq. 8)
q	[mg/g]	Amount adsorbed on the surface of adsorbent
q_m	[mg/g]	Adsorption capacity corresponding to a complete monolayer
Q	[J/mol]	Additional heat of adsorption of the last adsorbed layer when the pores are filled completely (Eq. 13)
$-r_{total}$	[mmol/(L.min)]	Total reaction rate in the system, sum of homogeneous and heterogeneous reaction rates
$-r_{homo}$	[mmol/(L.min)]	Rate of homogeneous reactions in the bulk phase
$-r_{hetero}$	[mmol/(L.min)]	Rate of heterogeneous reaction at the catalyst surface
$-r_A'$	[mmol/(g.min)]	Catalytic reaction rate, degradation rate of component A (in Weisz- Prater criterion)
$(-r_A'\rho_b)_{obs}$	[mmol/(L.min)]	Observed catalytic reaction rate, degradation of component A
ε	[--]	Porosity of the catalyst particle
τ	[--]	Turuosity factor of the catalyst particle
ρ_b	[g/L]	Catalyst density in the system

INTRODUCTION

Methyl *tert*-butyl ether (MTBE) has been used as a fuel additive since mid 1980s. Because of its high solubility in water, low biodegradability and low adsorption on soil ingredients, MTBE can contaminate surface and underground water sources. MTBE has been detected in measurable concentrations in water sources around the world (Achten et al., 2002; Klinger et al., 2002; Squillace et al., 1996; Kolb and Puttmann 2006a; Kolb and Puttmann 2006b; Tanabe et al. 2005; Hsieh et al., 2006). Due to its high solubility in water and low Henry's law constant, MTBE is not readily amenable to removal by conventional techniques in water treatment.

MTBE biodegrades very slowly in soil and groundwater (Salanitro et al., 1994; Suflita and Mormile, 1993). Air stripping is a traditional and reliable technology for removal of volatile organic compounds (VOC) from groundwater. However, air stripping is not effective for treatment of MTBE, which has a low Henry's law constant (Robbins et al., 1993) and high partition coefficient in water.

Advanced oxidation processes (AOP) and ozonation processes are among the promising methods for destruction of MTBE in water. Both AOP and ozonation generate hydroxyl radicals and the destruction of MTBE in these processes proceeds mainly via hydroxyl radical mechanism. Hydroxyl radicals are powerful oxidants but nonselective in their reactions. Therefore, unfavorable reactions may proceed in oxidation processes of water treatment. For example, formation of bromate ion (a suspected carcinogen) is one of the major problems in ozonation of contaminated waters. Oxidation of bromide ion by hydroxyl radicals is the main pathway of bromate formation in ozonation processes (von Gunten and Salhi, 2003; Manassis and Constantinos, 2003; Pinkernell and von Gunten, 2001; Legube et al., 2004). Direct oxidation of pollutants by molecular ozone is one of the possible solutions to alleviate this problem. The molecular mechanism of ozone reactions is more selective, but it is slower than radical mechanism. Therefore, enhancement of the reaction rate of molecular mechanism of ozonation reactions is an important goal from the process engineering viewpoint.

Use of nonpolar organic solvents such as fluorocarbons for extracting both pollutants and ozone from aqueous phase into organic phase and subsequent ozonation in nonpolar organic phases is a possible method to increase the rate of direct ozonation reaction (Bhattacharyya et al., 1995; Stich and Bhattacharyya 1987; Freshour et al., 1996; Chang and Chen, 1994; Chang and Chen, 1995). Although this method increases the rate of ozonation reactions, it leads to new process engineering challenges due to the contact of two liquid phases.

By fixing a nonpolar phase on a solid surface, it is possible to conduct the ozonation reactions on the solid surface and avoid practical challenges of two-phase liquid contact. Perfluorooctyl alumina (PFOAL) catalyst, which is prepared by interacting perfluoro-octanoic acid with alumina support is an example of such a catalyst. In a PFOAL catalyst, the perfluorinated chains are attached to the surface of the solid support from one end of the chain. Ozonation in the presence of PFOAL is a catalytic process in which the oxidation reactions on the surface of the catalyst can proceed via molecular mechanism. The nonpolar end of the chain is free; hence, the surface of the catalyst has hydrophobic and nonpolar characteristics. The organic molecules present in the aqueous phase tend to distribute preferentially on the nonpolar surface of the catalyst. In addition, solubility of ozone in this nonpolar medium is about ten times higher than aqueous phase (Bhattacharyya et al., 1995;

Stich and Bhattacharyya 1987; Freshour et al., 1996; Chang and Chen, 1994; Chang and Chen, 1995). As a result, there is a high concentration of both ozone and organic pollutant molecules on the surface of perfluorinated alumina and so higher reaction rates can be achieved. Kasprzyk et al. used perfluorinated alumina for removal of MTBE in aqueous medium (Kasprzyk-Hordern and Nawrocki, 2002; Kasprzyk-Hordern and Nawrocki, 2003; Kasprzyk-Hordern et al., 2004a; Kasprzyk-Hordern et al., 2004b; Kasprzyk-Hordern et al., 2004c; Kasprzyk-Hordern et al., 2005). They studied the catalytic efficiency of PFOAL for removal of MTBE and a number of other organic pollutants from water. They also compared catalytic ozonation process with the conventional aqueous phase ozonation.

Study of the kinetics of the ozonation reactions on the surface of PFOAL catalysts is crucial for elucidating the nature of ozonation reactions and determining the contribution of homogeneous and heterogeneous reactions in the catalytic ozonation system. A working kinetic model for heterogeneous ozonation reactions on the surface of PFOAL catalysts is essential for evaluating feasibility of design of large scale processes. In this chapter, ozonation of MTBE in the presence of PFOAL was studied from kinetic point of view and an appropriate kinetic model is proposed for the heterogeneous ozonation reactions of MTBE on the surface of PFOAL catalysts.

Studies showed that PFOAL catalyst have a considerable adsorption capacity for MTBE and other organic pollutants in aqueous medium (Kasprzyk-Hordern et al., 2002-2005; Ebadi et al., 2007). Hence, it may be used simply for adsorption of the pollutants from contaminated water. The adsorption techniques for removal of the pollutants are among the low cost and safe techniques of water and waste water treatment methods. They use no additional agents and there are no reactions and so no harmful by-products in the system. This capability gives a dual role for application of PFOAL in treatment of contaminated waters.

EXPERIMENTAL

γ-alumina, and perfluorooctanoic acid (purity>97%) used in preparation of perfluorooctyl alumina (PFOAL) catalyst and MTBE (purity>99%) were purchased from Merck.

PFOAL was prepared using γ-alumina by a procedure similar to Wieserman and Wefer's method (Wieserman and Wefer, 1991). Specific surface area and pore size of the base alumina support and prepared PFOAL catalysts were determined by physisorption of N_2 at its atmospheric boiling point. Details of the synthesis of PFOAL and its characterization are given elsewhere (Ebadi et al., 2007). MTBE solutions used in ozonation and adsorption experiments were prepared by dissolving appropriate amounts of MTBE in distilled water.

Ozonation experiments: Ozonation experiments were carried out in a batch reactor. The configuration of the experimental setup is shown in Figure 1. To maintain the desired temperature in the reactor, a constant temperature water bath coil with adequate insulation around the reactor was used.

Ozone was generated by an Ozomatic Lab 802 (Ozomatic GmbH, Germany) ozone generator using pure oxygen as the feed gas. The feed gas flow rate was 50 ml/min and the concentration of ozone in the outlet of ozone generator was controlled at 100 g/Nm^3. Ozone concentrations in aqueous phase and in outlet gas stream of the reactor were measured using online Anseros TIZ-OEM and GM-6000-RTI (Anseros, Germany) ozone analyzers, respectively. Ozone remaining in the outlet gas stream was destroyed catalytically before purging into the vent.

In a typical experiment, the reactor was first filled with 200 ml distilled water and then ozone-rich pure oxygen gas stream was bubbled through the reactor to establish the desired level of aqueous ozone concentration in water. The gas flow rate was about 50 ml/min and the ozone concentration at the reactor inlet was about 100 g/Nm^3. Then the gas flow was stopped and 10 ml MTBE solution of 200 mg/L was added to the ozonated water. In this way, the initial MTBE concentration of about 10 mg/L was obtained. At the same time, 1 g PFOAL catalyst was added to the reactor. The catalyst was used in powder form and its largest particle size was 0.2 mm. The reaction mixture was stirred thoroughly during the whole reaction time. Changes in concentration of MTBE and ozone with reaction time were recorded. The pH of the bulk liquid phase was 4.9 and it remained constant over the whole reaction time. The ozonation experiments were carried out at three different temperature levels of 25°C, 30°C, and 40°C.

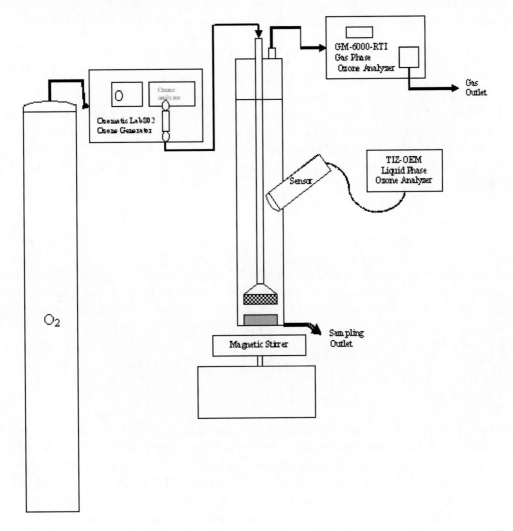

Figure 1. Schematics of the experimental setup for liquid phase ozonation. (constant temperature coil is not shown).

To measure concentrations of MTBE and reaction products in aqueous medium, a head-space injection method using a gas chromatograph equipped with TRACE MS PLUS mass spectrometer (Thermo Finnigan, Italy) was used. Immediately after sampling, sodium thiosulfate ($Na_2S_2O_3$) was added to sample vials for destruction of ozone and quenching the ozonation reactions. Addition of the $Na_2S_2O_3$ salt to sample vials enhances the volatilization of relatively volatile reaction components from aqueous medium due to the salting out effect. Separation was achieved by a DB1 (SGE) nonpolar capillary column (25 m, 0.22 mm, 0.25 μm). A constant temperature of 38°C was used for column oven. The injector temperature was 130°C. For quantitative analysis of the components of the reaction mixture, selected ion monitoring (SIM) method was used in the mass spectrometer detector. The 73 and 59 mass numbers were used for quantification of MTBE and *tert*-butyl formate (TBF), respectively. Appropriate statistical repeatability tests showed that the relative standard deviation of measurements was less than 3% for MTBE analysis.

Adsorption experiments: The adsorption experiments were carried out at 25°C. A wide range of aqueous phase MTBE concentrations in the range of 5 to 1000 mg/L was used for experiments. Details of adsorption experiments are reported previously (Ebadi et al, 2007).

RESULTS AND DISCUSSION

Specific surface area and average pore size of the alumina support catalyst were determined by physisorption of N_2 as 130 m^2/g and 84 Å, respectively. The surface coverage of the prepared PFOAL catalyst by perfluorooctyl groups is 3.6 $μmol/m^2$. The detail of the evaluation tests of the alumina support and the prepared PFOAL catalysts are reported before (Ebadi et al., 2007).

Catalytic Ozonation

In catalytic ozonation of MTBE, the MTBE degradation reactions proceed in both bulk homogeneous liquid phase and at the heterogeneous catalyst surface. Accordingly, the MTBE degradation rate in the presence of PFOAL designated as total rate ($-r_{total}$), is the sum of the homogeneous reaction rate ($-r_{homo}$) and the heterogeneous reaction rate ($-r_{hetero}$):

$$-r_{total} = (-r_{homo}) + (-r_{hetero}) = \left(-\frac{d[MTBE]}{dt} \right)_{homo} + \left(-\frac{d[MTBE]}{dt} \right)_{hetero} \tag{1}$$

where [*MTBE*] is the MTBE concentration in aqueous phase. The value of ($-r_{hetero}$) can be obtained from difference between ($-r_{total}$) and ($-r_{homo}$). The homogeneous reaction rate ($-r_{homo}$) can be evaluated by appropriate rate equation in terms of ozone and MTBE concentrations by using results of experiments of homogeneous ozonation of MTBE in aqueous phase in the absence of catalyst. Figure 2 shows results of MTBE degradation by homogeneous liquid phase ozonation at 30°C in the absence of catalyst. Figure 2(a) shows the ozone concentration versus reaction time. The change of MTBE concentration versus reaction time, which is shown in Figure 2(b), can be correlated in empirical form by Eq. (2). Degradation rate of MTBE is calculated by differentiating Eq. (2) and is shown in Fig 3(c).

$$[MTBE] = a + b*t + \frac{c}{d+t} \tag{2}$$

$$\left(-\frac{d[MTBE]}{dt}\right) = -\left(b - \frac{c}{(d+t)^2}\right) \tag{3}$$

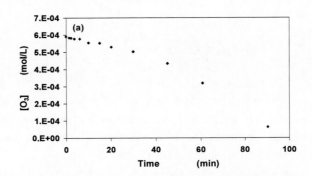

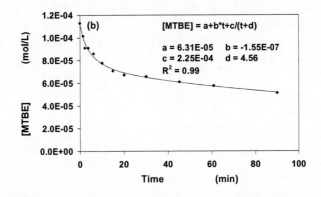

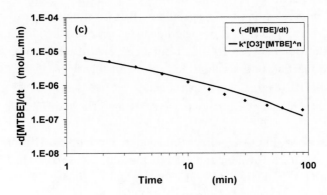

Figure 2. MTBE degradation by homogeneous ozonation in aqueous phase in the absence of catalyst, T = 30°C, pH = 4.9. (a) Decline of ozone concentration. (b) Decline of MTBE concentration. (c) Homogeneous reaction rate of MTBE degradation.

Table 1. Parameters of the rate equation for noncatalytic ozonation of MTBE, Eq. (4)

T(°C)	k (mol/[L.min.(mol/L)$^{1+n}$])	n
25	1.250×1019	5.33
30	2.164×1019	5.33
40	6.002×1019	5.33

As shown in Figure 2(c), a power law rate equation in terms of concentrations of MTBE and ozone can be obtained for degradation of MTBE in the homogeneous phase by fitting the power law kinetic equation i.e. Eq. (4) to the calculated rates of MTBE degradation:

$$\left(-\frac{d[MTBE]}{dt}\right)_{\hom o} = k[O_3][MTBE]^n \tag{4}$$

where $[O_3]$ is the aqueous ozone concentration. From statistical analysis, the rate constant $k = 2.164 \times 10^{19}$ and the exponent $n = 5.33$ as shown in Figure 3(c) were obtained. It is worthwhile to note that Eq. (4) has no relationship to the mechanism of ozonation reaction. At this stage, it is only used to fit the experimental data at 30°C and pH = 4.9.

Similar experiments were conducted for homogeneous ozonation of MTBE at 25°C and 40°C and the measured reaction rates were fitted by Eq. (4). Table 1 shows the parameters of the rate equation at different reaction temperatures.

Using the Arrhenius equation for the rate constant of homogeneous reactions in the bulk aqueous phase, empirical kinetic parameters of homogeneous ozonation of MTBE were calculated as:

$$E_{\hom o} = 81.1 \text{ kJ/mol}$$
$$k_{\hom o} = k_0 \exp(-E_{\hom o}/RT) = 1.986 \times 10^{19} \exp(-E_{\hom o}/RT) \tag{5}$$

Figure 3 shows the results of MTBE degradation by catalytic ozonation in the presence of 5 g/L PFOAL catalyst at 40°C. Parts (a) and (b) of Figure 3 depict profiles of concentration of ozone and MTBE with reaction time, respectively. Part (c) shows the total reaction rate, rate of homogeneous reaction and rate of heterogeneous reaction on the surface of PFOAL obtained from difference between total and homogeneous reaction rates. As shown in this figure, the surface reaction rate accounts for approximately 85% of the total reaction rate. Similar catalytic MTBE degradation experiments were conducted at 25°C and 30°C. The contributions of the surface reaction rate were about 50% and 75% at 25°C and 30°C, respectively.

On the surface of PFOAL, direct molecular mechanism (Kasprzyk-Hordern and Nawrocki, 2002; Kasprzyk-Hordern and Nawrocki, 2003; Kasprzyk-Hordern et al., 2004a; Kasprzyk-Hordern et al., 2004b; Kasprzyk-Hordern et al., 2004c; Kasprzyk-Hordern et al., 2005) is mainly responsible for degradation of MTBE, but in the homogeneous phase, the degradation of MTBE occurs by both indirect hydroxyl radical mechanism and direct molecular mechanism of ozone. It is reported that the rates of hydroxyl radical reactions are higher than the molecular ozone reactions (Legube and Karpel Vel Leitner, 1999). The contribution of heterogeneous surface reaction accounts for about 50-85% of the total reaction rate in the system at the temperature range of 25-40°C. From the results of catalytic ozonation, especially at 40°C, it can be concluded that the catalyst acts very effectively in promoting molecular ozonation, because the surface reaction rate is very high compared with the rate of the homogeneous reactions in bulk phase. This is mainly due to the high concentration of the reactants on the surface of the catalyst.

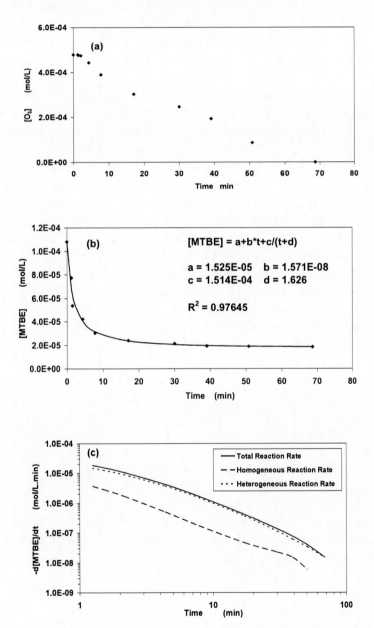

Figure 3. MTBE degradation by catalytic ozonation in aqueous phase in the presence of PFOAL as the catalyst, T = 40°C, pH=4.9, mass of catalyst = ~5 g/L. (a) Decline of ozone concentration. (b) Decline of MTBE concentration. (c) Total reaction rate and homogeneous reaction rate.

It should be noted that the pH of the distilled water decreases from 6.4 to 4.9 as a result of ozonation and it does not change during catalytic ozonation of MTBE. The results obtained for the catalytic ozonation rates at different temperatures showed that the contribution of surface reactions increased by increasing reaction temperature. This point is an evidence for the fact that the increase in temperature influences the surface reactions more than the homogeneous reactions, i.e. the heterogeneous surface reactions are more sensitive to the increase in temperature than homogeneous reactions. This can lead to two important conclusions: Firstly, this indicates that the chemical reaction at the catalyst surface is the rate-controlling step, because the chemical reaction at the catalyst surface is more sensitive to temperature change than transport steps in a heterogeneous reactive system. Secondly, it shows that the activation energy of the heterogeneous surface reaction is higher than the activation energy of the homogeneous reactions. This conclusion is in agreement with the results of Mitani et al. (2002). They calculated the activation energy of the direct molecular reaction of O_3 and MTBE as 95.4 kJ/mol and the activation energy of $^\bullet OH$ and MTBE as 4.6 kJ/mol.

It should be emphasized that the mechanism of the catalytic activity of the PFOAL differs from that of the conventional heterogeneous catalysts. On the surface of the conventional heterogeneous catalysts, at least one of the reactants interacts with the active sites of the catalyst changing its molecular structure to make it more susceptible to interaction with other reactant species. However, in the case of PFOAL catalyst, both of the reactants distribute preferentially on the catalyst surface and their molecular structure is not influenced by interaction with the catalyst surface. The main reason for increase of the reaction rate is the higher concentrations of the reactants in the perfluorooctyl phase on the catalyst surface. The mechanism of reaction between ozone and organic pollutants in the organic phase of the two phase ozonation systems is a confirmation for this conclusion (Bhattacharyya et al., 1995; Stich and Bhattacharyya 1987; Freshour et al., 1996; Chang and Chen, 1994; Chang and Chen, 1995).

In the heterogeneous reaction sequence, mass transfer of reactants takes place from the bulk fluid to the external surface of the catalyst particle. The reactants then diffuse from the external surface into and through the pores within the particles. In order to determine the intrinsic kinetic parameters, the bulk diffusion resistance and pore diffusion resistance should be determined. Since in this work, the catalyst was used in fine powder form and the reaction medium was stirred with a relatively high speed, the external resistance of mass transfer was negligible. Repeat experiments with higher speed of stirring confirmed that the external mass transfer was not controlling. The Weisz-Prater criterion was also used to evaluate the intra-particle diffusion resistance. The Weisz-Prater parameter is in fact the ratio between observed reaction rate and the maximum diffusion rate in the pores of the catalyst particles and is defined as (Beltrán, 2004; Fogler, 1992):

$$E = \frac{(-r_A' \rho_b)_{obs} L^2}{D_{eA} C_{As}} \tag{6}$$

In this equation $(-r_A' \rho_b)_{obs}$ is the observed catalytic reaction rate. In Weisz-Prater criterion it is assumed that the external resistance of mass transfer is negligible and $C_{As} = C_{Ab}$.

According to this criterion if $E \ll 1$ then the internal mass transfer is negligible and the surface reaction is the controlling step.

At the extreme case of maximum temperature, i.e. 40°C, which corresponds to maximum reaction rates, the diffusivities of O_3 and MTBE in aqueous medium were calculated by Wilke-Chang equation as 2.841×10^{-5} and 1.375×10^{-5} cm^2/s, respectively (Perry and Green, 1997). The porosity ε and tortuosity factor τ of the particles were taken approximately as 0.4 and 1.3 respectively. Considering the largest particle size of 0.2 mm, and the maximum reaction rate in the reactor, the Weisz-Prater parameter is calculated as:

for MTBE diffusion:

$$E = \frac{(-r'_A \rho_b)_{obs} L^2}{D_{eA} C_{As}} = \frac{(9.018 \times 10^{-3} \, mmol/L.min) \times (3.333 \times 10^{-3} \, cm)^2}{(2.538 \times 10^{-4} \, cm^2/min) \times (0.0556 \, mmol/L)} = 7.103 \times 10^{-3} \quad \ll 1$$

for O_3 diffusion:

$$E = \frac{(-r'_A \rho_b)_{obs} L^2}{D_{eA} C_{As}} = \frac{(9.018 \times 10^{-3} \, mmol/L.min) \times (3.333 \times 10^{-3} \, cm)^2}{(5.245 \times 10^{-4} \, cm^2/min) \times (0.4624 \, mmol/L)} = 4.132 \times 10^{-3} \quad \ll 1$$

Evidently, the Weisz-Prater parameter for this catalytic system is three orders of magnitude smaller than one and it is a confirmation that the diffusion rates of reactants are not controlling.

By considering the fact that the surface reaction is the most probable rate controlling step and the mass transfer steps and the adsorption rates are not controlling, it is believed that MTBE and O_3 are distributed between the bulk aqueous phase and the perfluorooctyl phase on the surface of the catalyst in a pseudo-equilibrium state. Under these conditions, the Quasi-Homogeneous (QH) model (Helfferich, 1962) is an appropriate kinetic model for modeling the catalytic reaction system.

The Quasi-Homogeneous model was proposed by Helfferich (1962) for modeling the catalytic reactions on the ion exchange resins. In this model, the catalyst and the reactants are assumed to be present in the same phase, i.e. the heterogeneous catalyst was considered as a homogeneous catalyst phase. The QH model is particularly suitable for systems in which the mass transfer and the adsorption rates are not significant and the reactants are distributed between the bulk homogeneous phase and heterogeneous phase.

The Quasi-Homogeneous model for the catalytic ozonation of MTBE on the surface of PFOAL can be written as:

$$(-r_{MTBE})_{hetero} = -\left(\frac{d[MTBE]}{dt}\right)_{hetero} = k_{hetero} f([O_3],[MTBE]) \tag{7}$$

By considering the fact that the reaction between O_3 and MTBE on the surface of PFOAL proceed by molecular mechanism and it starts by direct attack of O_3 molecule to the MTBE molecule, it is reasonable to write the concentration term in Eq. (7) as in Eq (8):

$$(-r_{MTBE})_{hetero} = -\left(\frac{d[MTBE]}{dt}\right)_{hetero} = k_{hetero}[O_3]^m[MTBE]^n \qquad (8)$$

where $[O_3]$ and $[MTBE]$ are the ozone and MTBE concentrations in the bulk aqueous phase, respectively. In fact, in the QH model the distribution coefficients of the reactants are combined with the actual rate constant and k_{hetero} is an apparent rate constant.

The results obtained by fitting the QH model, Eq. (8), to the experimental data at 40°C are shown in Table 2. Similar results were obtained for other temperatures. At each temperature, appropriate values of m and n were obtained from experimental results. By averaging the numerical values of m and n at different temperatures the optimal values of $m = 4$ and $n = 2$ were determined. Therefore, the rate equation of QH model for the system of catalytic ozonation of MTBE on the surface of PFOAL takes the final form of Eq. (9):

$$(-r_{MTBE})_{hetero} = -\left(\frac{d[MTBE]}{dt}\right)_{hetero} = k_{hetero}[O_3]^4[MTBE]^2 \qquad (9)$$

Table 2. Quasi-Homogeneous model fitted to the experimental data of catalytic ozonation of MTBE on the surface of PFOAL, T = 40°C

Kinetic model			Parameter value	Prob(t)
(-r)hetero = khetero[O₃][MTBE]		khetero	0.11966	0
		R^2	0.71497	
		SSR	1.43E-05	
$k_{hetero}:\left[\dfrac{mmol}{mmol\,PFO.\min.(mmol/L)^2}\right]$	Statistical criteria	Prob(F)	0	
(-r)hetero = khetero[O₃]^m[MTBE]^n	Parameters	khetero	28.49909	0
		m	4.2	0
		n	1.9	0
		R^2	0.99997	
		SSR	1.25E-09	
$k_{hetero}:\left[\dfrac{mmol}{mmol\,PFO.\min.(mmol/L)^{m+n}}\right]$	Statistical criteria	Prob(F)	0	
(-r)hetero = khetero[O₃]^4[MTBE]^2		khetero	33.1495	0
		R^2	0.99981	
		SSR	9.52E-09	
$k_{hetero}:\left[\dfrac{mmol}{mmol\,PFO.\min.(mmol/L)^6}\right]$	Statistical criteria	Prob(F)	0	

R2 = Correlation index

SSR = Sum of square residuals

Prob(t) = (or p value) = Test criterion for null hypothesis for each parameter. The smaller the value of Prob(t), the less likely the parameter is actually zero.

Prob(F) = (or F value) = Test criterion for the overall significance of the regression model. The larger the value of Prob(F), the less likely relationship between the dependent variable and the regression model.

As shown in Table 2, Eq. (9) correlates the experimental data very well ($R^2 = 0.99981$).

Table 3. Rate constants of heterogeneous reaction between O3 and MTBE, Eq. (10)

T(°C)	khetero ([mmol/(mmol PFO.min.(mmol/L)^6)])
25	4.84
30	4.03
40	33.15

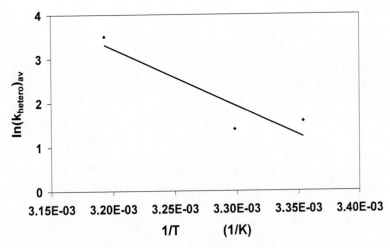

Figure 4. Arrhenius plot for heterogeneous rate constant ($-r_{MTBE} = k_{hetero}[O_3]^4[MTBE]^2$).

By fitting Eq. (9) to the experimental data at other temperatures, the rate constants shown in Table 3 are calculated.

Figure 4 shows the Arrhenius plot for the heterogeneous rate constant of catalytic ozonation of MTBE on the surface of PFOAL. The apparent activation energy of the heterogeneous reaction can be evaluated using the slope of the line fitted to the experimental data as, $E_{hetero} = 108.4$ kJ/mol.

The calculated value of activation energy for the heterogeneous reaction is another confirmation of the fact that the heterogeneous reactions in the perfluorooctyl layer are dominated by direct molecular mechanism. Activation energy of direct reaction of O_3 and MTBE by molecular mechanism is reported as 95.4 kJ/mol by Mitani et al. (2002). The Arrhenius equation for the heterogeneous rate constant can be written as Eq. (10).

$$k_{hetero} = 3.257 \times 10^{19} \exp(-E_{hetero}/RT) \tag{10}$$

The overall reaction rate of MTBE ozonation in the presence of PFOAL can be expressed as the sum of homogeneous and heterogeneous reaction rates:

$$(-r_{MTBE})_{total} = (-r_{MTBE})_{homo} + (-r_{MTBE})_{hetero}$$
$$= k_{homo}[O_3][MTBE]^{5.33} + m_{cat}f_{cat} k_{hetero}[O_3]^4[MTBE]^2 \tag{11}$$

where $(-r_{MTBE})_{total}$ is the overall reaction rate in the system, mmol/(L.min); m_{cat} is the catalyst mass in the system, g/L; f_{cat} is the perfluorooctyl content of the catalyst, mmol PFO/g catalyst; k_{hetero} is the heterogeneous rate constant given by Eq. (10), mmol/(mmol PFO.min.(mmol/L)^6); and k_{homo} is the rate constant of homogeneous reactions in the bulk phase given by Eq. (5), mmol/(L.min.(mmol/L)$^{6.33}$).

Application of LHHW and ER approach in catalytic ozonation of MTBE leads to unacceptable results such as negative values for the equilibrium constants of adsorption. Such difficulties are common in case of LHHW and ER models and are discussed in detail by Hill (1977). LHHW and ER kinetic models cannot express the heterogeneous reaction between O_3 and MTBE on PFOAL catalyst. The detail of a systematic discussion of this problem was given elsewhere (Ebadi et al, 2009a).

Adsorption Performance

Blank-test experiments were conducted to compare adsorption by bare alumina and PFOAL adsorbents. These experiments showed that no MTBE was adsorbed on bare alumina. On the contrary, adsorption experiments using PFOAL adsorbents showed that these adsorbents have considerable adsorption capacity for MTBE. The BET (Brunauer-Emmet-Teller) and BDDT (Brunauer-Deming-Deming-Teller) isotherms were considered to model experimental adsorption data. Because the original forms of these isotherms were developed by Brunauer et al (1938, 1940) for the gas phase adsorption, the suitable forms of these isotherms for the liquid phase adsorption (Ebadi et al. 2009b) were employed for modeling the adsorption data:

$$q = q_m \frac{K_S C_{eq}}{(1 - K_L C_{eq})(1 - K_L C_{eq} + K_S C_{eq})} \tag{12}$$

In Eq. (12) q and q_m are the amount adsorbed and monolayer adsorption capacity, respectively. K_S is the equilibrium constant of adsorption of the first layer and K_L is the equilibrium constant of adsorption for upper layers of adsorbate on the adsorbent. C_{eq} is the equilibrium concentration of the liquid phase. The parameters q_m, K_S, and K_L, should be determined by fitting the equation to the experimental data.

BET isotherm can only model types II and III of van der Waals adsorption isotherms. To model types IV and V of van der Waals adsorption isotherms Brunauer et al. revised the BET isotherm and developed a general form of the equation to account for pore filling after which no increase was observed in amount adsorbed by increasing the fluid phase concentration (Brunauer et al , 1940):

$$q = q_m \left\{ \frac{x}{1-x} + \frac{2(c-1)x + 2(c-1)^2 x^2 + Dx^m + Ex^{m+1} + Fx^{m+2}}{2[1 + 2(c-1)x + (c-1)^2 x^2 + Lx^m + Mx^{m+1} + hx^{m+2}]} \right\} \tag{13}$$

in which:

$x = K_L C_{eq}$ (for liquid phase adsorption)

$c = K_S/K_L$ (for liquid phase adsorption)

$h = (mc^2-c^2+2c)g$

$g = e^{Q/RT}$

m is the total number of adsorbed layers that fill the pores, and Q is the additional heat of adsorption of the last adsorbed layer when the pores are filled completely.

$D = mc^2+mh-2mc-m^2c^2$

$E = 2c+m^2c^2+2mc-2c^2-mc^2-2h-2mh$

$F = mh+2h$

$L = c^2+h-2c-mc^2$

$M = mc^2+2c-2c^2-2h$

Frequently the general form of BET equation is called BDDT isotherm. In the above equations only C_{eq} and q are measured experimentally and the other parameters are model parameters found by nonlinear regression analysis of the experimental adsorption data.

The experimental adsorption data of MTBE on PFOAL adsorbent are shown in Figure 5. The increasing trend of the amount adsorbed versus liquid phase concentration continues up to a liquid phase MTBE concentration of about 700 mg MTBE/L. As shown by experimental data in Figure 5, PFOAL adsorbent has considerable adsorption capacity for MTBE, and the maximum adsorption capacity of PFOAL was 7.1 mg MTBE/g adsorbent. Beyond these maximum values the amount of adsorbed MTBE did not increase with increasing liquid phase concentration.

By considering the correlation coefficients R^2, (see Figure 5), and other statistical criteria of the regression calculations for the isotherm models, it was shown that the BET multilayer adsorption isotherm can represent the experimental data at lower concentration range and it can model the S-shaped trend of experimental data at this range. While BDDT multilayer isotherm proved to be a better model in expressing the adsorption data over a wide range of concentration. The type IV adsorption pattern of the experimental data has been expressed very well by BDDT isotherm model. The BET and BDDT isotherms provide a conceptual insight to the physical nature of adsorption process on the surface of PFOAL adsorbent.

The results show that pore-filling mechanism dominates at high concentration range, while at low concentrations the adsorption is directly related to hydrophobic characteristics of the surface.

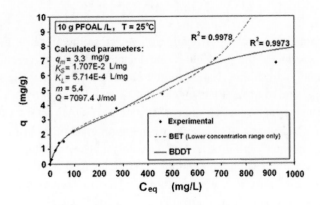

Figure 5. Comparison of experimental data and performance of isotherm models in aqueous phase adsorption of MTBE on PFOAL adsorbent, T = 25°C.

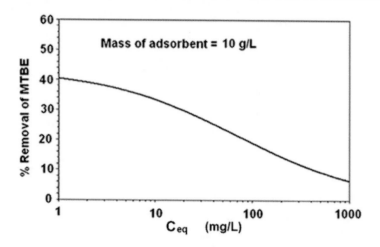

Figure 6. Percentage of MTBE removed from water by PFOAL adsorbent at different liquid phase equilibrium concentrations, %Removed = $(C_0-C_{eq})/C_0$.

The monolayer adsorption capacity (q_m) of PFOAL adsorbent was 3.3 mg MTBE/g adsorbent. It is possible to calculate the active surface area of PFOAL for the adsorption of MTBE on the basis of the monolayer adsorption capacity (q_m). Area occupied by one MTBE molecule may be calculated as $a = 3.329E-19$ m^2/molecule using the kinetic diameter of the molecule which is 6.2 Å (Li et al., 2003). The active surface area of PFOAL for adsorption of MTBE is calculated as 7.4 m^2/g. This is in a very good agreement with the surface coverage of PFOAL (3.6 μmol/m^2). This is very low compared to the total surface area of the adsorbent. Therefore, if the surface coverage of PFOAL could be increased then its active surface area and its adsorption capacity can be increased.

Figure 6 shows the efficiency of MTBE removal from water by PFOAL adsorbents. At low concentrations (<~5 mg MTBE/L), MTBE removal by using 10 g PFOAL/L was about 40%, and even at very high concentration range (~930 mg MTBE/L) MTBE removal efficiency is considerable (~ 7%).

CONCLUSION

The results obtained for catalytic ozonation of MTBE in the presence of PFOAL showed that this catalyst enhances the molecular mechanism of ozone reactions. Because of hydrophobic and nonpolar characteristics of the surface of PFOAL, the organic pollutant molecules and ozone tend to accumulate on catalyst surface leading to high concentrations of both reactants and hence high reaction rates. With 5 g/L PFOAL catalyst at the temperature range of 25°C- 40°C, 50-85% of the total degradation rate of MTBE proceeds through heterogeneous reaction route on the surface of the catalyst. The contribution of heterogeneous reactions increases with increasing temperature. This indicates that the surface reaction is the rate controlling step and also is a confirmation for the molecular mechanism of surface reactions with high activation energy.

A quasi-homogeneous kinetic model was proposed for the reaction of ozone and MTBE in the presence of PFOAL. The corresponding activation energy was evaluated as 108.4 kJ/mol.

Unlike fast hydroxyl radical mechanism, the molecular reactions of ozone are slower but more selective. Enhancement of the molecular mechanism of the ozonation reactions by perfluorinated solid catalysts such as PFOAL can improve the potentials of application of ozone in water and wastewater treatment.

The results of MTBE adsorption on the prepared PFOAL showed that it has a high adsorption capacity for MTBE, while bare alumina support did not adsorb MTBE. The monolayer adsorption capacities of the prepared PFOALs was 3.3 mg MTBE/g PFOAL and the maximum adsorption capacity was 7.1 mg MTBE/g PFOAL. At high concentration range, pore-filling mechanism dominates the adsorption. If one could increase the surface coverage of PFOAL, its adsorption capacity at low equilibrium concentrations can be increased and it can be used as a more efficient adsorbent for removal of organic pollutants from water.

REFERENCES

Achten C., Kolb A., Püttmann W. (2002). Methyl *tert*-Butyl Ether (MTBE) in river and wastewater in Germany. *Environ. Sci. Technol.*, 36(17), 3652-3661.

Beltrán F.J. (2004). *Ozone Reaction Kinetics for Water and Wastewater Systems*, Page 250. Boca Raton, Lewis Publishers.

Bhattacharyya D., Van Dierdonck T.F., West S.D., Freshour A.R. (1995), Two-phase ozonation of chlorinated organics. *J. Hazard. Mater.* 41(1), 73-93.

Brunauer S., Emmet P.H., Teller E. (1938). Adsorption of gases in multimolecular layers, *J. Am. Chem. Soc.* 60, 309-319.

Brunauer S., Deming L.S., Deming W.E., and Teller E. (1940). On a theory of the van der Waals adsorption of gases, *J. Am. Chem. Soc.* 62, 1723-1732.

Chang C.Y., Chen J.N. (1994). Ozonolysis of 2,4-dichlorophenol in a two-phase solvent/water system. *Water Sci. Technol.*, 29(9), 343-346.

Chang C.Y., Chen J.N. (1995). Application of a fluorinated solvent to the conventional ozonation process for the destruction of 2,4-dichlorophenol. *Environ. Int.*, 21(3), 305-312.

Ebadi A., Soltan Mohammadzadeh J.S., Khudiev A. (2007). Adsorption of methyl tert-butyl ether on perfluorooctyl alumina adsorbents-high concentration range. *Chem. Eng. Technol.*, 30(12), 1666-1673.

Ebadi A., Soltan Mohammadzadeh J.S., Shafiei S. (2009a). Kinetics of Catalytic Ozonation of Methyl *tert*-Butyl Ether in the Presence of Perfluorooctyl Alumina, *Chem. Eng. Technol.* 32(5), 778-788.

Ebadi A., Soltan Mohammadzadeh J.S., Khudiev A. (2009b).What is the correct form of BET isotherm for modeling liquid phase adsorption?, *Adsorption*, 15(1), 65-73.

Fogler H.C. (1992). *Elements of Chemical Reaction Engineering*, 2nd ed., Pages 625-626. Prentice-Hall, Englewood Cliffs, NJ.

Freshour A.R., Mawhinney S., Bhattacharyya D. (1996). Two-phase ozonation of hazardous organics in single and multicomponent systems. *Water Res.*, 30(9), 1949-1958.

Helfferich F. (1962). *Ion Exchange*, 1962 edition, Pages 76, 127, 258, 279. Published by Courier Dover Publications, 1995

Hill C.G. (1977). *An Introduction to Chemical Engineering Kinetics and Reactor Design*, Pages 190-192. John-Wiley and Sons, New York.

Hsieh L.-T., Yang H.-H., Chen H.-W. (2006). Ambient BTEX and MTBE in the neighborhood of different industrial parks in southern Taiwan. *J. Hazard. Mater. A*, 128(2-3), 106-115.

Kasprzyk-Hordern B., Nawrocki J. (2002). Preliminary results on ozonation enhancement by a perfluorinated bonded alumina phase. *Ozone Sci. Eng.*, 24(1), 63-68.

Kasprzyk-Hordern B., Nawrocki J. (2003). The feasibility of using a perfluorinated bonded alumina phase in the ozonation process. *Ozone Sci. Eng.*, 25(3), 185-197.

Kasprzyk-Hordern B., Dabrowska A., Swietlik J., Nawrocki J. (2004a). The application of the perfluorinated bonded alumina phase for natural organic matter catalytic ozonation. *J. Environ. Eng. Sci.*, 3(1), 41-50.

Kasprzyk-Hordern B., Andrzejewski P., Dabrowska A., Czaczyk K., Nawrocki J. (2004b). MTBE, DIPE, ETBE and TAME degradation in water using perfluorinated phases as catalysts for ozonation process. *Appl. Catal. B*,, 51(1), 51-66.

Kasprzyk-Hordern B., Dabrowska A., Swietlik J., Nawrocki J. (2004c). Ozonation enhancement with non-polar bonded alumina phases *Ozone Sci. Eng.*, 26(4), 367-380.

Kasprzyk-Hordern B., Andrzejewski P., Nawrocki J. (2005). Catalytic ozonation of gasoline compounds in model and natural water in the presence of perfluorinated alumina bonded phases *Ozone Sci. Eng.*, 27(4), 301-310.

Klinger J., Stieler C., Sacher F., Branch H.J. (2002). MTBE (methyl *tertiary*-butyl ether) in groundwaters: monitoring results from Germany. *J. Environ. Monit.*, 4(2), 276-279.

Kolb A., Püttmann W. (2006a). Methyl *tert*-butyl ether (MTBE) in finished drinking water in Germany. *Environ. Pollution*, 140(2), 294-303.

Kolb A., Püttmann W. (2006b). Methyl *tert*-butyl ether (MTBE) in snow samples in Germany. *Atmospheric Environment*, 40(1), 76-86.

Legube B., Parinet B., Gelinet K., Berne F., Croue J.-P. (2004). Modeling of bromate formation by ozonation of surface waters in drinking water treatment *Water Res.*, 38(8), 2185-2195.

Legube B., Karpel Vel Leitner N. (1999). Catalytic ozonation: a promising advanced oxidation technology for water treatment. *Catal. Today*, 53(1), 61-72.

Li S., Tuan V.A., Noble R.D., Falconer J.L.; MTBE adsorption on all silica β zeolite, *Environ. Sci. Technol.* 37, 4007-4010, 2003

Manassis M., Constantinos S. (2003). Conditions affecting bromate formation during ozonation of bottled water. *Ozone Sci Eng.*, 25(3), 167-175.

Mitani M.M., Keller A.A., Bunton C.A., Rinker R.G., Sandall O.C. (2002). Kinetics and products of reactions of MTBE with ozone and ozone/hydrogen peroxide in water. *J. Hazard. Mater.*, B89(2-3), 197-212.

Perry R.H., Green D.W. (eds.) (1997). Perry's Chemical Engineers Handbook, 7th ed., Chapter 2, Page 2-371. McGraw-Hill Book Company.

Pinkernell U., von Gunten U. (2001). Bromate minimization during ozonation: Mechanistic considerations. *Environ. Sci. Technol.*, 35(12), 2525-2531.

Robbins G.A., Wang S., Stuart J.D. (1993). Using the static headspace method to determine Henry's law constants. *Anal. Chem.*, 65(21), 3113-3118.

Salanitro J.P., Diaz L.A., Williams M.P., Wisniewski H.L. (1994). Isolation of a bacterial culture that degrades Methyl t-Butyl Ether. *Appl. Environ. Microbiol.*, 60(7), 2593-2596.

Squillace P.J., Zogorski J.S., Wilber W.G., Price C.V. (1996). Preliminary assessment of the occurrence and possible sources of MTBE in groundwater in the United States, 1993-1994. *Environ. Sci. Technol.*, 30(5), 1721-1730.

Stich F.A., Bhattacharyya D. (1987). Ozonolysis of organic compounds in a two-phase fluorocarbon-water system. *Environ. Prog.*, 6(4), 224-229.

Suflita J.M., Mormile M. R. (1993). Anaerobic biodegradation of known and potential gasoline oxygenates in the terrestrial subsurface. *Environ. Sci. Technol.*, 27(5), 976-978.

Tanabe A., Tsuchida Y., Ibaraki T., Kawata K., Yasuhara A., Shibamoto T. (2005). Investigation of methyl *tert*-butyl ether levels in river-, ground-, and sewage-waters analyzed using a purge-and –trap interfaced to a gas chromatograph-mass spectrometer *J. Chromatogr. A* , 1066(1-2), 159-164.

von Gunten U., Salhi E. (2003). Bromate in drinking water, a problem in Switzerland?. *Ozone Sci Eng.*, 25(3), 159-166.

Wieserman L.F., Wefer K. (1991). Surface-modified adsorbent comprising metal oxide/hydroxide particles reacted with one or more perfluorinated organic acids. US Pat. *4,983,566*, Aluminum Company of America.

In: Water Production and Wastewater Treatment
Editor: B. Antizar-Ladislao et al.

ISBN 978-1-61728-503-5
© 2011 Nova Science Publishers, Inc.

Chapter 10

PHOTOCATALYTIC DEGRADATION OF PHENOLIC CONTAMINANTS USING TITANIUM DIOXIDE NANO-PARTICLES: STATISTICAL MODELING AND PROCESS OPTIMIZATION USING *P*-CRESOL

S. Ray[1] *and J. A. Lalman*[2]

Department of Civil and Environmental Engineering,
University of Windsor,
401 Sunset Avenue, Windsor, Ontario, Canada, N9B 3P4

ABSTRACT

Titanium dioxide (TiO_2) was examined as a potential heterogeneous photocatalyst for degrading phenolic compounds. In this chapter, various factors affecting TiO_2 photocatalysis are discussed and the significance of using a statistical model to understand the impact of the factors on the photocatalytic rate is explained. The statistical model development procedure presented is based on the Box Benkhen design (BBD) technique. A BBD-model reported by other researchers to calculate the photocatalytic rate of phenol degradation using TiO_2 nanoparticles was used to compare with the rates predicted by *p*-cresol (a phenol derivative) model.

A case study was conducted to validate data derived from the model for *p*-cresol with experimental data. The *p*-cresol degradation rate computed from the model was compared with the experimental value at various levels of the four independent model variables. The variables included TiO_2 nanoparticle size, TiO_2 concentration, dissolve oxygen (DO) concentration and *p*-cresol concentration. The case study reported a maximum degradation of *p*-cresol for 10 nm TiO_2 particles. In comparison to the various conditions under evaluation, higher degradation of *p*-cresol was recorded at high DO (31 mg/l) and low *p*-cresol (40 mg/l) concentration. An activation energy of 10.77 kJ/mol·K was computed for *p*-cresol photocatalytic degradation with 10 nm TiO_2 particles. The activation energy and quantum yield calculations revealed that *p*-cresol degrades faster than phenol. Overall, the case study demonstrated that the statistical model accurately

---

[1] Graduate Student, email: uwindsor.rays@gmail.com.
[2] Associate Professor, email: lalman@uwindsor.ca.

predicted the photocatalytic degradation rate of *p*-cresol for the conditions under investigation.

1. INTRODUCTION

Many global environmental and health concerns facing our planet are linked to anthropogenic and industrial activities. Large number of organic pollutants are relentlessly released into the environment by many industrial manufacturing sectors as well as municipal treatment facilities (Schindler, 2001; McFarlane and Nilsen, 2003; United Nations Educational, Scientific and Cultural Organization (UNESCO), 2006). Phenolic compounds with total annual production of approximately 3 million tonnes are major contributors to global pollution (EHC 161, 1994; EHC 168, 1995). Phenolic chemicals are routinely used in the manufacture of various chemicals, structured polymers, and resins products (Bukowska and Kowalska, 2003). These products have widespread industrial and commercial applications in the manufacture of insulation panels, paints and lubricants. Phenol based compounds are constituents of animal wastes (Bruce et al, 1987). They are also produced from coal tar formation and from microbiological degradation of organic matter (EHC 161, 1994; EHC 168, 1995). Because of widespread releases into the environment, humans and other organisms are exposed to phenolic compounds (Meknassi *et al.*, 2004). Human health problems related to growth retardation, reproduction, foetal immaturity, genetic disruption, and endocrine system disruption are a direct result from exposure to these compounds (Meknassi *et al.*, 2004; Safe, 2004; Martinez *et al.*, 2006). These toxicological health effects coupled with the widespread use of phenolic compounds as chemical intermediates and large-scale discharge of phenolic wastes in the environment suggest the need for developing effective treatment option for removing these contaminants.

2. TREATMENT OPTIONS FOR PHENOLIC CONTAMINANTS

Many conventional treatment processes are not designed to effectively remove or degrade phenolic contaminants from water or wastewater sources (Smith et *al.*, 1991; Westerhoff, 2003; Li *et al.*, 2005). The removal efficiency of phenolic compounds using primary treatment methods such as coagulation and flocculation (alum or ferric chloride) and lime softening is very low, as removal is mostly due to adsorption onto settling solids. No more than 20% removals of phenolic compounds are expected in these treatment processes (Smith et *al.*, 1991, Westerhoff, 2003). Some studies have shown that the biological removal of phenolic contaminants is often impaired beyond a threshold concentration (Autenrieth et *al.*, 1991; Martinez *et al.*, 2006). Moreover, biological treatment requires longer residence time (Pera-Titus et *al.*, 2004; Kavitha and Palanivelu, 2005). Following the limitations of conventional treatment methods, tertiary treatment processes are often recommended for removing phenolic compounds from contaminated water supplies (Li *et al.*, 2005). Enzymatic treatment using peroxidase and laccase enzymes have been reported to accomplish approximately 95% removal of phenols by partial polymerization and phase transfer (Caza et *al.*, 1999; Kurniawati and Nicell, 2005). Granular activated carbon (GAC) adsorption has been identified by the United States Environmental Protection Agency (USEPA) as the best available treatment method (BAT) for treating phenolic contamination (USEPA, 2001). However, because these tertiary treatment processes rely on phase transfer, phenolic compounds are not completely removed from the environment.

3. HETEROGENEOUS PHOTOCATALYSIS: A TREATMENT OPTION

In recent years, the oxidative degradation of organic pollutants in aqueous phase using a photo-illuminated catalyst has emerged as a potential technology for treating industrial effluents (Ollis *et al.*, 1991). The process, generically identified as heterogeneous photocatalysis, relies on using hydroxyl ($^{\cdot}$OH) radicals to mediate the oxidation of organic contaminants into carbon dioxide (CO_2) and water using specific wavelengths of light (Bhatkhande et *al.*, 2001; Lee and Mills, 2004). Heterogeneous photocatalysis offers a unique advantage over other alternative treatment methods because it degrades toxic organic pollutants into carbon dioxide (CO_2) in presence of light. The treatment method is classified as 'green' in some reports because CO_2 is produced as an ultimate end product (Bhatkhande et al., 2001; Herrmann, 2005). Among the reported photocatalysts (Fe_2O_3, CdS, WO_3, ZnO, TiO_2) which have been used, titanium dioxide (TiO_2) has received the most attention due to its chemical inertness, lower biological toxicity, excellent photo-stability, high relative abundance and above all, oxidative potential which is best suited for generating $^{\cdot}$OH radicals (Rajeshwar, 1995; Bhatkhande *et al.*, 2001; Carp *et al.*, 2004; Herrmann, 2005).

4. MECHANISM OF HETEROGENEOUS PHOTOCATALYSIS WITH TiO_2

The oxidative potential of TiO_2 originates from its semiconductor band gap (E_g). When illuminated with light of wavelengths less than 380 nm (photons having energy higher than the band gap (E_g)), TiO_2 produces electrons (e^-) and holes (h^+) at different energy levels (Linsebigler et *al.*, 1995; Lee and Mills, 2004). The charge carriers (electron-hole pairs) either recombine or migrate to the particle surface and initiate oxidative – reductive reactions (Rajeshwar, 1995; Herrmann, 2005). In an aqueous phase, the holes (h^+) are scavenged by surface hydroxyl (OH^-) ions to generate $^{\cdot}$OH radicals. The electron (e^-) on the catalyst surface reacts with other oxidizing species, namely dissolved oxygen in water and this result in formation of more $^{\cdot}$OH radicals. These $^{\cdot}$OH radicals mediate the subsequent degradation of organic molecules (Matthews, 1992; Bhatkhande et al., 2001).

5. FACTORS AFFECTING TiO_2 PHOTOCATALYSIS

The ability of a heterogeneous catalyst to photocatalytically degrade organic compounds depends upon many factors which include the catalytic material properties (crystal structure and surface area), catalyst loading, radiation intensity, radiation wavelength, substrate concentration, dissolve oxygen concentration, pH and temperature. The impact of these factors on the reaction rates of TiO_2 catalyzed photodegradation of phenolic compounds, particularly phenols and substituted phenols has been reported in several studies (Blake, 2001; Bhatkhande et al., 2001; Herrmann, 2005).

5.1. TiO$_2$ Material Properties

The crystal structure (Rajeshwar, 1995) and catalytic surface area (Carp et al., 2004) are factors known to affect the photo-oxidative properties of TiO$_2$. The crystal structure dictates the bandgap energy (E$_g$) and the oxidative potential (Gogate and Pandit, 2004). The different crystalline forms of TiO$_2$ includes anatase (kinetically stable), rutile (thermodynamically stable), brookite and monoclinic. In comparison to the other crystal forms, the anatase form (distorted orthogonal structure) has the highest E$_g$ (3.2 eV) value and greatest photocatalytic activity (Carp et al., 2004). Consequently, the anatase form is selectively utilized in many studies because it is photocatalytically more active than the other crystalline forms (Tsai and Cheng, 1997; Blake 2001; Bhatkhande et al., 2001; Gogate and Pandit, 2004).

The specific surface area (SSA) is a function of the particle size for any heterogeneous catalyst. Hence, smaller diameter TiO$_2$ photocatalysts are associated with larger SSA. An increase in the total number of free charge carriers (e$^-$ and h$^+$) on the TiO$_2$ surface with increasing SSA is expected to increase the efficiency of the catalyst. The number of free carriers is affected by the number and the lifetime of free e$^-$ and h$^+$, and the latter depends upon the particle size. In the case of large particles, the volume recombination of e$^-$ and h$^+$ dominates and the result is a reduction of free charge carriers on the TiO$_2$ surface. Ultimately, the photocatalytic activity is reduced and the efficiency decreases (Shah et al., 2002).

TiO$_2$ particle size within the micrometer range is normally used in the manufacture of a variety of industrial and consumer products. However, TiO$_2$ particles within this range are not utilized in photocatalysis because they are not photoactive (Allen et al., 2004; Hurum et al., 2006). In addition, the light scattering phenomenon for micrometric TiO$_2$ particles leads to a loss of photon energy (Allen et al., 2004). Because of these problems associated with using micrometer size particles, a growing research interest has recently emerged into utilizing nanoparticles. Increasing innovations in manufacturing processes have resulted in production of different nanometer size TiO$_2$ particles. Several nanometer size TiO$_2$ particles have been tested over past years for their photocatalytic potential to degrade organic compounds (Blake 2001; Bhatkhande et al., 2001; Gogate and Pandit, 2004).

5.2. Incident Light Characteristics

The generation of photo-electrons depends on the wavelength and intensity of the incident radiation. The energy barrier for discharge of a photo-electron (E$_g$) depends on the catalyst material. The energy of the impinging photons, required to overcome the E$_g$ barrier, is a function of the wavelength of the illuminating light. Due to the bandgap energy of approximately 3.2 eV, photo-excitation of electrons in TiO$_2$ is mediated by incident radiation with wavelengths below 380 nm (Matthews, 1992; Herrmann, 2005). TiO$_2$ has been reported to be photocatalytically active over the entire zone of the ultra-violet (UV) region (200-380nm). However, because of the health hazards associated with using UV radiation below

280 nm, radiation with an average wavelength of 300 nm is preferred for TiO_2 photocatalytic studies (Tsai and Cheng, 1997).

Another factor affecting the photocatalysis is the number of photons impinging on the TiO_2 surface. The number of incident photons is directly proportional to the intensity or irradiance of the UV source. In several batch photocatalytic studies, the UV light irradiance may vary from 4-10 mW/cm^2 (Lee and Mills, 2004). According to Ray et al. (2007), selecting a UV source with an output of 10 mW/cm^2 is expected to generate the most number of photons per unit area of reaction surface.

5.3. Photocatalysis Process Variables

The number of catalyst particles in the reaction zone is related to the TiO_2 concentration or the TiO_2 mass loading and the photocatalytic degradation rate is affected by these two parameters (Herrmann, 2005). . Typically, an increase in the photocatalytic rate is associated with an increase in the TiO_2 loading (Mills et al., 1993). However, a threshold is often observed in studies with suspended TiO_2 particles. The threshold level in photocatalytic rates is related to an increase in the turbidity of the suspension at higher TiO_2 concentration and the limited penetration depth of the incident UV radiation (Gogate and Pandit, 2004).

Another major factor affecting the catalytic activity is the dissolved oxygen (DO) concentration (Herrmann, 2005). The availability of oxygen facilitates the generation of $^{\bullet}OH$ radicals and minimizes the loss of charge carriers (electron-hole pairs) (Fox and Dulay, 1993). Thus, enhanced photocatalytic rates are reported at elevated DO levels (Matthews and McEvoy, 1992).

Photocatalysis is strongly influenced by the number of substrate molecules adsorbed to the catalytic active sites on the TiO_2 surface (Lee and Mills, 2004; Herrmann, 2005). Thus, the dissociation form (dissociated or undissociated) and initial concentration of substrate are reported to alter the photocatalytic rates (Dalrymple et al., 2007). In the millimolar concentration range, the substrate adsorption is reported to be monolayer, and according to Lee and Mills (2004), monolayer adsorption is preferred for maximum reaction rates. Additionally at elevated substrate levels, the availability of photons at the catalyst surface decreases due to the direct absorption of photons by substrate (organic) molecules. For phenolic compounds, the adsorption of substrates on the catalyst surface is strongly correlated with the type of functional groups and substitution patterns. Hence, different photocatalytic rates are reported for phenols with different substitution (mono-, di- or tri-) patterns and varied substituted functional groups (cresol to chlorophenol to nitrophenol) (Tsai and Cheng, 1997; Bhatkhande et al., 2001; Gogate and Pandit, 2004; Pera-Titus et al., 2004; Kusvuran et al., 2005).

5.4. Environmental Variables

The iso-electric point or point of zero (zpc) surface charge of TiO_2 in solution is approximately pH 7.0 (Guzman et al., 2006). The aggregation tendency of TiO_2 nanoparticles and adsorption of the substrate onto the TiO_2 surface is controlled by surface charges (Ray and Lalman, 2010). Thus, monitoring and control of pH is crucial for photocatalytic reactions, particularly in an aqueous medium. However, pH is often not considered a factor in phenol photocatalytic degradation with TiO_2 due to their high dissociation pH and strong adsorption on TiO_2 surface in the undissociated form (Bhatkhande et al., 2001).

Temperature is another variable whose effect is not clearly reported in literature. Some studies have reported that photocatalytic reaction rates are temperature dependent and follow an Arrhenius type behavior (Kartal et al., 2001; Bhatkhande et al., 2001). However, other studies have contradicted that photocatalytic reactions are not sensitive to temperature changes particularly within the region from 20 to 80°C (Fox and Dulay, 1993; Hermann, 1999).

6. Factors Affecting TiO_2 Photocatalysis: Bridiging the Research Gap

Several earlier studies have described the impact of individual factors on the degradation of phenolic compounds (Kartal et al., 2001; Blake, 2001; Lee and Mills, 2004; Herrmann, 2005; Kusvuran et al., 2005). However, the photocatalytic rates reported in these studies are difficult to compare because of differences in reporting units and experimental conditions (Bhatkhande et al., 2001; Carp et al., 2004). Also, many studies have varied multiple experimental parameters simultaneously in order to improve the photocatalytic reaction rates (Chen and Ray, 1998; Blake, 2001). Reports describing the impact of individual factors on the photocatalysis is lacking in the literature. Moreover, consolidating these variables into a unified statistical model to predict the photocatalytic degradation rates has not been reported (Sakkas et al., 2010; Ray, 2010). Consequently, a pressing research need is to consolidate all the various factors into a unified model. A complex method to evaluate the effects of different variables on TiO_2 photocatalysis of phenolic compounds is one-factor-at-a-time (OFAT) approach. This OFAT approach assesses one factor at a time instead of all simultaneously, hence, the method is time-consuming, expensive and often leads to misinterpretation of results when interactions between different components are present (Myers and Montogomery, 2002; Ray, 2006). Another approach of accurately evaluating the impact of the variables on the degradation process is to vary all the factors simultaneously in a systematic manner using a statistical experimental design.

7. Statistical Design and Photocatalytic Rate Modeling

A statistical experimental design is a tool that is often used to establish relationships between several independent variables and one or more dependent variables. Developing a polynomial model for photocatalytic degradation rate can be performed using a statistical experimental design approach (Box et. al., 1978; Box and Draper, 1987).

7.1. Statistical Design

Several experimental designs have been used to model the photocatalytic degradation of different substrates (Sakkas *et al.*, 2010). Among the available experimental design methods, a full factorial design (FFD) is often considered unpractical because a large number of experiments are required. Based upon the desirable feature of accurate prediction throughout the factor space central composite design (CCD) and Box-Benkhen design (BBD) are commonly selected experimental designs for modeling purpose (Box and Draper, 1987; Myers and Montogomery, 2002; Ray *et al.*, 2009; Sakkas *et al.*, 2010). However, for a quadratic model with three or more factors, the BBD procedure is more advantageous than the CCD.

7.2. Selecting Experimental Factors And Factor Levels

An experimental design leading to the development of a model to predict the photocatalytic rate must carefully screen the factors in order to reduce the complexity of the model and minimize the number of experiments (Box *et. al.*, 1978; Ray, 2006). Screening of various experimental factors is based on data from preliminary experiments (Ray *et al.*, 2009). Use of an experimental design to model the degradation rate of phenol was recently reported by Ray *et al.* (2009). The independent variables considered by these researchers were TiO_2 particle size, TiO_2 concentration, DO concentration and substrate (phenol) concentration. Other factors influencing the photocatalytic rates, namely, radiation intensity, wavelength and pH were set at the optimum values (Ray *et al.*, 2009).

The number of factors levels is defined by the experimental design under consideration. For the BBD (or CCD) procedure, each experimental factor is examined at three different levels (Box and Draper, 1987; Myers and Montogomery, 2002). The factor levels are defined by the region of interest for the factor space under evaluation. Many practical constraints including experimental and analytical limitations also influence the levels of the experimental factors which are selected for statistical modeling (Ray, 2006). Selecting the different TiO_2 catalyst sizes is often limited by the availability of particle sizes bearing the same crystal structure. Similarly, in the case of selecting the TiO_2 concentration, the lowest level is defined in a region where the photocatalytic rate is slightly greater than the degradation rate of the substrate in the presence of UV only, without any TiO_2 (photolysis). The upper level of the TiO_2 concentration depends on the photo-hindrance effect imposed by the turbidity of the medium. The substrate concentrations are chosen to ensure formation of a mono-layer of the substrate on the TiO_2 surface (Lee and Mills, 2004; Ray *et al.*, 2009).

7.3. Model Development

The development of a statistical model involves data collection, model formulation and model verification (Box *et. al.*, 1978; Box and Draper, 1987; Myers and Montogomery, 2002; Ray, 2006). The computed reaction rates from the photocatalytic experiments conducted at the different factor levels were used to develop the model (Ray *et al.*, 2009; Ray, 2010). The purpose of the model is to define the photodegradation rate (model response) in terms of several independent photocatalytic process variables (model terms). The coefficients for the different model terms were computed using regression analysis. The final statistical model for the photocatalytic rates was formulated by refining a full quadratic model (for BBD or CCD) through sequential deletion of the statistically insignificant terms in the model (Box *et. al.*, 1978; Myers and Montogomery, 2002; Ray, 2010). The accuracy and prediction error was determined to verify and validate the model. The prediction error of the final model was determined by comparing the predicted rates (response) with the experimental rates. Differences between the experimental and the predicted response (residual) were statistically analyzed to determine the accuracy of the model (Box *et. al.*, 1978; Box and Draper, 1987; Myers and Montogomery, 2002; Ray *et al.*, 2009).

7.4. Factor Level Optimization

Statistical models coupled with statistical optimization tools are often utilized to locate the factor settings for an optimal process response (Box and Draper, 1987). Some commonly used optimization tools include optimality plot and optimality criterion (Myers and Montogomery, 2002). Among the available optimization techniques, computation of the optimality criterion is a popular method (Redhe *et al.*, 2002). The numerical algorithm is first used to compute the optimality criterion for each possible combination of the factor levels. The optimality criterion is thereafter optimized (maximized or minimized) to identify the factor level combinations for the optimal response (Titterington, 1975). Recent studies by Ray *et al.* (2009) and Sakkas *et al.* (2010) have reported optimizing the factor setting to obtain a maximum photocatalytic degradation rate.

8. STATISTICAL MODELING OF PHENOL PHOTOCATALYSIS: A LITERATURE REVIEW

An emerging treatment technology for degrading phenolic compounds from contaminated water supplies is to employ TiO_2 photocatalysis using nanoparticles. Although some reports are available, evidence describing the effects of different process variables on the photocatalytic rate is limited (Bhatkhande *et al.*, 2001; Kartal *et al.*, 2001; Sakkas *et al.*, 2010). In a recent study by Ray *et al.* (2009), the BBD procedure was used to statistically model the photocatalytic degradation rate of phenol. These researchers developed a second-order (quadratic) model which included the following factors: TiO_2 size, TiO_2 concentration, DO concentration and substrate (phenol) concentration. Ray *et al.* (2009) observed first (pseudo) order kinetics for the photocatalytic degradation of phenol in presence of TiO_2 nanoparticles. The phenol model equation for an apparent first order rate constant (k) is shown as Equation 1.

$$k = 0.0022244 * (TiO_2\ size) + 0.0037492 * (DO) - 0.0000523 * (TiO_2\ size) - 0.0224267 * (TiO_2\ Conc)^2$$
$$- 0.0000430\ * (TiO_2\ size) * (DO) + 0.0008159\ * (TiO_2\ Conc) * (DO) - 0.0000414\ * (DO) * (Substrate\ Conc)\ \textbf{(1)}$$

The optimal TiO_2 and DO concentration, which yield the maximum photocatalytic degradation of phenol using TiO_2 nanoparticles, was located by computing the D-optimality criteria involving the model designated as Equation 1. The model was subsequently validated over a range of phenol concentrations, ranging from 0.4 to 1.0 mmol/l.

9. STATISTICAL MODELING OF P-CRESOL PHOTOCATALYSIS: A CASE STUDY

The objective of the case study presented in this chapter is to confirm the validity of the phenol model for a mono-substituted phenol derivative such as *p*-cresol. The experimental factors evaluated were TiO_2 particle size (dry), TiO_2 concentration, DO concentration and *p*-cresol concentration. Photocatalytic experiments were conducted at selected levels of the experimental factors. The *p*-cresol degradation rates were computed from the photocatalytic experiments and the first-order reaction rate constant was in agreement with the reaction order for phenol degradation. The experimental photocatalytic rates were compared against the model predicted rates to confirm the validity of the model. Finally, the photocatalytic behavior of *p*-cresol was compared against phenol with respect to the activation energy and the quantum yield.

9.1. Experimental Factor Levels

The TiO_2 nanoparticles selected for the *p*-cresol degradation studies were 5, 10 and 32 nm. Confirming the crystal structure as the anatase form for each nanoparticle size was accomplished by X-ray diffraction. The levels selected for the TiO_2 nanoparticle size were based on the commercial availability of the photocatalyst with the same crystal structure. The only difference in the catalyst particles was the size (dry powder) and hence, the specific surface area (SSA). The SSA was determined by physisorption of nitrogen using the Brunner Emmett Teller (BET) method (Nova 1200e, Quantachrome Instruments, FL). The TiO_2 concentration was varied between 0.1 to 1.0 g/l. Preliminary experiments showed that at less than 0.1g/l TiO_2, improvement in photocatalytic rate due to the presence of TiO_2 nanoparticles was negligible and at TiO_2 concentration greater than 1.0 g/l, the photocatalytic degradation rate was hindered by the turbidity of the suspension.

Table 1. Factors and levels selected for p-cresol degradation

Factors / Levels	Size of TiO_2 nanoparticles (nm)/Specific surface area (m^2/g)[a]	TiO_2 catalyst concentration (g/l)	DO concentration (mg/l)	Initial *p*-cresol concentration (mg/l)
1	5 / 275±15[b]	0.1	0.04	40
2	10 / 131±12[b]	0.5	7.80	70
3	32 / 47±2[b]	1.0	31.0	100

Notes: [a] Specific surface area (m^2/g) of TiO_2 particles (dry).

[b] Average and standard deviation for triplicate samples.

To validate the model over the entire range of the DO concentration, the maximum and minimum boundaries were set at 0.04 mg/l and 31.0 mg/l, respectively. The level of the *p*-cresol concentration was selected within the limits of mono-layer (Langmuir type) substrate adsorption on the photocatalyst surface (Lee and Mills, 2004; Herrmann, 2005; Ray *et al.*, 2009). The experimental factors and their respective levels are summarized in Table 1.

9.2. Experimental Methodology

Photocatalytic experiments were conducted in a customized photocatalytic reaction chamber which was equipped with sixteen 300 nm monochromatic UV lamps (Tsai and Cheng, 1997; Ray et *al.*, 2009) on the outer perimeter (Figure 1). The average intensity of the UV radiation was maintained at 9 mW/cm^2 (Lee and Mills, 2004; Ray et *al.*, 2009). The experimental apparatus was identical with that reported for developing the phenol model (Ray et *al.*, 2009). Photocatalysis of *p*-cresol was conducted in a reactor constructed from quartz tubing (UV transmitant).

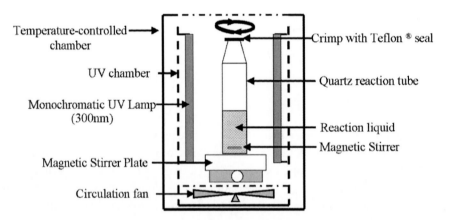

Figure 1. Schematic of photocatalytic reactor and the experimental setup (Ray et al, 2009).

The photocatalytic reaction rates were reported to be least affected by the solution pH near neutral pH condition (zpc of TiO_2) (Bhatkhande *et al.*, 2001). Hence, all the experiments were conducted in ultra-pure water at pH 7.0±0.5 without any further pH adjustment. Photocatalytic experiments, except for those performed to evaluate the temperature effect, were performed at 37±2°C (Ray et *al.*, 2009). Liquid samples were removed at regular intervals and analyzed for residual *p*-cresol using a high performance liquid chromatograph (HPLC) operated in a reverse phase mode. The eluent (acetonitrile-water mixture (2:5)) flow rate was set at 0.4 ml/min and the temperature was maintained at 45°C. The headspace gas was analyzed for CO_2 using a gas chromatograph (GC) configured with a thermal conductivity detector. The GC analytical methods were adopted from work reported by Ray et *al.* (2009). The detection limit for *p*-cresol and CO_2 were 0.01mg/l and 0.2kPa, respectively. All experimental conditions were examined in triplicates.

9.3. Kinetic Study of p-Cresol Photocatalysis

The residual p-cresol concentration was monitored over a duration of 1 hour in the presence of TiO_2 (photocatalysis) and in absence of TiO_2 (photolysis) (Figure 2A). In both cases, the p-cresol degradation reaction followed first-order kinetics (Equation 2).

$$-(dC/dt) = kC \qquad (2)$$

where, k is the apparent first order reaction rate constant, referred herein as apparent degradation rate constant (min^{-1}), C is the p-cresol concentration (mg/l) and $(-dC/dt)$ is the first order disappearance (removal) rate. $[-\ln(C/C_o)]$ was plotted against the reaction time to determine the apparent degradation rate constant (Figure 2B). The photolysis rate (without TiO_2) contributed to 10% of the p-cresol degradation while the remaining 90% was attributed to photocatalysis (with TiO_2). Recall the output of the phenol model is the apparent first order rate constant for the photocatalytic degradation with TiO_2 nanoparticles. The apparent first order rate constant for p-cresol photocatalysis was confirmed by the plot shown in Figure 2B.

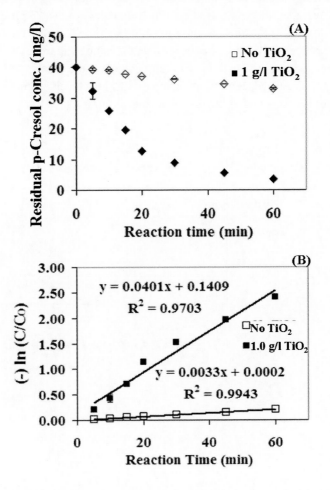

Figure 2. p-Cresol degradation profiles for photocatalysis and photolysis (A) Residual concentration (B) Removal rate. [Averages with standard deviation (SD) for triplicate samples are shown].

9.4. Validation of the Statistical Model for p-Cresol Photocatalysis

The phenol model (Equation 1) predicted the apparent degradation rate constant (k, min^{-1}) for p-cresol photocatalysis from the values of four independent factors (TiO$_2$ size, TiO$_2$ concentration, DO concentration, and p-cresol (reactant) concentration), which were varied at three different levels (Table 1). The apparent degradation rate constant was determined using Equation 1 and the computed k value from the model was compared with the corresponding experimental k value for each factor level combination.

The model predictions were in close agreement with the experimental results for 0.4 mg/l DO and 7.8 mg/l DO; however, at 31 mg/l DO the model over estimated the apparent degradation rate constant by 33.4% (Figure 3A). Notice a large variation in the degradation rate was observed at a high DO level. Maintaining high DO levels in the reactor was difficult and this likely caused a large variability in the degradation rate constant. The predicted values for the degradation rate constants correlated closely with the experimental values for all the TiO$_2$ concentration levels under examination (Figure 3B). Higher degradation rates constants were associated with higher TiO$_2$ concentrations. Low p-cresol concentration was observed to degrade the reactant faster than at a high p-cresol concentration. The experimental rate constant was lower than the value predicted by the model at lower p-cresol concentration. At 70 mg/l and 100 mg/l p-cresol concentration, the predicted values for the degradation rate constant correlated closely with the experimental value (Figure 3C). Photocatalysis is a surface phenomenon and competition for active sites on the catalyst surface is expected to increase at high p-cresol concentrations compared to low levels. Hence, high photocatalytic degradation rates are expected at low p-cresol concentrations.

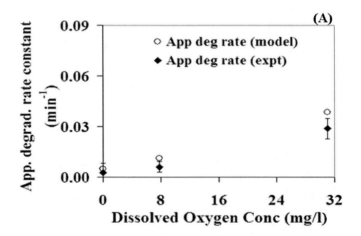

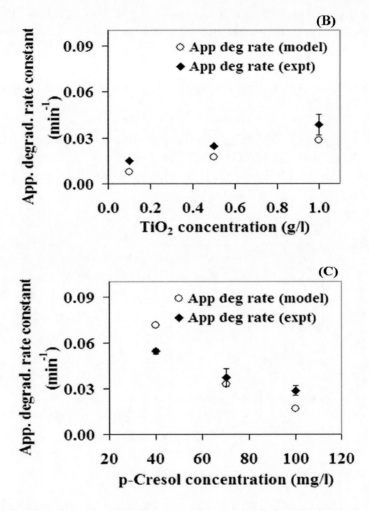

Figure 3. Comparison of the apparent degradation rate for the model with experimental values for different (A) DO concentration, (B) TiO$_2$ concentration, (C) p-cresol concentration [Averages with standard deviation (SD) for triplicate samples are shown].

9.5. Verification of Optimal Condition from the Statistical Model

The optimization of TiO$_2$ nanoparticle size for maximum photocatalytic degradation was reported in studies conducted by Ray *et al.* (2009). The D-optimality criterion, computed from the phenol model using numerical algorithm was used to identify the TiO$_2$ nanoparticle size associated with the greatest photocatalytic degradation rate constant (k). The maximum photocatalytic rate was predicted for a TiO$_2$ particle size of approximately 10 nm (9.091 nm) (Ray *et al.*, 2009). The experimental degradation rate data for *p*-cresol verified the predicted TiO$_2$ particle size of approximately 10 nm when a maximum degradation rate was observed. A plot of the experimental apparent degradation rate constant and SSA against the particle size showed a maximum rate constant for 10 nm TiO$_2$ particles (Figure 4). In spite of an increase in the SSA, a lower apparent degradation rate was observed below 10 nm. The lower photocatalytic degradation rate below the optimum TiO_2 size of 10 nm could be likely due to a phenomenon known as quantum size effect (Linsebigler et *al.*, 1995; Carp *et al.*, 2004).

9.6. Comparison of Activation Energy, Quantum Yield and Mineralization Rate

The photocatalytic degradation of *p*-cresol with 10 nm TiO_2 catalyst was conducted at 23°C (300K), 30°C (303K) and 37°C (310K). The degradation rate constant in mol/s (k_t) was computed and a plot of [- ln k_t] versus [1/T] showed an Arrhenius dependency of the rate constant (Figure 5).

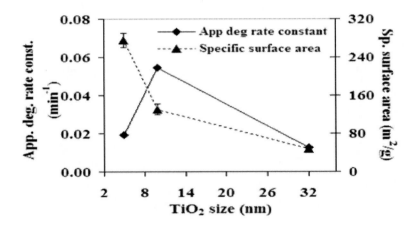

Figure 4. Apparent degradation rate constant and specific surface area versus TiO_2 particle size (dry). [Averages with standard deviation (SD) for triplicate samples are shown)].

An activation energy of 10.77 kJ/mol·K was computed for the photocatalytic degradation of *p*-cresol using the 10 nm TiO_2 nanoparticles. The observed activation energy for *p*-cresol was comparable to the value reported for phenol (13.55 kJ/mol·K) (Ray *et al.*, 2009). The activation energy in photocatalytic reactions is influenced by the affinity of the reactant for active sites on the catalyst surface. The pk_a values of phenol (9.99) and *p*-cresol (10.09) could be a major reason for similar affinities of phenol and *p*-cresol for the catalyst surface (EHC 161, 1994; EHC 168, 1995). The quantum yield for the 10 nm TiO_2 nanoparticles was computed for phenol and *p*-cresol to confirm the difference in activation energy. The quantum yield is defined as the ratio of the number of substrate molecules (phenol or *p*-cresol) degraded to the number of photons irradiated (Lee and Mills, 2004).

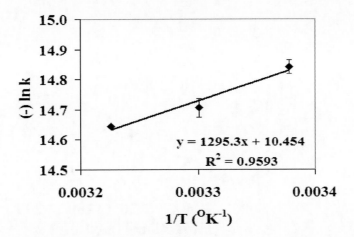

Figure 5. Arrhenius plot of photocatalytic degradation rate constant for p-cresol [Averages with standard deviation (SD) for triplicate samples are shown].

The yield for p-cresol degradation (41 ± 1.8%) was statistically greater than the reported value of 35±2.5 % for phenol (Ray *et al.*, 2009). A two-sample t-test indicated that the quantum yields for the two substrates (p-cresol and phenol) were statistically different (The $t_{computed}$ value (3.4) was greater than the $t_{tabulated}$ (3.2) value (Box *et al.*, 1978)).

The higher quantum yield for p-cresol correlated with lower activation energy compared to phenol. A slightly greater quantum yield for p-cresol when compared to phenol suggested that the degradation rate for p-cresol is larger than that for phenol.

Complete degradation (or mineralization) was estimated by measuring the quantity of CO_2 in the reactor headspace. Complete degradation of p-cresol was evident 4 hours after the reaction was initiated (Figure 6A). The mineralization rate followed zero-order kinetics (Figure 6B) with a rate constant of 0.0013 mmol CO_2/minute. The mineralization rate observed for p-cresol was in agreement with the value reported for phenol (0.0012 mmol CO_2/minute) (Ray et al., 2009).

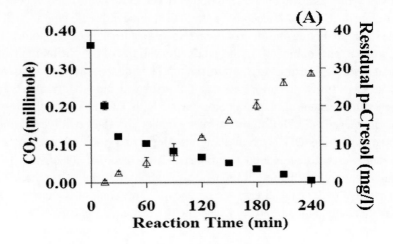

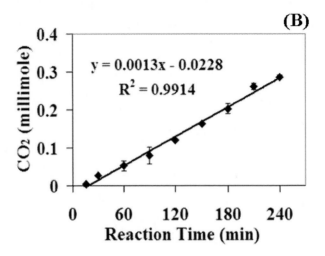

Figure 6. Photocatalytic profile - (A) Residual p-cresol concentration and CO_2 formation (B) Mineralization rate [Averages with standard deviation (SD) for triplicate samples are shown].

Based on a comparison of the quantum yield and activation energy, faster photocatalytic degradation of *p*-cresol with TiO_2 nanoparticles is expected in comparison to phenol. However, note the phenol model is only valid for assessing the degradation of *p*-cresol within the factor space under consideration.

10. CONCLUSION

The photocatalytic degradation of phenolic contaminants with TiO_2 is a promising treatment option when compared to other techniques. The photocatalytic process is affected by factors which include catalytic material properties, incident radiation characteristics, catalyst loading, DO concentration and temperature. Statistical experimental design is a very effective tool for assessing the interaction between these factors and to consolidate the factors into a statistical model. Recently, a statistical model based on the BBD procedure was reported for predicting the degradation rate constant of phenol photocatalysis using TiO_2 nanoparticles (phenol model). In this study, the validity of the phenol model for predicting the photocatalytic degradation of *p*-cresol using TiO_2 nanoparticles was assessed. The results from the case study demonstrated that the statistical model formulated for predicting the apparent rate constant of phenol photocatalysis with TiO_2 nanoparticles was also valid for *p*-cresol photocatalysis. Deviation between predicted values with experimental values was observed when the DO concentration was high and *p*-cresol concentration was low. A maximum *p*-cresol degradation rate constant was recorded for 10 nm TiO_2 particles. The activation energy and mineralization rate for photocatalysis of *p*-cresol were in agreement with that reported in the literature for phenol. The computed quantum yield calculations showed that degradation of *p*-cresol was slightly faster than phenol.

ACKNOWLEDGMENTS

Financial support for the work presented in this chapter was provided by the Natural Sciences and Engineering Research (NSERC) of Canada and the University of Windsor.

REFERENCES

Allen, N.S.; Edge, M.; Ortega, A.; Sandoval, G.; Liauw, C. M.; Verran, J.; Stratton, J.; McIntyre, R. B. *Polym. Degrad. Stab.* 2004, 85, 927-946.

Autenrieth, R.L.; Bonner, J.S.; Akgerman, A.; Okaygun, M. *J. Hazard. Mat.* 1991, 28, 29-53.

Bhatkhande, D.S.; Pangarkar, V.G.; Beenackers, A.A.C.M. *J. Chem. Technol Biotechnol.* 2001, 77 102-116.

Blake, D.M. Bibliography of work on the heterogeneous photocatalytic removal of hazardous compounds from water and air; *National Renewable Energy Laboratory: Golden, CO,* Technical Report 2001, 4, 3-16.

Box, G.E.P.; Draper, N.R. Empirical Model Building and Response Surfaces; *John Wiley and Sons: New York, NY,* 1987, 205-477.

Box, G.E.P.; Hunter, W.G.; Hunter, W.S. Statistics for Experimenters: An Introduction to Design, Data Analysis, and Model Building; *John Wiley and Sons: New York, NY,* 1978, 510-536.

Bruce, R.M.; Santodonato, J.; Neal, M.W. Summary review of the health effects associated with phenol. *Toxicol Ind Health.* 1987. 3, 535-68.

Bukowska, B.; Kowalska, S. *Curr. Top. Biophys.* 2003, 27, 47-51.

Carp, O.; Huisman, C.L.; Reller, A. Prog. *Solid State Chem.* 2004, 32, 33-177.

Caza, N.; Bewtra, J.K.; Biswas, N.; Taylor, K.E. *Water Res.*1999, 33, 3012-3018.

Chen, D.; Ray, A.K. *Wat. Res.* 1998, 32, 3223-3234.

Dalrymple, O.K.; Yeh, D.H.; Trotz, M.A. *J. Chem. Technol. Biotechnol.* 2007, 82, 121-134.

Environmental Health Criteria (EHC) No. 161, Phenol; *World Health Organization. Geneva, Switzerland,* 1994.

Environmental Health Criteria (EHC) No. 168, Cresol; *World Health Organization. Geneva, Switzerland,* 1995.

Filali-Meknassi, Y;.; Tyagi, R.D.; Surampalli, R.Y.; Barata, C.; Riva M.C. *Prac. Period. Hazard. Toxic. Radioactive Waste Manag.* 2004, 8, 39-56.

Fox, M.A. Dulay, M.T. *Chem. Rev.* 1993, 93, 341-357.

Gogate, P.R.; Pandit, A.B. *Adv. Environ. Res.* 2004, 8, 501-551.

Guzman, K.A.D.; Finnegan, M.P.; Banfield, J. F. *Environ. Sci. Technol.* 2006, 40, 7688-7693.

Herrmann, J.M. *Catal. Today.* 1999, 53, 115-129.

Herrmann, J.M. *Top. Catal.* 2005, 34, 49-65.

Hurum, D.C.; Agrios, A.G.; Crist, S.E.; Gray, K.A.; Rajh, T.; Thurnauer, M. C. J. *Electron. Spectrosc. Relat. Phenom.* 2006, 150, 155-163.

Kartal, O.E. ; Erol, M. ; Oguz, H. *Chem. Eng. Technol.* 2001, 24, 645-649.

Kavitha, V.; Palanivelu, K. *Water Res.* 2005, 39, 3062-3072.

Kurniawati, S.; Nicell, J.A. *Biotechnol. Bioeng.* 2005, 91, 114-123.

Kusvuran, E.; Samil, A.; Atanur, O.M. ; Erbatur, O. *Appl. Catal. B.* 2005, 58, 211-216.

Lee, S.K.; Mills, A. J. *Ind. Eng. Chem.* 2004, 10, 173-187.

Li, L.; Zhang, P.; Zhu, W.; Han, W.; Zhang, Z. *J. Photochem. Photobiol.* A. 2005, 171, 145-151.

Linsebigler, L.; Lu, G.; Yates Jr, J.T. *Chem. Rev.* 1995, 95, 735-758.

Martinez, A.B.; Barbot, E.; Marrot, B.; Moulin, P.; Roche, N. J. *Membrane. Sci.* 2006, 281, 288-296.

Matthews, R.W. *Pure Appl. Chem.* 1992, 64, 1285-1290.

Matthews, R.W.; McEvoy, S.R. J. *Photochem. Photobiol. A.* 1992, 66, 355-366.

McFarlane, S.; Nilsen, E. Report -2003-10: On Tap - Urban Water Issues in Canada. *Canada West Foundation (CWF), Calgary, AB*, 2003, 1-14.

Mills, A.; Davies, R.H.; Worsley, D. *Chem. Soc. Rev.* 1993, 22, 417-425.

Myers, R.H.; Montogomery, D.C. Response surface methodology: Process and product optimization using designed experiment (second ed.); *John Wiley and Sons: New York, NY*, 2002, 343-350.

Ollis, D.F.; Pelezzetti, E.; Serpone, N. *Environ. Sci. Technol.* 1991, 25, 1522-1529.

Pera-Titus, M.; García Molina, V.; Baños, M.A.; Giméneza, J.; Esplugas, S. *Appl. Catal. B.* 2004, 47, 219-256.

Rajeshwar, K. J. *Appl. Electrochem.* 1995, 25, 1067-1082.

Ray, S. Developing an efficient nanocatalyst system for photocatalytic degradation of toxic aqueous contaminants. PhD Dissertation. University of Windsor, Windsor, ON, 2010, 1-90.

Ray, S. *Ind. Tex. Jour.* 2006, 117, 24-30.

Ray, S.; Lalman, J.A. Proc. AIChE Spring Meeting 2010, Mar. 21-25, San Antonio, TX. Paper 176710.

Ray, S.; Lalman, J.A.; Biswas, N. *Chem. Eng. J.* 2009, 150, 15- 24.

Ray, S.; Lalman, J.A.; Biswas, N. Proc. AIChE Annual Meeting. 2007, Nov. 4-7, Salt Lake City, UT. Paper 93215.

Redhe, M.; Forsberg, J.; Jansson, T.; Marklund, P-O.; Nilsson, L. *Struct. Multidisc. Optim.* 2002, 24, 185-194.

Safe, S. *Toxicology* 2004, 205, 3-10.

Sakkas, V.A.; Islam, M.A.; Stalikas, C.; Albanis, T.A. J. *Haz. Mat.* 2010, 175, 33-44.

Schindler, D.W. *Can. J. Fish. Aquat. Sci.* 2001, 58, 18-29.

Shah, S.I.; Li, W.; Huang, C.-P.; Jung, O.; Ni, C. *Proc. Natl. Acad. Sci. USA.* 2002, 99 (Suppl. 2): 6482-6486.

Smith, J.E.; Renner, R.C.; Hegg, B.A.; Bender, J.H. Technologies for Upgrading Existing or Designing New Drinking Water Treatment Facilities; *Noyes Data Corp. Park Ridge, NJ,* 1991, 3-158.

Titterington, D.M. *Biometrika* 1975, 62, 313-320.

Tsai, S.-J.; Cheng, S. *Catal. Today.* 1997, 33, 227-237.

United Nations Educational, Scientific and Cultural Organization (UNESCO), The 2nd UN World Water Development Report: Water, a shared responsibility; *Berghahn Books, New York, NY*, 2006, 6-40.

United States Environmental Protection Agency (USEPA). Removal of Endocrine Disruptor Chemicals Using Drinking Water Treatment Processes, EPA/625/R-00/015; *USEPA Office of Research and Development, Cincinnati, OH*, 2001, 1-27.

Westerhoff, P. *Southwest Hydrol.* 2003, 2, 18-19.

In: Water Production and Wastewater Treatment
Editor: B. Antizar-Ladislao et al.

ISBN 978-1-61728-503-5
© 2011 Nova Science Publishers, Inc.

Chapter 11

KINETIC AND REACTOR MODELING FOR THE DEGRADATION OF PHENOL IN WATER BY UV/H$_2$O$_2$

Masroor Mohajerani, Mehrab Mehrvar and Farhad Ein-Mozaffari

Department of Chemical Engineering, Ryerson University, 350 Victoria street,
Toronto, Ontario ,Canada, M5B 2K3

ABSTRACT

A dynamic kinetic model for the phenol degradation by the hydrogen peroxide and ultraviolet irradiation processes (UV/H$_2$O$_2$) as an advanced oxidation technology (AOT) in a single lamp tubular photoreactor as well as a multilamp tubular photoreactor is provided. The model contains main chemical and photochemical reactions in the medium flowing in laminar regime. An optimal concentration of 5,000 mgL^{-1} for hydrogen peroxide was predicted. The velocity field in the laminar flow is determined by Navier-Stokes equation using the finite element method. The model is validated with distilled water. The validation of the model is based on the experimental data reported in the open literature. The local volumetric rates of energy absorption and phenol concentration profiles inside the photoreactors are shown. The synergetic effect due to the presence of four UV lamps in a multilamp photoreactor for the phenol degradation was found to be 60%.

NOMENCLATURE

A	local volumetric rate of energy absorption (*Einstein $m^{-3}s^{-1}$*)
C_i	concentration of component i (*M*)
C_o	inlet concentration (*M*)
D	diffusivity (*m^2s^{-1}*)
f_i	fraction of photons absorbed by species i (-)
P	pressure (*pa*)
Q	volumetric flow rate (*m^3s^{-1}*)

q_o	radiant energy flux on the sleeve wall *(Einstein $m^{-2}s^{-1}$)*
q	radiant energy flux (*Einstein $m^{-2}s^{-1}$*)
r	position on *r*-axis for single lamp photoreactor (*m*)
R	photoreactor radius (*m*)
Re	Reynolds number
R_i	quartz sleeve radius (*m*)
$R_{rxn,i}$	rate of reaction of component i (*Ms^{-1}*)
S	surface area perpendicular to axial flow direction (*m^2*)
t	time (*s*)
$\overline{V}$	inlet velocity (*ms^{-1}*)
V	velocity (*ms^{-1}*)
v_r	radial velocity (*ms^{-1}*)
v_θ	tangential velocity (*ms^{-1}*)
v_z	axial velocity (*ms^{-1}*)
z	position on *z*-axis for single lamp photoreactor (*m*)

Greek Letters

ρ	density (*kgm^{-3}*)
μ	dynamic viscosity (*$kgm^{-1}s^{-1}$*)
θ	position on *θ*-axis for single lamp photoreactor (*m*)
ϕ	quantum yield (*mol.$Einstein^{-1}$*)
ε_i	molar absorptivity of component i (*M^{-1}*)
μ_w	extinction coefficient of water (*m^{-1}*)
μ_s	extinction coefficient of solution (*m^{-1}*)

Acronym

AOP	Advanced Oxidation Process
AOT	Advanced Oxidation Technology
CFD	Computational Fluid Dynamics
CFM	Computational Flow Modeling
FEM	Finite Element Method
LVREA	Local Volumetric Rate of Energy Absorption

1. INTRODUCTION

The presence of toxic and recalcitrant compounds in water supplies and the effluents of wastewater treatment plants is a topic of global attention. Various conventional and traditional treatment methods have their own inabilities to destruct organic compounds. Advanced oxidation processes (AOPs) are related to the generation of highly oxidizing agents (i.e., hydroxyl radicals) which result in the decolorization, detoxification, degradation, and biodegradability enhancement of the toxic, inhibitory, and biorecalcitrant wastewaters (Mohajerani et al., 2009, 2010a; Mehrvar et al., 2000, 2001).

Advanced oxidation technologies (AOTs) such as photocatalysis, Fenton and photo-Fenton processes, radiolysis, and ultrasonolysis are useful to enhance the generation of hydroxyl radicals (Mohajerani et al., 2010b). Despite the potential of AOTs, the development of an industrial scale wastewater treatment system has not been successfully accomplished yet due to the high capital and operating costs. These processes can be employed for contaminated groundwater, surface water, and wastewaters containing organic compounds with low biodegradability as well as for the purification and disinfection of drinking water. Advanced oxidation processes are those groups of technologies that lead to the generation of hydroxyl radicals ($^{\bullet}OH$) as the primary oxidant (second highest powerful oxidant after the fluorine). These radicals are produced by means of oxidizing agents such as H_2O_2 and O_3, ultraviolet irradiation, ultrasound, and homogeneous or heterogeneous catalysts. Today, most studies focus on finding better methods of $^{\bullet}OH$ production. Hydroxyl radicals are non-selective in nature and can react without any other additives with a wide variety of contaminants whose rate constants are usually in the order of 10^6 to 10^9 $M^{-1}s^{-1}$ (Ball et al., 1997; Kang and Hoffmann, 1998). These hydroxyl radicals attack organic molecules by either abstracting a hydrogen atom or adding a hydrogen atom to the double bonds. The products of the oxidation are new intermediates with lower molecular weights or carbon dioxide and water in the case of complete mineralization (Tabrizi and Mehrvar, 2006). A full understanding of kinetics and mechanisms of all chemical and photochemical reactions under the operating condition is necessary, by which, based on the well understood mechanisms, optimal condition could be obtained.

Among the AOPs, UV/H_2O_2 process has shown a better efficiency in organic degradation and facility in operation. Ultraviolet light and hydrogen peroxide are combined in an effective synergy to mineralize organic chemicals in aqueous solutions. These hydroxyl radicals are produced when the water containing H_2O_2 exposed to UV light. The generation of hydroxyl radicals by decomposition of hydrogen peroxide was first observed by Hoigné and Bader (1976). Nowadays, due to its advantages, UV/H_2O_2 has gained researchers' interest (Johnson and Mehrvar, 2008; Mohajerani et al., 2010a). UV/H_2O_2 is effective in oxidizing a wide range of organic compounds such as dye and textile (Aye et al., 2003, 2004), pesticides and herbicides (Glaze et al., 1995; Alfano et al., 2001; Benitez et al., 2004; Shemer and Linden, 2006), and pharmaceuticals (Shemer et al., 2006). The mathematical modeling of UV/H_2O_2 process helps to predict the treatment of polluted sources of drinking water and industrial effluents in a practical scale. Different studies on the kinetic modeling of the degradation of organic compounds by UV/H_2O_2 process have been conducted (Song et al., 2008; Crittenden et al., 1999; Edalatmanesh et al., 2008; Mohajerani et al., 2010a). Kinetic modeling of advanced oxidation technologies is a useful tool for studying the process parameters. The effect of different factors on the process efficiency such as initial organic concentration, residence time, H_2O_2 concentration, flow rate, and alkalinity concentrations could be investigated through the modeling without carrying out costly experiments. Defined flow models also help to design and scale up the industrial size photoreactors (Zhao et al., 2008).

Phenol is extensively found in many industrial wastewater streams such as coal conversion, resins, coatings, plastics, textiles, pulp and paper plants, and oil refineries. These compounds are released in the surface water that results in environmental hazard. The conventional biological wastewater treatment processes fail to completely destruct phenol because it is refractory to microorganisms. As a result, new powerful advanced wastewater treatment methods are required to degrade such compounds. Wastewater containing phenol even in low concentration is toxic and cannot be directly discharged into sewage systems. It is toxic to fish at a 1-2 mgL^{-1} concentration level (Araña et al., 2001). Phenol is used as a model component in wastewater treatment studies. The oxidative destruction of phenol and other organic pollutants in aqueous solutions has been investigated by several studies such as Fenton's reagent (Azevedo et al., 2004), Fenton-like process (Bremner et al., 2006), photo-Fenton (Maciel et al., 2004), ozonation (Utsumi et al. 1998), UV/H_2O_2 (Edalatmanesh et al., 2008), heterogeneous photocatalysis (Mehrvar et al., 2000, 2001; Wang et al., 2005), catalytic wet air oxidation (Santos et al., 2005), and electro-Fenton (Pimentel et al., 2008) processes.

In this chapter, a free radical and molecular model is proposed to predict the behavior of the oxidation of phenol by using UV/H_2O_2 process in single and multilamp photoreactors. Moreover, the modeling of the UV/H_2O_2 process is performed by the aid of computational fluid dynamics (CFD), in which the momentum, radiation energy, and mass balances for each component are considered. The UV lamp spectrum falls within the range of 400-600 nm which is very effective for photochemical reactions but it does not show thermal effects; thus, thermal effects of photochemical reactions are normally negligible.

2. GEOMETRY OF PHOTOREACTORS

The schematic diagram of the two photoreactors used in this study are shown in Figure 1, (a) for the single lamp photoreactor and (b) for multilamp photoreactor. The single lamp photoreactor is composed of two concentric cylinders with annulus laminar flow. Inner cylinder is a quart sleeve with the radius R_i in which a UV lamp is inserted. Two equal sized UV lamps in series with 1.2 m length are equal to a photoreactor length of 2.4 m, therefore, there is no dark zone in the photoreactors. The multilamp photoreactor is also composed of a cylinder containing four equal sized parallel UV lamps so that each of them is located in the quarter of the reactor radius with the same characteristics of the single lamp photoreactor. The photoreactor radius is R. The physical properties and operating conditions of the processes are provided in Table 1. Cylindrical coordinates were used for the modeling of the photoreactors. For the modeling purpose, various H_2O_2 concentrations from 25 to 10,000 mgL^{-1} have been chosen. The main assumptions for the flow modeling are isothermal reaction at 25°C, steady state, and laminar flow. Also, physical properties of water are assumed.

The photoreaction modeling was carried out by momentum and mass balances exist in the Chemical Engineering Module of COMSOL Multiphysics (Version 3.5). The momentum balance has been solved by the use of the Navier-Stokes equation in COMSOL.

3. MOMENTUM BALANCE

Momentum balance was developed in laminar flow regime. The continuity equation and momentum balances at steady state for an incompressible fluid are developed by following equations (Bird et al., 2002):

$$\nabla \cdot V = 0 \tag{1}$$

$$\rho V \cdot \nabla V = -\nabla P + \nabla \cdot \mu \left(\nabla V + (\nabla V)^T \right) + F \tag{2}$$

where ρ, V, P, μ, and F represent the density, velocity, pressure, dynamic viscosity, and the external force on the control volume, respectively.

Boundary conditions for momentum balance are as follows:

1. Inlet of the photoreactor: the velocity of inflow is specified by dividing the volumetric flow rate by the surface area $(\bar{V} = Q/S)$.

2. Outlet of the photoreactor: a normal flow is assumed so that the output pressure is atmospheric.

3. Walls of the photoreactor: no slip boundary condition was assumed for the photoreactors and all the lamps' walls.

Table 2. Characteristics and operating conditions of the photoreactors

Parameter	Single lamp photoreactor	Multilamp photoreactor
	Photoreactors in series	
Number	2	2
Overall length (m)	2.4	2.4
Radius (mm)	200	200
	UV lamps	
Number	2 × 1	2 × 4
Type	Low pressure	Low pressure
Nominal length of each photoreactor (m)	1.2	1.2
Nominal radius (R_t) (mm)	13	8.5
Input current (amps)	0.84	1.2
Input watts (W)	75	120
UV Output (W)	25.5	36
	Quartz Sleeve	
Outer radius (R_j) (mm)	17	17
	Operating conditions	
Wastewater volumetric flow rate Ls^{-1}	0.1	0.1
Re	237.4	293.5
[phenol]$_o$ (mM)	2.23	2.23
[H$_2$O$_2$]$_o$ (mgL^{-1})	25-10,000	25-10,000

At steady state condition, the simultaneous solution of Equations (1) and (2) as well as applying boundary conditions give various flow characteristics such as velocity distribution and the minimum and maximum velocities. The details are discussed in Section "Results and Discussion".

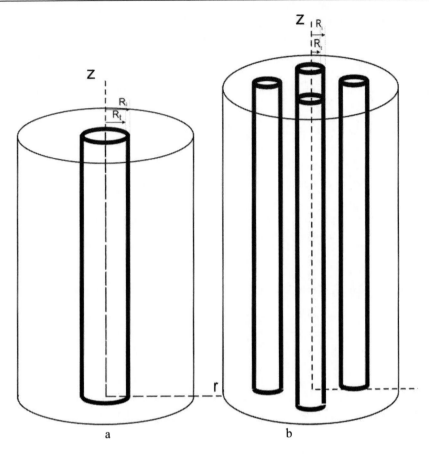

Figure 1. Schematic diagram of the photoreactors a) single lamp photoreactor b) multilamp photoreactor.

3.1.Computational Fluid Dynamics (CFD) Modeling

The 3-D flow field in the single lamp and multilamp photoreactors was simulated using commercial CFD package (COMSOL Multiphysics V3.5). CFD codes and packages have been used to predict internal and external flows in the past decades. The necessity of employing CFD packages for chemical engineering applications is also obvious. COMSOL Multiphysics is a type of CFD package based on finite element method (FEM) which is useful for computational flow modeling (CFM). The momentum and mass conservation equations in the laminar regime were solved using the finite element method (FEM). The division of the photoreactors' domain into discrete elements is the first stage (grid generation) where the number of grids per volume (cells density) is required to be fine enough to capture the flow details. Due to the boundary layer formation around lamps and photoreactor walls, it is essential to increase the number of grids around lamps and photoreactor walls. The number of grids employed for the discretization was specified by conducting a grid independence study. The grid independence was carried out by comparing the changes in velocity along the photoreactor by cell density increment. The additional cells did not change the calculated velocity and kinetic energy rate by more than 1 and 5%, respectively. The final 3-D mesh of the model had 7,442 and 14,376 elements for single lamp and multilamp photoreactors, respectively.

4. MASS BALANCE

The mass balance or continuity equation for each compound in the system should be solved simultaneously to find the concentration profile of each compound inside the photoreactor. At steady state, the general continuity equation for each compound in cylindrical coordinates could be written as follows (Bird *et al.*, 2002):

$$v_r \frac{\partial C_i}{\partial r} + v_\theta \frac{1}{r} \frac{\partial C_i}{\partial \theta} + v_z \frac{\partial C_i}{\partial z} = D \left(\frac{1}{r} \frac{\partial}{\partial r} \left(r \frac{\partial C_i}{\partial r} \right) + \frac{1}{r^2} \frac{\partial^2 C_i}{\partial \theta^2} + \frac{\partial^2 C_i}{\partial z^2} \right) + R_{rxn,i} \tag{3}$$

where D is the diffusivity of species i in the mixture ($m^2 s^{-1}$) and v_z, v_r, and v_θ are the axial, radial, and tangential velocities (ms^{-1}), respectively. C_i and $R_{rxn,i}$ are the concentration (M) and the rate of the reaction (Ms^{-1}) for component i, respectively. Equation (3) is general mass transport equation for laminar flow. Assumptions for solving mass balances are steady state flow and impermeable wall. Considering the small ratio of the diameter to the length of the photoreactors, radial and tangential velocities are assumed to be zero. Axial diffusion is neglected with respect to the axial convective flux. The tangential diffusion is also neglected due to symmetry.

The three boundary conditions are provided as follows:

- Inlet ($z=0$): the influent phenol concentration is specified ($C_o=2.23\ mM$);
- Lamps' wall ($r=R_i$): the concentration gradient on the quartz sleeve wall is zero because the diffusion of phenol in quartz sleeve is basically zero; and
- Photoreactor wall ($r=R$): the mole flux and consequently the concentration gradient on the reactor wall are also zero.

Based on the above mentioned assumptions, the governing mass balance equation can be written as follows:

$$v_z \frac{\partial C_i}{\partial z} = D \left(\frac{1}{r} \frac{\partial}{\partial r} \left(r \frac{\partial C_i}{\partial r} \right) \right) + R_{rxn,i} \tag{4}$$

5. REACTION MECHANISMS

The main photochemical reactions R1 and R2 (Baxendale and Wilson, 1957; Alnaizy and Akgerman, 2000) and chemical reactions R3 to R7 (Christensen *et al.*, 1982; Buxton *et al.*, 1988; Bielsky *et al.*, 1985; Schested *et al.*, 1968) in the system are provided as follows (phenol is shown by *RH*):

$$H_2O_2 + hv \xrightarrow{\phi_1} 2^{\bullet}OH \qquad (\phi_1 = 0.5 \text{ mol Einstein}^{-1}) \tag{R1}$$

$$RH + hv \xrightarrow{\phi_2} intermediates \longrightarrow CO_2 + H_2O \ (\phi_2 = 0.12 \text{ mol Einstein}^{-1}) \tag{R2}$$

where ϕ is the quantum yield, the fraction of the absorbed radiation consumed by the photolytic decomposition reaction. In other words, quantum yield is the number of moles of the irradiated substance decomposed per mole of photons absorbed (*Einstein*).

$$H_2O_2 + {}^{\bullet}OH \xrightarrow{k_1} HO_2^{\bullet} + H_2O \ (k_1 = (1.4 - 4.5) \times 10^7 \ M^{-1}s^{-1}) \tag{R3}$$

$$2^{\bullet}OH \xrightarrow{k_2} H_2O_2 \qquad (k_2 = (5.0 - 8.0) \times 10^9 \ M^{-1}s^{-1}) \tag{R4}$$

$$2HO_2^{\bullet} \xrightarrow{k_3} H_2O_2 + O_2 \ (k_3 = (0.8 - 2.2) \times 10^6 \ M^{-1}s^{-1}) \tag{R5}$$

$$HO_2^{\bullet} + {}^{\bullet}OH \xrightarrow{k_4} H_2O + O_2 \ (k_4 = 6.6 \times 10^9 \ M^{-1}s^{-1}) \tag{R6}$$

$$RH + {}^{\bullet}OH \xrightarrow{k_5} intermediates \longrightarrow CO_2 + H_2O \qquad (k_5 = 6.8 \times 10^9 \ M^{-1}s^{-1}) \tag{R7}$$

6. PHOTON (IRRADIATION) BALANCE

The radiant energy distribution is not uniform inside the photoreactor due to several reasons. Among them, the extinction coefficient produced by the species absorption is always present. The photon balance must be coupled with momentum and mass balances in the modeling of photoreactors. For the mathematical modeling of the photoreactors, the local volumetric rate of energy absorption (LVREA), the local rate of absorbed radiation per unit time and unit volume, must be estimated. The rate of organic degradation by direct photolysis is proportional to the LVREA. The LVREA is a function of the spatial variables of the concentration of the absorbing species and other physio-chemical parameters. The LVREA is not uniform inside the photoreactors due to the light attenuation caused by the species absorption; thus, LVREA depends on the radiation field exist in the photoreactor. The fraction of the incident light absorbed by the specific compound (f_i) is as follows (Jacob and Dranoff, 1966):

$$f_i = \frac{\varepsilon_i C_i}{\sum\limits_{i=1}^{n} \varepsilon_i C_i} \tag{5}$$

where ε_i and C_i are the molar absorptivity $(m^{-1}M^{-1})$ and the concentration of species i (M), respectively. The radiation balance for a single lamp UV photoreactor can be written as follows (Jacob and Dranoff, 1966):

$$\frac{1}{r}\frac{d(rq)}{dr} = -q(2.303\mu_s)$$

(6)

where q is the radiant energy flux $(Einstein.m^{-2}s^{-1})$ and μ_s is the extinction coefficient (m^{-1}) of the solution. The latter parameter could be defined as follows:

$$\mu_s = \mu_w + \sum_{i=1}^{n}\varepsilon_i C_i$$

(7)

where μ_w is the pure water extinction coefficient $(0.7\ m^{-1})$. The integration of the irradiation governing Equation (6) gives:

$$q = q_0\frac{R_i}{r}\exp(\mu_s(r-R_i))$$

(8)

where q_o is the radiant energy flux on the sleeve wall before any attenuation $(Einstein.m^{-2}s^{-1})$ and R_i is the inner reactor radius (m).

LVREA (A) is the product of μ_s and q; thus, the LVREA expression is:

$$A = \mu_s q_0 e^{-2.303\mu_s(r-R_i)}$$

(9)

Based on the mechanism of UV/H_2O_2 (Reactions R1 to R7), the reaction rates of different species exist in the system could be developed as follows:

$$R_{RH} = -k_5[RH][{}^{\bullet}OH] - \phi_2 f_{RH} A$$

(10)

$$R_{H_2O_2} = -\phi_1 f_{H_2O_2} A - k_1[H_2O_2][{}^{\bullet}OH] + k_2[{}^{\bullet}OH]^2 + k_3[HO_2^{\bullet}]^2$$

(11)

$$R_{{}^{\bullet}OH} = 2\phi_1 f_{H_2O_2} A - k_1[H_2O_2][{}^{\bullet}OH] - k_2[{}^{\bullet}OH]^2 - k_4[{}^{\bullet}OH][HO_2^{\bullet}] - k_5[RH][{}^{\bullet}OH]$$

(12)

$$R_{HO_2^{\bullet}} = k_1[H_2O_2][{}^{\bullet}OH] - k_3[HO_2^{\bullet}]^2 - k_4[HO_2^{\bullet}][{}^{\bullet}OH]$$

(13)

7. RESULTS AND DISCUSSION

Figure 2 illustrates the velocity profile of the center slice of the photoreactors (on xz plane). It is clear from Figure 2 that the velocity profile in the single lamp photoreactor is more uniform compared to that of the multilamp photoreactor. Figure 3 depicts the dimensionless velocity (velocity divided by the average velocity) profile in the outlet of the single and multilamp photoreactors. It is clear from Figure 3 that by increasing the number of lamps, the maximum velocity increases so that velocity distribution in the single lamp photoreactor is more uniform. In the multilamp photoreactor, the maximum velocity is observed at the center of the photoreactor which has the lowest residence time. Local volumetric rate of energy absorption (LVREA) is higher at the center of the multilamp photoreactor due to the light intensity fluxes of the four UV lamps.

The phenol degradation in single lamp and multilamp photoreactors by UV/H_2O_2 was modeled based on the published experimental data (Alnaizy and Akgerman, 2000).

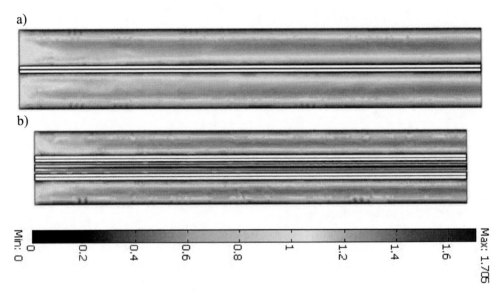

Figure 2. Dimensionless velocity profile in the axial cross section of the photoreactors a) Single lamp photoreactor b) multilamp photoreactor.

In the first step of the model, the reaction rate constant between phenol and hydroxyl radicals was specified by trial and error. The comparison of experimental results with the simulation run was carried out to obtain a reasonable error between experimental results and the predicted model. Therefore, k_5 was specified to be $6.8 \times 10^9\ M^{-1}s^{-1}$, which was in the expected range of 1.0×10^9 to $10 \times 10^9\ M^{-1}s^{-1}$ (Beltran et al., 1999). The developed model in this study was also validated by Alnaizy and Akgerman's (2000) experimental results. Figure 4 depicts that the developed model in the present study was able to predict the phenol degradation rate for two different molar concentration ratios of influent H_2O_2/phenol (288 and 495). The residuals between the predicted model and the experimental results were sketched (not shown) for the difference between the predicted dynamic model and the experimental data, where there was no trend among the data and a good random gun-shot pattern was observed, confirming a good agreement between the model and the experimental results, with less than 5% error.

Figure 5 illustrates the effect of inlet hydrogen peroxide concentration on the phenol degradation. This figure shows that the optimal inlet hydrogen peroxide concentration is 5,000 mgL^{-1}. For higher hydrogen peroxide concentrations, excess molecules react with hydroxyl radicals and acts as hydroxyl radical scavengers and results in a lower degradation rate and efficiency.

The modeling of the photoreactor requires the evaluation of local volumetric rate of energy absorption (LVREA). The LVREA is a function of radiant energy flux and extinction coefficient and can be evaluated by Equation (9). Figure 6 shows the distribution of the axial LVREA inside the single and multilamp photoreactors.

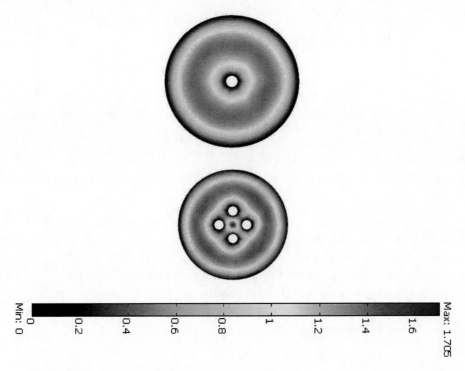

Figure 3. Dimensionless velocity profile in the radial cross section of the photoreactors a) single lamp photoreactor b) multilamp photoreactor.

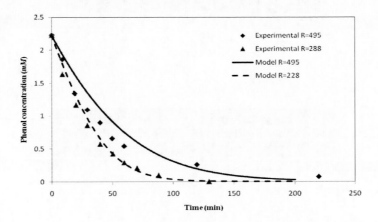

Figure 4. Phenol concentration by developed model and the experimental data from literature (Alnaizy and Akgerman, 2000). R is the molar concentration ratio of influent H_2O_2/phenol.

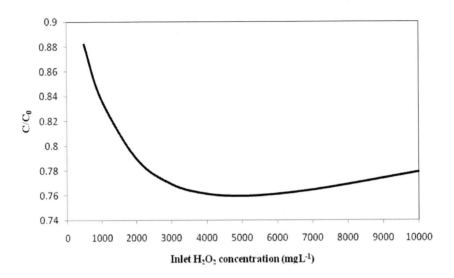

Figure 5. Optimal H_2O_2 for phenol removal in the photoreactor (5,000 mgL^{-1} H_2O_2 performs a greater phenol reduction).

As shown in Figure 6, the LVREA is drastically decreased near the UV lamps. The multilamp photoreactor provide higher LVREA than that of the single lamp photoreactor (almost four times greater than that of the single lamp photoreactor). Figure 7 provides the radial LVREA profile in the single and multilamp photoreactors. The presence of four UV lamps inside the photoreactor provides the synergetic effect. The summation of LVREA of these UV lamps results in the enhancement of the photolytic degradation of organic compounds in the reaction medium.

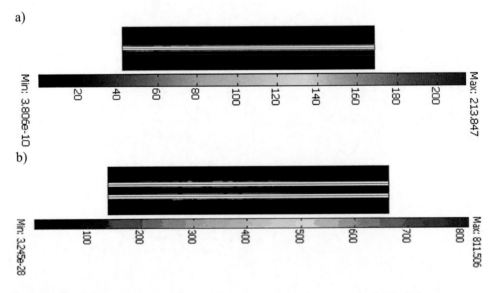

Figure 6. LVREA distribution in the axial cross section of the photoreactors a) Single lamp photoreactor b) multilamp photoreactor.

Mohajerani, M.; Mehrvar, M.; Ein-Mozaffari, F. An overview of the integration of advanced oxidation technologies and other processes for water and wastewater treatment. *International Journal of Engineering,* 2009, 3, 120-147.

Mohajerani, M.; Mehrvar, M.; Ein-Mozaffari, F. CFD modeling of metronidazole degradation in water by UV/H_2O_2 process in single and multilamp photoreactors. *Industrial and Engineering Chemistry Research*, 2010a, 49, 5367-5382.

Mohajerani, M.; Mehrvar, M.; Ein-Mozaffari, F. Recent achievements in combination of ultrasonolysis and other advanced oxidation processes for wastewater treatment. *International Journal of Chemical Reactor Engineering*, 2010b, 8, 1-78.

Pimentel, M.; Oturan, N.; Dezotti, M.; Oturan, M.A. Phenol degradation by advanced electrochemical oxidation process electro-Fenton using a carbon felt cathode. *Applied catalysis B: Environmental*, 2008, 83, 140-149.

Santos, A.; Yustos, P.; Cordero, T.; Gomis, S.; Rodríguez, S.; García-Ochoa, F. Catalytic wet oxidation of phenol on active carbon: Stability, phenol conversion and mineralization. *Catalysis Today,* 2005, 102-103, 213-218.

Schested, K.; Rasmussen, O.L.; Fricke, H. Rate constants of OH with HO_2, O_2^-, and $H_2O_2^+$ from hydrogen peroxide formation in pulse-irradiated oxygenated water. *Journal of Physical Chemistry,* 1968, 72, 626-631.

Shemer, H.; Linden, K.G. Degradation and by-product formation of diazinon in water during UV and UV/H_2O_2 treatment. *Journal of Hazardous Materials,* 2006, 136, 553-559.

Shemer, H.; Kunukcu, Y.K.; Linden, K.G. Degradation of the pharmaceutical Metronidazole via UV, Fenton and photo-Fenton processes. *Chemosphere*, 2006, 63, 269-276.

Song, W.; Ravindran, V.; Pirbazari, M. Process optimization using a kinetic model for the ultraviolet radiation-hydrogen peroxide decomposition of natural and synthetic organic compounds in groundwater. *Chemical Engineering Science,* 2008, 63, 3249-3270.

Tabrizi, G.B.; Mehrvar, M. Pilot-plant study for the photochemical treatment of aqueous linear alkylbenzene sulfonate. *Separation and Purification Technology,* 2006, 49, 115-121.

Utsumi, H.; Han, S.-K.; Ichikawa, K. Enhancement of hydroxyl radical generation by phenols and their reaction intermediates during ozonation. *Water science and technology*, 1998, 38, 147-154.

Wang, W.; Serp, P.; Kalck, P.; Faria, J.L. Visible light photodegradation of phenol on MWNT-TiO2 composite catalysts prepared by a modified sol-gel method. *Journal of Molecular Catalysis A: Chemical*, 2005, 235, 194-199.

Zhao, Z.F.; Mehrvar, M.; Ein-Mozaffari, F. Mixing study in an agitated multi-lamp cylindrical photoreactor using electrical resistance tomography. *Journal of Chemical Technology and Biotechnology*, 2008, 83, 1676-1688.

In: Water Production and Wastewater Treatment   ISBN 978-1-61728-503-5
Editor: B. Antizar-Ladislao et al.   © 2011 Nova Science Publishers, Inc.

Chapter 12

STATISTICAL OPTIMIZATION OF REACTIVE BLUE 221 DECOLORIZATION BY FUNGAL PEROXIDISE

Hamid-Reza Kariminia[1] and Vajihe Yousefi

School of Chemical and Petroleum Engineering, Sharif University of Technology,
P.O. Box 11155-9465, Azadi Ave., Tehran, Iran

ABSTRACT

The conventional one-factor-at-a-time (OFAT) method and two statistical methods including factorial design and response surface methodology (RSM) were applied for optimization of reactive blue 221 (RB221) decolorization using *Coprinus cinereus* peroxidase (CIP). Through the OFAT analysis the optimal conditions was at the temperature of 22 °C, pH 9.0, H_2O_2 concentration of about 4.258 mM and initial dye concentration of 80 ppm for the 100% decolorization of RB221 in only 30 seconds. In the statistical analysis, factorial design method was primarily applied for screening the most significant parameters on RB221 decolorization. Then two stage optimization using RSM was performed through central composite design (CCD). Finally, a reduced cubic model with a good fit of regression equation ($R^2=0.9943$, Adj.$R^2=0.9916$) and not significant lack of fit (*P*-value=0.94) was generated. ANOVA analysis indicated that the hydrogen peroxide concentration was the most significant parameter on decolorization of RB221. The optimum conditions through RSM were the hydrogen peroxide concentration of around 7.5 mM, and pH values between 5.5 and 7.5. Higher activity of CIP improved the decolorization in all conditions.

INTRODUCTION

Reactive dyes contain chromophoric groups such as azo, anthraquinone, triarylmethane and reactive groups e.g. vinyl sulphone, chlorotriazine, trichloropyrimidine that form covalent bonds with the fiber [Sumathi and Manju, 2000]. Most of these dyes are toxic, potentially carcinogenic and their removal from industrial effluents is a major environmental problem

---

[1] Corresponding author. Tel: +98 21 66166426; fax: +98 21 66022853.E-mail address: kariminia@sharif.ir.

[Reife *et al.*, 1995]. Recently, enzymatic approach has attracted much interest in decolorization of synthetic dyes as an alternative strategy to the conventional physical and chemical methods as well as microbial treatments that pose some serious limitations [Husain, 2006]. In this study, we tried to find out the optimal conditions for removal of reactive blue 221 using crude *Coprinus cinereus* peroxidase (CIP) enzyme. The optimization was conducted through conventional one-factor-at-a-time (OFAT) method as well as statistical approach. The response surface methodology (RSM) is a collection of mathematical and statistical techniques useful for developing, improving and optimizing processes and can be used to evaluate the relative significance of several affecting factors even in the presence of complex interactions [Montgomery, 1991]. This methodology has been successfully applied in optimization of decolorization by fungal cultures [Karacan *et al.*, 2007; Nagarajan and Prasad, 2008; Sharma *et al.*, 2008; Trupkin *et al.*, 2003] as well as enzymatic decolorization using LiP [Alam *et al.*, 2009], MnP [Li *et al.*, 2009] and Laccase [Murugesan *et al.*, 2007]. However, to the best of our knowledge this is the first research on decolorization of a reactive dye using CIP that encompasses the combined effect of operational parameters on optimum decolorization process.

MATERIALS AND METHODS

Microorganism, Chemicals and Culture Media

All chemicals used in this research were of analytical grades available commercially. The peroxidase was produced using *Coprinus cinereus* NBRC 30628, prepared from National Biological Resources Center, Japan. The fungal strain was stored on PDA slants at 4°C. The liquid medium used to cultivate *C. cinereus* for the production of peroxidase contained 30 g/l glucose, 10 g/l pepton, 5 g/l yeast extract and pH adjusted to 4. The sterilized medium (100 ml in 250 ml Erlenmeyer flasks) was inoculated using a piece (a 1 cm diameter disk) of agar block cut out from actively growing fungal culture on PDA plates. The fungi were cultured at 30°C on a rotary shaker (150 rpm). At the end of cultivation, the culture broth was filtered to remove the fungal pellets. The resulting clear solution was stored at 4 °C and used for dye decolorization experiments.

Assays

The enzyme activity was assayed under the following conditions. A reaction mixture containing 65 mM phosphate buffer (pH 7.0), 0.63 mM 4-AAP, 10 mM phenol, 3.1 mM hydrogen peroxide and 0.97 g/l Triton X-100 in a total volume of 3.1 ml was incubated at 37°C for 10 min. The reaction was then started by adding 0.1 ml of enzyme solution and the initial increase in absorbance was monitored at 500 nm for one minute. One unit of peroxidase activity was defined as the amount of the enzyme consuming 1 μmol of hydrogen peroxide per minute under the assay conditions [Sakurai *et al.*, 2001].

Concentration of the dye was measured photometrically at the maximum absorption wavelengths for reactive blue 221 (RB221) at 613 nm using a UV-Vis recording double beam spectrophotometer. The decolorization efficiency (DE) was expressed as the percentage ratio of decolorized dye concentration to that of initial one.

OFAT Optimization

Medium optimization by one-factor-at-a-time method involves changing an independent variable while fixing the others at certain levels. Selection of appropriate pH, temperature, H_2O_2 and dye concentration are crucial in the development of an efficient and economic process. Hence, these parameters were selected to be optimized by OFAT method, first.

The experiments were conducted in 100 ml glassy reactor containing 23 ml of synthetic dye solution, peroxidase and buffer, which placed in a water bath at a certain temperature. Reactor contents were stirred To evaluate the effects of operational and environmental factors on the efficiency of color removal, the batch decolorization experiments were carried out at different experimental conditions as bellows: initial dye concentration (43.475-214 ppm), hydrogen peroxide concentration (1.42-14.19 mM), temperature (22-60 °C) and pH (2.0–10.0). The pH of solutions during decolorization were adjusted using different type of buffers including 47.423 mM potassium chloride/HCl buffer (pH 2.0), 32.864 mM citrate/phosphate buffer (pH 4.0), 47.423 mM phosphate buffer (pH 6.0, 7.0, 8.0), 23.71 mM borax/boric acid buffer (pH 9.0), 20.74 mM borax/NaOH buffer (pH 10.0). Enzyme activity was fixed to 1.2 U/ml in all experiments. Table 1 indicates different experimental conditions for the OFAT optimization. All experiments were conducted in duplicate and their average values are reported.

Statistical Optimization

For statistical optimization, experiments were conducted in test tubes containing 2.5 ml dye solution, buffer and enzyme. The tubes were incubated for 10 min, in water bath at certain temperature and were periodically mixed using a tube vortex.

Table 1. Effect of different parameters on decolorization of reactive blue 221, using OFAT method

Studied parameter	Dye concentration (mg/L)	pH	H2O2 concentration (mM)	Temperature (°C)
Effect of H2O2 concentration	86.95	7.0	1.42-14.19	22 ± 1
Effect of temperature	86.95	9.0	4.258	(22-60) ± 0.5
Effect of pH	86.95	2.0-10.0	4.258	22 ± 0.5
Effect of dye concentration	43-214	9.0	4.258	22± 0.5

Table 2. Levels and actual values of independent variables examined in 2- factorial design

	Range and Levels Coded	
Factors	-1	+1
A- pH	3	10
B- Enzyme (U/ml)	0.65	38.8
C- H_2O_2 Concentration (mM)	0.5	30
D- Temperature (^{o}C)	15	50
E- Dye Concentration (mg/l)	20	200

Screening of Significant Parameters Using Two Level Factorial Design

The 2- factorial design method for five factors was primarily used for screening significant factors. This design permits the estimation of all main effects and all interaction effects. Low and high levels of factors are given in Table 2. All the experiments were performed in duplicate and their mean values are reported here. Data were analyzed using Design Expert 7.0 Stat-Ease, Inc. (trial version), including ANOVA to find out the significant factors among these variables. The buffer solutions were the same as those applied in OFAT optimization.

Optimization Using Response Surface Methodology

Optimization was performed in two steps. First, central composite design (CCD) model [Khuri and Cornell, 1987] for four variables including H_2O_2 concentration, pH, CIP activity and temperature was applied. As results of this analysis indicated that temperature did not have important effect on decolorization of RB221, another optimization was conducted for the remaining three significant parameters through CCD. All the experiments were performed in triplicates and the mean values of response (DE) were reported. The value of alpha in each case was set as rotatable.

RESULTS AND DISCUSSION

Optimization Using OFAT Methodology

Effects of H_2O_2 Concentration
The effect of H_2O_2 concentration on decolorization by crude CIP was investigated. Decolorization did not occur without the addition of H_2O_2. Approximately, in all H_2O_2 concentrations %100 decolorization was achieved, but in higher H_2O_2 concentrations decolorization took place relatively slower. This may be attributed to the inactivation of enzyme in higher concentrations of H_2O_2 [Palma *et al.,*1997]. However, this negative effect can be neglected because of very high decolorization rates.

Effect of Ph

Decolorization efficiency was increased sharply with increase of pH from 2 to 4, then became less sensitive to pH. Decolorization of RB221 by CIP occurred satisfactorily in a broad range of pH (4-10), where the best pH was 9.0. As textile wastewater is characterized by a neutral to alkaline pH (around 7–11) [Jahmeerbacus *et al.*, 2004], the CIP enzyme is supposed to be a suitable choice for treatment such alkaline wastewaters.

Effect of Temperature

Effect of temperature was examined in the range of 22 °C to 60 °C. Nearly 90% of dye was removed in initial 30 seconds. The problem of enzyme inactivation at high temperatures was not very important in decolorization of RB221 by CIP up to 60 °C. At 60 °C, minor decolorization occurred due to enzyme inactivation.

Effect of Initial Dye Concentration

Decolorization efficiency was increased quickly as initial dye concentration increased from 43.5 ppm to 87 ppm, then decreased with further increase in dye concentration.

Statistical Optimization

First Stage of Optimization: Screening of Significant Factors Using Factorial Design

Since the conventional method of optimization, OFAT' approach is laborious, time consuming and does not depict the combined effect of all the factors involved in enzymatic decolorization, statistical methods is applied. In this study, 2^4 factorial experimental design was primarily used to assess the most significant parameters. Each one of the five variables including pH (A), enzyme activity (B), H_2O_2 concentration (C), temperature (D) and dye concentration (E) received two values. A second order polynomial model that fitted to decolorization results of RB221 was obtained as shown in Eq.(1).

$$DE\ (\%) = 16.27 - 1.77 \times A - 4.25 \times B - 6.12 \times C - 2.54 \times D + 5.82 \times E + 2.66 \times A \times C + 5.09 \times A \times D - 2.34 \times A \times E + 4.89 \times B \times C - 4.78 \times B \times E + 5.46 \times C \times D - 4.90 \times C \times E \quad (1)$$

Statistical analysis indicated that the coefficients of A, B, C, AB, AC, BC, CD and DE were statistically significant. Altogether, it was observed that among five initial parameters, four factors, in order of significance include pH, H_2O_2 concentration, and enzyme activity. Temperature had no significant contribution on decolorization of RB221.

Second Stage of Optimization by Response Surface Methodology

In accordance with the results of factorial design, four variables of pH (A), enzyme activity (B), H_2O_2 concentration (C) and temperature (D) were selected for optimization using response surface methodology. Initial dye concentration in all experiments was adjusted in 100 mg/l. As many as 29 experiments were designed using four factor CCD experimental design with five replicates in central point. These experiments were performed in triplicate and their average values were reported. The significance of various models including linear, 2FI, quadratic and cubic were evaluated by ANOVA. However, the ANOVA results clearly show that temperature did not have significant effect on decolorization of RB221.

Final Optimization Using Central Composite Design

In this step of optimization, the effect of three variables including pH (A), enzyme activity (B) and H_2O_2 concentration (C) on decolorization of RB221 was investigated using central composite design. Levels of these variables are presented in Table 3. Totally 38 experiments was designed and performed in duplicate. The approximating function of decolorization was obtained in the form of Eq.(2).

$$DE\ (\%) = 98.33 - 2.43 \times A + 1.19 \times B + 6.02 \times C + 3.40 \times A \times B - 2.33 \times A \times C + 2.72 \times B \times C - 1.11 \times A^2 - 3.47 \times C^2 + 2.53 \times A \times B \times C + 2.66 \times A^2 \times B - 8.65 \times A^2 \times C \qquad (2)$$

ANOVA results of this quadratic model indicated in Table 4. The F-value of 367.27 implies that the model is significant for dye decolorization. All of the model terms are significant according to P-values. The model also revealed statistically insignificant lack of fit (P-value = 0.9427). For testing the goodness of fit of the regression equation, the determination coefficient, R^2 was evaluated. The R^2 value equal to 0.9943 advocated a high correlation between observed and predicted values. The value of the adjusted determination coefficient (Adj.R^2=0.9916) was also very high to indicate a high significance of the model. The adequate precision ratio of 81.245 indicates an adequate signal where it measures the signal to noise ratio; a ratio greater than four is desirable.

Table 3. levels of indipendant variables selected for final optimization using RSM

Factors	Range and Levels Coded				
	-1.68	-1	0	+1	+1.68
A- pH	4	5.5	7.0	8.5	10
B- Enzyme (U/ml)	0.135	5.58	13.57	21.55	27
C- H2O2 Concentration (mM)	0.1	2.11	5.05	7.99	10

Table 4. ANOVA results for final step of optimization of RB221 decolorization using RSM

Source	Sum of Squares	df	Mean Square	F-value	p-value Prob > F	
Block	0.013228	1	0.013228			
Model	1192.202	11	108.382	367.2682	< 0.0001	significant
Residual	6.78737	23	0.295103			
Lack of Fit	2.898248	15	0.193217	0.39745	0.9412	not significant
Pure Error	3.889123	8	0.48614			
Total	*1199.002*	*35*				

R2=0.9943, Adj. R2=0.9916.

Interactive Effect of H_2O_2 Concentration and pH

Figure 1 represents the effect of H_2O_2 concentration and pH on decolorization of RB221 at average enzyme activity (13.57 U/ml). The decolorization efficiency increased with hydrogen peroxide concentration up to an optimum level and decreased thereafter. This optimum level was around 5.05 mM H_2O_2 concentration at pH value of 5.22, enhanced (7.52 mM) at pH values between 6.0 and 7.5, and then decreased at higher pH values.

Interactive Effect of H_2O_2 Concentration and Enzyme Activity

The mutual effect of H_2O_2 concentration and enzyme activity on decolorization of RB221 and the 3D surface plot as well as counter plot at average pH of 7.0 are shown in Figure 2. Decolorization efficiency is more sensitive to H_2O_2 concentration than enzyme activity. In all enzyme activity, the increase in decolorization efficiency was observed for increase in H_2O_2 concentration from 0.1 mM to around 5.5 mM and then sharp decrease occurred at higher concentrations. Nevertheless, this optimum value slightly enhance with increase in enzyme activity. Approximately, at enzyme activities higher than 13.5 U/ml and hydrogen peroxide concentrations higher than 6.0, complete decolorization of RB221 would achieve.

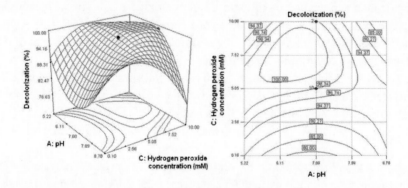

Figure 1. Left: 3D surface plot for the removal of RB221 as a function of pH and hydrogen peroxide concentration Right: Contour surface plot for removal of RB221 as a function of pH and hydrogen peroxide concentration. (at average enzyme activity of 13.57 U/ml).

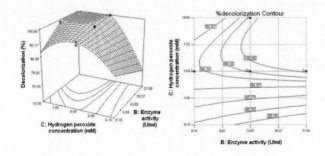

Figure 2. Left: 3D surface plot for the removal of RB221 as a function of hydrogen peroxide concentration and enzyme activity Right: Contour surface plot for removal of RB221 as a function of hydrogen peroxide concentration and enzyme activity. (at average pH value of 7.0).

CONCLUSION

Response surface methodology was effectively used for the optimization of enzymatic decolorization of reactive blue 221. After screening of significant parameters using the conventional OFAT method, RSM was applied and in average enzyme activity (13.57 U/ml), the optimum decolorization of RB221 can be achieved in H_2O_2 concentrations in the range of 6.0 mM to 9.5 mM and pH values between 5.5 and 7.5. Higher enzyme activities can improve decolorization of RB221 in all H_2O_2 concentrations and pH values.

REFERENCES

Alam, Md.Z.; Mansor, M.F.; and Jalal, K.C.A. (2009). Optimization of decolorization of methylene blue by lignin peroxidase enzyme produced from sewage sludge with *Phanerocheate chrysosporium*. J. Hazard. Mater, 162, 708-715.

Husain, Q. (2006). Potential applications of the oxidoreductive enzymes in the decolorization and detoxification of textile and other synthetic dyes from polluted water: a review. *Crit Rev. Biotechnol, 26,* 201-221.

Ikehata, K.; Buchanan, I.D.; Pickard, M.A.; and Smith, D.W. (2005). Purification, characterization and evaluation of extracellular peroxidase from two *Coprinus* species for aqueous phenol treatment. *Biores. Tech, 96,* 1758–1770.

Jahmeerbacus, M.I.; Kistamah, N.; and Ramgulam, R.B. (2004). Fuzzy control of dyebath pH in exhaust dyeing. *Coloration Technol, 120,* 51–55.

Karacan, F.; Ozden, U.; and Karacan, S. (2007). Optimization of manufacturing conditions for activated carbon from Turkish lignite by chemical activation using response surface methodology. *Appl. Therm. Eng. 27,* 1212-1218.

Khuri, A.I.; and Cornell, J.A. (1987), *Response Surface Methodology*, Marcel Dekker, New York

Li, X.; Jia, R.; Li, P.; and Ang, S. (2009). Response surface analysis for enzymatic decolorization of Congo red by manganese peroxidase, *Catal B: Enzym, 56,* 1-6.

Montgomery, D.C. (1991), *Design and Analysis of Experiments* (3rd ed.), Wiley, New York.

Murugesan, K.; Dhamija, A.; Nam, I.; Kim, Y.; and Chang Y. (2007). Decolourization of reactive black 5 by laccase: Optimization by response surface methodology. *Dyes and Pigments, 75,* 176-184.

Nagarajan, G.; and Annadurai, G. (1999). Biodegradation of reactive dye (Verofix Red) by the white rot fungus *Phanerochaete chrysosporium* using Box- Behnken experimental design. *Bioprocess Eng, 20,* 435-440.

Palma, C., M.T. Moreira, G.J. Feijoo and M. Lema (1997). Enhanced catalytic properties of MnP by exogenous addition of manganese and hydrogen peroxide. Biotechnol Lett, 19, 263–267.

Prasad, R.K. (2008). Color removal from distillery spent wash through coagulation using *Moringa oleifera* seeds: Use of optimum response surface methodology, *J. Hazard. Mater., 165,* 804-811.

Reife, A.; and Freeman, H.S.; and Freeman, H.C. (1995). *Environmental Chemistry of Dyes and Pigments*, Wiley–Interscience, USA.

Sharma, P.; Singh, L.; and Dilbaghi, N. (2008). Response surface methodological approach for the decolorization of simulated dye effluent using *Aspergillus fumigatus fresenius*. *J. Hazard. Mater, 161*, 1081-1086.

Sumathi, S.; and Manju, B.S. (2000). Uptake of reactive textile dyes by *Aspergillus foetidus*. *Enzyme Microbial Technol*, 27, 347–355.

Trupkin, S.; Levin, L.; Forchiassin F.; and Viale, A. (2003). Optimization of a culture medium for ligninolytic enzyme production and synthetic dye decolorization using response surface methodology. *J. Ind. Microbiol. Biotechnol. 30*, 682-690.

In: Water Production and Wastewater Treatment   ISBN 978-1-61728-503-5
Editor: B. Antizar-Ladislao et al.   © 2011 Nova Science Publishers, Inc.

Chapter 13

ARSENIC CONTAMINATION IN GROUNDWATER IN LATIN AMERICA: THE CHALLENGE OF PROVIDING SAFE DRINKING WATER IN THE DEVELOPING WORLD

María Fidalgo de Cortalezzi[1,2], Fernando Yrazu[1] and Paola Sabbatini[1]

(1) Center for Environmental Engineering, Department of Chemical Engineering, Instituto Tecnológico de Buenos Aires, Av. Madero 399, Buenos Aires, Argentina
(2) CONICET, Argentina

ABSTRACT

The supply of safe drinking water has become a subject of increasing concern due to new evidence on constituent toxicity, which provides the grounds for an adjustment of regulated maximum contaminant levels to lower values. Arsenic is of particular importance, since its high toxicity requires removal levels that challenge the state of the art in both analytical and treatment methods. In addition to this, arsenic is naturally present in groundwater in many areas around the world, affecting populations with diverse economic, cultural, and educational backgrounds. Addressing this issue, a wide array of treatment options has been proposed, but very few of them have proved successful in the field. The reasons for their failure rely not so much on technical performance, but rather on user acceptance, commitment and understanding of the risks. An analysis of the current situation is presented with a focus on the Latin American region, in an attempt to elucidate the underlying causes for this unresolved problem in the developing world.

INTRODUCTION

Water is a vital resource, both for drinking or industrial applications, that has been long taken for granted. Though it can be argued that water can be indefinitely recycled and that there are large reservoirs in the world that are very unlikely to be depleted, the problem of a regular distribution across nations and water quality have risen as the new challenges. While some areas will probably observe an increase in rainfall and flooding events, others are expected to suffer severe water scarcity. Even in the same location, the unbalanced distribution of rainfalls throughout the year calls for a well-orchestrated water resource management plan to face the challenges of a changing climate [1].

Water quality is another issue of growing importance in the last decade. The availability of improved analytical techniques allowed for the detection of chemicals that even at very low concentrations could be harmful for human consumption and the environment, such as pharmaceuticals and personal care products. In addition to this, new evidence has suggested that toxic levels for some of the more traditional contaminants may be lower than initially thought, thus causing a shift in regulations to lower maximum concentrations allowed in drinking water. Therefore, there is a need for new treatment processes to achieve the removal levels required by the updated regulation.

While this goal can be relatively easy reached in developed countries, it still constitutes a huge challenge to provide safe drinking water to the developing world. Low economic resources, lack of technological information, and dispersed population are some of the difficulties observed. Many researchers have been working on developing treatment options specially tailored to overcome these obstacles, with mixed results. Political and socio-economical aspects have proved to play an important role in solving this public health issue.

In this chapter, we explore the case of arsenic contamination of drinking water, with focus on Latin America. An overview of detection and treatment options already in place will be presented, as well as other technologies still in pilot stages.

ARSENIC CONTAMINATION IN GROUNDWATER IN LATIN AMERICA

It is estimated that around 4 million people are affected by groundwater arsenic contamination in the region, mainly in the inorganic trivalent and pentavalent forms [2]. The source of this contamination is predominantly natural, stemming from the geological characteristics of the region. It occurs under natural conditions as a result of volcanic emissions, weathering reactions and biological activity. Anthropogenic factors such as mining effluents or crop pesticide runoff represent a minor but increasing proportion of the problem. The most affected countries in the region are Argentina, Chile, Mexico, Peru, and Bolivia; given a combination of the extension of land affected and population density in those sites.

Arsenic is present in central and northern Chile, naturally or derived from mining activities. An estimated 200,000 people are at risk of exposure to high concentrations in their drinking water source, between 0.2 and 0.9 ppm [3].

In the case of Mexico, the origin of phreatic contamination is the influence of the Trans-Mexican Volcanic Belt. Given the fact that 75% of the population relies on potable water extracted from the ground, the presence of arsenic in some areas represents a grave threat to public health. In fact, studies have shown that arsenic concentration levels higher than that recommended by WHO have been detected in multiple well sites across the country [4] exposing both rural and urban populations.

In Bolivia and Peru, considerable aquifer contamination results from natural causes, given the mountainous characteristics of a sizeable part of their territory. In spite of this, the actual number of people at risk is less than in the previous countries´ examples, since the hardships of living in this type of terrain result in a low population density.

Argentina probably has one of the largest areas with groundwater contamination (1 million square kilometers) with predominance of As(V), in concentrations ranging from less than 0.01 to more than 1 ppm. Its origin is mostly natural, with a probable very minor contribution from crop pesticide runoff. Due to a combination of the extension of the affected territory and the fact that its population relies mainly on groundwater sources, it is estimated that more than 2 million people are at risk. Though there has not been a comprehensive mapping of the presence of this element in groundwater in the territory, it can be said that the main affected areas are the Chaco-Pampean plains, and the North and West Andean regions. The presence of volcanic glass ash in the soil is considered to be the source of the arsenic that leaches into the aquifers [5]. The vastness of the affected territory poses a challenge for authorities, since cost-effective solutions have to be provided for a spectrum that ranges from a constellation of isolated rural populations to small cities.

ANALYTICAL METHODS FOR ARSENIC DETECTION AND QUANTIFICATION

The very high toxicity of this element implies that even extremely low concentrations in water can pose a hazard to human health. Therefore, detection methods have to be able to accurately assess concentration levels below 10 ppb, which is not a simple task [6]. Natural presence of arsenic has been observed in many remote areas, often without access to high tech analytical instrumentation. A group of field kits have been developed for arsenic detection but they still lack the accuracy and detection limits of bench-scale instruments. The accurate measurement of arsenic concentrations in remote suspected contaminated areas is still a pending task, and the development of a much-needed reliable field test kit still constitutes a very active area of research.

Groundwater contamination with arsenic is predominantly associated with its trivalent and pentavalent inorganic forms (rather than organic species), in agreement with the genesis of the compound. In general, inorganic arsenic is more easily detectable in its trivalent form, therefore most methods include a pre-reduction step in order to reduce any pentavalent forms present in the sample when assessing total arsenic content [7]. The most common pre-reductants are sodium borohydride and potassium iodide, which requires a strong acidic medium [8]; alternatives include L-cysteine and mercaptoacetic acid. In cases where it is required to differentiate between As (III) and As (V), pre-separation steps are added to the process.

Perhaps the most popular arsenic detection methods are the spectrometric ones, including atomic absorption, atomic fluorescence and graphite furnace atomic absorption spectrometry. Both atomic absorption (AAS) and atomic fluorescence spectrometry (AFS) require the generation of arsenic hydride, which is accomplished by reaction with either sodium or potassium borohydride [9] . These reducing agents can also be useful for species differentiation, since As (V) reacts with BH_4- at a lower pH than As (III). Other techniques such as HPLC can be coupled with either AAS or AFS in order to achieve a higher level of sensitivity.The presence of transition metals might cause interference when using hydride generation; this can be prevented by the use of the flow injection (FI) technique. The application of FI for atomic absorption spectrometry can yield a limit of detection of less than 0.05 ppb [10].

Graphite furnace atomic absorption spectrometry (GFAAS) is considered to be one of the most reliable techniques, and it does not require hydride generation [11]. However, this method generally requires pre-concentration of the sample.

Another very sensitive technique, although not widely used, is neutron activation analysis. This method is often used as a reference for testing new procedures, but it is impractical for routine analysis since a dedicated high-energy neutron source is required.

Electrochemical methods such as polarography, cathodic stripping voltammetry and anodic stripping voltammetry are not generally used. This is because these techniques generally suffer from sensitivity, interference or reproducibility issues [12].

Commercial on-site detection systems use colorimetric analysis based mostly on a number of chemical reaction steps, which include hydride generation. These systems are generally regarded as not very reliable, partly due to the inherent imprecision of the colorimetric methods [13].

Other types of analytical tools used for arsenic detection are the inductively coupled plasma (ICP) methods. ICP can be used in conjunction with mass spectrometry (MS) [14], which is one of the most widely used techniques, or with atomic emission spectrometry (AES) [15]. The advantage of using ICP is that in principle there is no need for sample conditioning as, for example, with atomic absorption spectrometry. However, in order to overcome sensitivity issues when analyzing samples with low concentration of arsenic, hydride generation can be coupled with ICP-MS to achieve best results. Also, in ICP the high temperature of the plasma ionises all forms of arsenic present, meaning that no distinction is made between As (III) and As (V). One way to achieve non-volatile speciation analysis is to couple HPLC and ICP-MS.

One drawback of ICP-MS is its cost and for this reason, it is not commonly found in developing countries, where atomic absorption spectroscopy is the most popular analytical method for arsenic determination.

ARSENIC AND PUBLIC HEALTH: EVOLUTION OF THE WORLD HEALTH ORGANIZATION GUIDELINES AND NATIONAL REGULATIONS FOR DRINKING WATER

The World Health Organization (WHO) publishes the document "Guidelines for Dinking Water Quality", which is periodically updated based on new studies and the analytical and technical feasibility of achieving the recommended contaminant levels. The main objective of these guidelines is the protection of human health, and thus no economic considerations are taken into account. It is important to note that WHO guidelines are recommended values and not mandatory limits. They have been used worldwide as a basis for setting national standards for public water supplies, combined with local environmental, social, economic, and cultural aspects for each country [16].

In the 1950s, WHO conducted a survey asking all member states about their water treatment plants and the quality of the drinking water produced. The outcome of this survey exposed a grim situation and an urgent need for WHO to establish drinking water standards. In 1958, WHO published the first International Standards for Drinking Water. While some countries adopted the WHO document as the legal national standards for water quality, others developed local standards based on the WHO declaration, and it soon became a widely used reference for water quality and water treatment practices.

As techniques for detecting and quantifying contaminants improved, increased knowledge on the effect on human health of various substances called for revisions and changes to the International Standards for Drinking Water in 1963 and 1971.

In 1984, the standards were replaced by the WHO Guidelines for Drinking Water Quality, stressing the idea that they do not represent imposed regulations but rather a recommendation from a public health perspective. While it was recognized that not all countries would be able to attain the specified levels, it was expected that states would develop national standards as close as possible to these guidelines.

The methodology for establishing the guideline values vary according to the type of toxicity of the contaminants. In the case of chemicals for which a threshold for toxic effects can be determined, the values were calculated based on the assumed volume of daily consumption and a tolerable intake. For carcinogens, however, no threshold can be established and the guidelines were obtained by means of a risk-based approach. The values correspond to the concentration in drinking water associated with an estimated increase in the lifetime risk of developing cancer of 10^{-6} (i.e. one additional case per 1 million people), assuming the ingestion of water containing the chemical at a concentration equal to the guideline value for 70 years. However, there are some cases in which the value obtained by these calculations results impractical, either for analytical, technological or economic reasons. In these cases, a provisional value is set at a practical level, which will be reviewed and eventually lowered as new developments overcome the initial limitations, and the corresponding risk level is informed alongside the guideline value. An example of such a compound is arsenic.

Arsenic was included in WHO standards since their first version in 1958, establishing a limit of 0.20 mg/l, above which it was thought to cause health problems. The 1963 version lowered the maximum allowable concentration of arsenic to 0.05 mg/l, but offered no specific explanation for the change. In 1971, arsenic was first introduced as a possible carcinogen (no human data), and although the standard was maintained at the same value as in 1963, it was recommended to keep its level in drinking water as low as possible.

The first WHO Guidelines in 1984 categorized arsenic as an inorganic constituent of significance to health and sets its maximum concentration at 0.05 mg/l, based on human data showing no adverse effect at that level. However, in 1993, a provisional value was established at 0.01 mg/l, on the basis of an increased cancer incidence observed in China where arsenic naturally occurs in groundwater. The 2002 edition keeps the guideline value as provisional at 0.01 mg/l, recognizing that although there is evidence of hazard, the available information on health effects is limited.

Most developed countries have adopted the 0.01 mg/l guideline as their national standard. This required a significant effort to ensure compliance at all water treatment facilities, in terms of economic investment, operator training, analytical capabilities and community informational campaigns. It is reasonable to assume that the regulatory level will be attained, given the state of the art on arsenic treatment processes and detection methods. However, many of these treatments and analytical equipment are unavailable in developing countries. This fact is particularly important given the high incidence of arsenic contamination in groundwater in middle to low income regions.

Figure 1. Map of maximum contaminant levels for Latin American countries.

Table 1. Arsenic standards for drinking water in several countries affected by its natural presence in groundwater and WHO guidelines

Country	Max arsenic concentration	Source
WHO	0.01 mg/l (provisional)	(16)
Argentina	0.01 mg/l	Código Alimentario Argentino (2007)
USA	0.01 mg/l	Environmental Protection Agency
Uruguay	0.005 mg/l	Decreto 253/79
Chile	0.01 mg/l	NCH 409/1 actualización 2005/2007
Bolivia	0.01 mg/l	NB 512 – October 2004
Perú	0.01 mg/l	Decreto Supremo N 002-2008-MNAM
México	0.025 mg/l	NOM-127-SSA1-1994 modificación año 2000
Ecuador	0.01 mg/l	NTE INEN 1-108-2006
Colombia	0.01 mg/l	Decreto 475/98
Costa Rica	0.01 mg/l	Ministerio de Salud – Reglamento de Calidad de Agua Potable D-25991
Canada	0.01 mg/l	Health Canada – Guidelines for Drinking Water Quality
India	0.05 mg/l	
Bangladesh	0.05 mg/l	

The widespread adoption of the lower standard is hampered by socio-economical aspects in these countries, exposing the population to a higher risk. In fact, the real tragedy of arsenic poisoning comes from communities exposed to concentrations 10 to 50 times the WHO guideline level that have no treatment available at all. In this context, it seems reasonable for many countries to focus their efforts on attaining a moderately safe arsenic level of 0.05 mg/l for the entire population, rather than setting a lower standard that is not feasible to achieve in a widespread manner under the current scenario. Table 1 lists the national standard values for many Latin and North American countries. Most countries in America have now adopted the WHO guideline value for national standard, as shown in Figure 1. However, the degree of compliance with the regulated values is extremely low in the areas naturally affected by arsenic contamination, making the standard updates have little or no impact on population health.

TECHNOLOGIES FOR ARSENIC REMOVAL

There is a wide variety of technologies that can be applied to arsenic removal. The most commonly used are, based on cost, effectiveness and simplicity: coagulation-coprecipitation/filtration, membrane filtration, adsorption and ion exchange processes.

Coagulation/filtration is the most commonly used and well-documented process. Coagulants are aluminum salts such as alum, and ferric salts such as ferric chloride or ferric sulfate. High efficiency has been reported in laboratory settings, but full-scale plants usually report lower values, making the process sometimes unable to attain the required concentrations. The separation step is key, and proper design of the unit will determine the overall effectiveness of the process. Microfiltration successfully separates flocs, but it is impractical in the field. Gravity sedimentation is used in household units that treat very small volumes; however, sand filtration is applied in the majority of coagulation processes.

Membrane processes, e.g. reverse osmosis (RO), have been successfully applied to arsenic removal. RO removes to a certain degree all ions present, and the produced water must be reconditioned to be used as drinking water. The treatment can result in extremely low levels of arsenic, and has the advantage of removing many other toxic components. The operation is simple, but operators should at least have minimal training in order to avoid fouling of the membranes and extend the modules' lifetime. RO systems operate at high transmembrane pressure (>200 psi) and the recoveries are generally low (20- 30 %). As a consequence, high volumes of concentrated wastewater are produced, which must be disposed of in a safe manner. The technology has relatively higher capital and operational costs, making it more suitable for municipal treatment plants than for household use. Availability of chemicals for water pretreatment and membrane cleaning, as well as membrane module replacement may be an issue to consider in certain locations.

Synthetic ion exchange resins are widely used in water treatment to remove many undesirable dissolved solids, most commonly hardness, from water. These resins are based on a cross-linked polymer skeleton, called the 'matrix', with charged functional groups covalently attached. Strong basic resins, e.g. quaternary amines, have been applied to arsenic removal. Ions need to be charged in order to be removed by ion exchange resins; therefore, if significant amounts of arsenite (uncharged) are present, a pre-oxidation step is required to convert them to arsenate in order for the process to be effective. Resin regeneration produces a concentrated arsenic waste solution that requires monitoring to ensure the sustainability of the treatment.

Adsorption processes have also been extensively used for arsenic removal. Traditional adsorbents (activated alumina, activated carbon) have been tested but usually required pre-treatment to reach acceptable performance levels. Adsorption processes are pH-dependent and usually fast desorption occurs at unfavorable pH ranges. Being a surface phenomenon, adsorption capacity is highly dependent on the specific surface area of the material. Therefore, newly developed high surface area adsorbents synthesized from nanomaterials have been proposed and applied to arsenic removal with significant success (see section in this chapter on Nanotechnology and Water Treatment).

Even though there exists a wide range of well known and proven treatment options for arsenic removal, the supply of safe water to the entire population exposed to contaminated groundwater is a goal that has not been reached yet. One of the most important reasons for this may be the cost of installation and operation of some of these technologies, that makes them unreachable for many communities. Additionally, there seems to be an educational and cultural barrier to overcome, since many of the affected people in developing countries ignore or underestimate the health threat posed by long term ingestion of arsenic contaminated water As a consequence, they place little value in the improved water treatment process, and thus there is a lack of compromise on the users' side that prevents them from investing their time and money to attain arsenic free drinking water.

An example of the depicted situation is a study conducted in India over a 2-year period. The objective of the study was to evaluate the effectiveness of commercially available small scale treatment plants, from US, European and local manufacturers, and its outcome exposed an underlying problem in arsenic abatement [17]. Most of the treatment plants were based on adsorption or ion exchange technology, and one used a coagulation-filtration process. The plants performed poorly, mainly because of the user unfriendliness of the units, unclear maintenance operations and users' lack of awareness of the problem, rather than pure technological obstacles.

Within Latin America, Chile is probably the country that has been the most successful in reducing arsenic exposure, with several full-scale treatment plants. The first one was built in the northern city of Antofagasta as early as 1970, with arsenic abatement capabilities up to only 0.110 ppm. Newer plants and improved operational procedures enabled reaching the present 0.010 ppm level. However, the problem of supplying safe water to small, scattered communities is still unresolved. Large scale treatment plants use $FeCl_3$ as coagulant, followed by separation and disposal of the sludge. At the household level the experience was not very successful. A treatment option also based in the coagulation-filtration process failed in practice due to lack of motivation of the people, who do not see a health problem in the elevated arsenic content as they are more worried about the organoleptic and microbiological characteristics of the water[3].

In Argentina, there have been some isolated efforts to treat arsenic contamination at the municipal level. Reverse osmosis is the most commonly used treatment option, in addition to coagulation/filtration plants. However, treatment facilities are the exception, and most municipal drinking water plants limit their operation to pumping and disinfection, regardless of the arsenic content of their source waters.

LOW COST TECHNOLOGIES FOR ARSENIC TREATMENT

In order to address some of the issues regarding the cost of the best known and established technologies, a group of alternative, more affordable treatments have been proposed worldwide.

The Kanchan filter, developed by researchers at the Massachusetts Institute of Technology (MIT) and NGOs from Nepal, is a domestic treatment unit based on coagulation/adsorption onto iron hydroxide and sand filtration [18]. It can achieve up to 90% removal, but its main advantages may be that it was constructed by trained locals using materials easily found on-site (Nepal), and that the cost was minimal. Several types of filters with the same operational principle (coagulation/sand filtration) have been developed, as for example the 3-Kolshi or SONO filter. It consists of three clay pitchers containing different materials (sand/charcoal). A third material is introduced into the first pitcher (small cast iron pieces, colloidal silver, etc), which is the reactive component [19]. The good performance and success of this particular technology was such that in 2007, it was awarded the Grainger Challenge, a scientific competition aimed at finding an economical way to remove arsenic from arsenic-contaminated groundwater, funded by the United States National Academy of Engineering and the Grainger Foundation. A similar approach for household level arsenic removal was tested in Bangladesh. The process was based on coagulation with ferric sulfate and calcium hypochlorite, followed by sand filtration, using only two 20 L buckets, construction sand and a piece of fabric. During the test period, arsenic removal was accomplished but disposal of the sludge produced was recognized as an obstacle to prevent widespread use. Also, users expressed their preference for a centralized water treatment unit that would supply safe water for the community [20].

Low cost options based on adsorption have also been proposed. Many natural adsorbents have been tested and proposed for the areas where they are indigenous: Mexican cactus mucilage[21]; zeolites; coconut shells; petroleum coke; pine saw dust; and so on [22]. Several researchers have also worked towards the development of an ionic exchange resin specifically designed for arsenic removal [23,24]. A removal unit based on ionic exchange coupled with iron oxide adsorption/precipitation was designed by Sengupta and coworkers and is found currently in operation in over 175 rural communities in India [25]. The treatment is community-based, and users are involved in its operation, thus increasing commitment through ownership of the solution. However, almost all of the low cost treatments have been designed and field tested in the Nepal-India-Bangladesh region. The lack of transfer of these technologies to Latin American countries raises the question of whether cultural, educational and socio-economical differences between the two regions could be the preventing factor.

The Panamerican Center for Sanitary Engineering and Environmental Science in Lima, Perú has developed a treatment called ALUFLOC [26]. The product is a mixture of adsorbent clays and coagulant that needs to be added to water and then removed by natural sedimentation or sand filtration. Good removal levels have been achieved, but due to the degree of handling required by the method, user acceptance was low. Other low cost technologies have been proposed in Latin America, but they are still in laboratory or pilot scale [27].

NANOTECHNOLOGY AND WATER TREATMENT

The removal of a constituent at such low concentrations as required in natural arsenic contaminated waters makes adsorption processes especially applicable. Adsorption is a surface phenomenon, and therefore the efficiency of the process is related to the specific surface area of the adsorbent. Nanoparticles are of special interest, given the high specific surface area attainable. There has been an important number of treatment processes using micro and nanoparticles, and nanostructured adsorbents. However, there is a trade-off between efficency of the process for very small particles, and manufacturing and operational costs associated with newer technologies and complicated synthesis processes.

Iron oxide is by far the main adsorbent used in arsenic abatement. It has several advantages: excellent affinity towards arsenate and arsenite, worldwide availability, known chemistry, low cost and negligible toxicity. There is a huge variety in sizes, shapes and modes of operation in which iron oxide-based systems are applied. Each process presents advantages and disadvantages with respect to the others, considering the water flow rate that needs to be treated, availability of special raw materials at a particular site, cost of fabrication, arsenic levels, operational characteristics, and so on, making a simple comparison and evaluation of merits between them an uneasy task. They should be considered as group of available tools, and the preferred technology should be selected taking into account the intended location. Generally, nanoparticles or nanostructured materials are used in two different schemes: fixed (chemically attached), coating an inert substrate material and forming adsorption columns, or individually suspended in the water to be treated, followed by a separation process.

Table 2. Main iron-based adsorbents for drinking water and their adsorption capacities

Adsorbent	pH	Concentration /range	Surface area (m^2/g)	T $(°C)$	Method	Capacity (mg/g) As(V)	Ref
Unsupported Material							
Akaganeite b-FeO(OH) nanocrystals	7.5	5–20 mg/L	330	25	Langmuir	141.3	[28]
FePO$_4$ (amorphous)	6–6.7	0.5–100 mg/L	53.6	20	-	10	[29]
FePO$_4$ (crystalline)	6–6.7	0.5–100 mg/L	35.9	20	-	9	[29]
Ferrihydrite	7	0–150 mg/L	-	-	Langmuir	68.75	[30]
Ferrihydrite	-	0.267–26.7 mmol/L	-	-	-	111.02	[31]
Fex(OH)y-Montm	9	0–60 mg/L	165	22	-	4	[32]
Goethite	9	0–60 mg/L	39	22	-	4	[32]
Goethite	5	-	103	29	Langmuir	5	[33]
Goethite	7.1	0–38 mg/L	-	-	Langmuir	442.8	[30]
Hematite	4.2	133.49 mmol/L	14.4	30	Langmuir	0.2	[34]
HFO	9	0–60 mg/L	200	22	-	7	[32]

Material	pH	Concentration	Surface area	Temp (°C)	Model	Capacity	Ref
Hematite supported ceramic	6.1	2-10 mg/L	41.879	25	Langmuir	5.99	[35]
	6.1	10 mg/L	26.149	25	Breakthrough	3.34	-
	6.1	0.09 mg/L	26.149	25	Breakthrough	0.22	-
Alumina/Fe(OH)$_3$	8,2–8,9	0.05 mg/L	-		Breakthrough	0.09	[36]
Fe/NN-MCM-41	6	0–1500 mg/L	310	25	-	119.8	[37]
Fe/NN-MCM-48	6	0–1500 mg/L	352	25	-	187.3	[37]
Fe10SBA-15	6.5	0.133–1.33 mmol/L	-	25	Langmuir	12.74	[38]
Ferric chloride impregnated silica gel	-	-	-	-	-	≤5.24	[39]
GAC-Fe (0.05 M)	4.7	0.10–30.0 mg/L	600–1000	25	Langmuir	2.96	[40]
GAC-Fe–H$_2$O$_2$ (0.05 M)	4.7	0.10–30.0 mg/L	600–1000	25	Langmuir	3.94	[40]
GAC-Fe–NaClO (0.05 M)	4.7	0.10–30.0 mg/L	600–1000	25	Langmuir	6.57	[40]
GAC-Fe–O$_2$ (0.05 M)	4.7	0.10–30.0 mg/L	600–1000	25	Langmuir	1.92	[40]
Granular ferric hydroxide (GIH)	8–9	5–100 mg/L	-	25	Column capacity	2.3	[41]
Iron hydroxide coated alumina	7.15–7.2	0.1–1.8 mmol/L	95.7	25	Langmuir	36.64	[36]
Iron oxide coated cement (IOCC)	7	0.5–10.0 mg/L	-	35	Langmuir	6.43	[42]
Iron oxide coated sand	7.6	100 mg/L	10.6	22 ± 2	Langmuir	0.043	[43]
Iron(III) alginate gel	4	0–10 mg/L	-	-	-	352	[44]
Iron(III) oxide with polyacrylamide	-	-	-	-	-	43	[45]
Iron(III) oxide-impregnated GAC	7	1 mg/L	840	20–23	-	4.5	[46]
Iron(III)-loaded chelating resin	-	-	-	-	-	60	[47]
Sulfate-modified iron oxide coated sand (SMIOCS)	7	0.5–3.5 mg/L	3.75	27	Langmuir	0.12	[48]
Sulfate-modified iron oxide coated sand (SMIOCS)	4	0.5–3.5 mg/L	3.74	27	Langmuir	0.13	[48]

The separation can be achieved by simple sedimentation if particles are large enough, or sand filtration. The advantage of the first operational procedure, even though it may involve higher fabrication costs, is that it avoids the separation operation. The separation of the spent adsorbent can be problematic, especially for very small particles, which in turn are of special interest due to their high adsorption capacity. Incomplete removal of the adsorbent material leads to health (arsenic ingest) and economic (loss of adsorbent material can be otherwise regenerated and reused) concerns. One interesting case is that of magnetic nanoparticles, which seems to combine the benefits of a dispersed material with the ease of removal using external magnets. The process worked successfully at small scale but questions have been raised about their scalability to full size municipal water treatment plants, which is still being investigated.

Mohan and Pittman compared the adsorption capacities of various adsorbents for arsenic removal [22]. Table 2 summarizes the capacity of As(V) removal for iron adsorbents in drinking water. It is important to note that while some adsorbents present smaller particles with the highest adsorption capacities, they are usually related to higher energy-associated manufacturing costs.

FERROXANE DERIVED CERAMICS

As shown, iron oxides are a class of material widely applied to arsenic removal due to its properties of low cost, availability, and negligible toxicity. The way iron oxides are used, however, exhibits great variation with respect to their size, shape, phase and mode of operation. In the search for an economic and user-friendly technology, there seems be a trade-off between technology input and final cost. For example, a group of very simple processes have been proposed using iron dissolved *in situ* (e.g. from nails, and other waste materials) followed by sand filtration. Although the final cost is minimal, the produced water often has a high dissolved iron concentration, giving it a yellowish color; also, its microbiological aspect is a concern. System performance is difficult to control, resulting in low user acceptance. On the other end, very high surface area iron nanoparticles exhibit outstanding performance, but cost and other practical issues involving manufacturing large quantities of the adsorbent, make widespread deployment of the technique inviable.

There is a need for yet another treatment option that correctly balances technology, cost and user-friendliness in a way that produces consistently good quality water at a negligible price, minimizing user intervention. There is also a social component to consider, since user acceptance will vary with location.

In this context, a method was proposed using nanostructured iron oxide ceramic membranes fabricated from ferroxane nanoparticles [49] as adsorbents. The nanoparticles can be deposited on different support materials to obtain composite ceramics [50]. The porous ceramic retains the high surface area property of the unsupported particles, while avoiding the separation step.

The use of ferroxane derived ceramics presents the advantage of achieving a high specific adsorbent surface on a fixed support, which retains the nanoparticles and prevents their leakage into the purified liquid. Additionally, this material presents a high resistance to wear for normal use, which means that the membrane can withstand multiple cycles of adsorption, saturation and regeneration without significant deterioration [35].

The raw material from which ferroxanes are obtained is a type of iron oxide (lepidocrocite), which can in turn be synthesized in a straightforward fashion from an abundant and relatively inexpensive compound, ferrous chloride. The reason for the choice of lepidocrocite resides in its crystalline structure, which can be schematically understood as planar sheets held together one over the other by means of hydrogen bonds. When this compound is reacted with an organic acid in order to synthesize ferroxanes, hydrogen bonds which hold the sheets together are broken, unbonding those sheets. Thus, smaller particles with a large specific surface are obtained.

A suspension of ferroxane nanoparticles can be then injected into a porous support, (e.g. porous alumina) and sintered at around 350°C, a temperature level which is sufficient to form the ceramic membrane but which does not significantly reduce its specific surface. After sintering, the material converts to hematite, the thermodynamically stable form, and therefore no further changes in phase or structure are expected. Experimental results show that on average, these membranes exhibit a specific surface area of around 40 m^2/g [35]. Their adsorptive capacity, which is dependent among other factors on the concentration of the input solution, is on a par with other types of adsorbents reported in the literature (see Table 2).

The adsorptive properties of ferroxane-derived iron oxide membrane vary with pH, favoring the retention of arsenic species at lower pH and releasing it at higher levels. This allows for the possibility of regenerating the membrane, since at normal groundwater pH levels adsorption is favored, whereas the passage of a basic solution causes desorption of the previously removed arsenic.

Another advantage of this material is that ionic strength variations do not alter its adsorptive capacity, which hints at a specific adsorption mechanism. Similarly, potential interferences that are usually present in groundwater, such as silicates and fluoride, do not hamper significantly the adsorption of arsenic (Figure 2). In fact, laboratory tests of ferroxane-derived membranes with natural waters samples from different locations in Argentina showed removal capacities in good agreement with the values previously obtained with synthetic waters.

a)

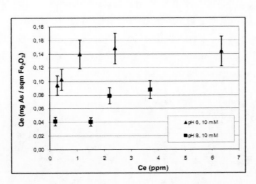

b)

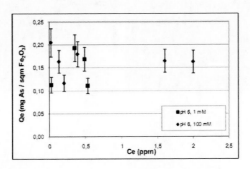

c)

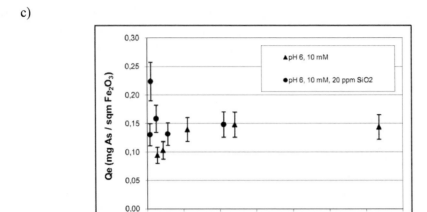

Figure 2. As(V) Adsorption isotherms for ferroxane derived ceramics under different relevant environmental conditions: (a) effect of pH; (b) effect of ionic strength; (c) effect of dissolved silica.

Although the material can be potentially applied in a variety of configurations, such as batch adsorption, packed columns, or deposited onto different support materials; effort was directed towards the fabrication of a simple point of use device that can be operated by non-technical personnel and that would provide safe water for daily consumption for a single family. The device consists of an array of ceramic tubes (Figure 3), housed in a plastic container, through which water flows tangentially. The first container collects water as it enters tangentially into each tube and exits radially through the walls of the tube. The treated water flows to a second plastic container that acts as clean water reservoir. A field study is currently underway in which the filter is being tested in both urban and rural environments. The outcome of this study is expected to provide important feedback about positive and negative aspects found by the users, in an effort to overcome the limitations of acceptance often seen in other technologies.

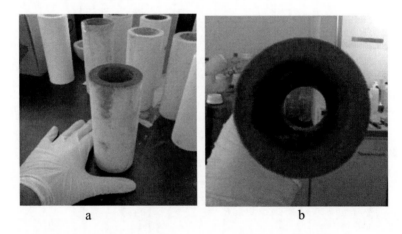

Figure 3. Alumina supported iron oxide ceramic tubes used in the Ferroxane derived filter for arsenic removal.

CONCLUSION

Natural presence of arsenic in groundwater is affecting many areas of the world, with millions of people affected. While urban populations in developed countries are served with good quality water due to affordability of treatment technologies, another is the case in rural settings or developing countries. To specifically address this issue, a wide variety of low cost technologies have been proposed by researchers worldwide. However, very few of them have made it past the laboratory environment and even fewer reached the needed population further from the initial trials. The main obstacles for a successful implementation were user-unfriendliness of the technique and lack of commitment of the users, stemming mostly from not recognizing the health threat posed by arsenic contaminated drinking water. In light of these observations, it can be concluded that the overall problem is more educational and cultural than technical. Although better technologies that remove arsenic without putting an extra burden on the affected population are highly desirable, alongside with better and more affordable analytical techniques for the detection of contaminants in the field, it seems that without education campaigns and strong involvement of local government and NGOs no complete solution can be reached. Interaction with potential users during the initial steps of treatment process design, and development of a sense of ownership in conjunction with specific public health informational campaigns are essential components to successfully address the challenge of providing arsenic-free water to the developing world.

REFERENCES

[1] Meigh, J.; McKenzie, A.; Sene, K. A Grid-Based Approach to Water Scarcity Estimates for Eastern and Southern Africa. *Water Resources Management* 1999, *13* (2), 85-115.

[2] Esparza, M. C. d. Presencia de arsénico en el agua de bebida en América Latina y su efecto en la salud pública. *International Congress Natural Arsenic in Groundwaters in Latin America*, Mexico City, 2006.

[3] C. Fereccio, A. M. S. Arsenic Exposure and Its Impact on Health in Chile. *Journal of Health Popul Nutr* 2006, *24* (2), 164-175.

[4] M. Armienta, N. S. Arsenic and fluoride in the groundwter of Mexico. *Environmental Geochemistry and Health* 2008, *30* (4), 345-353.

[5] Bundschuh, J.; Armienta, M.; Birkle, P.; Bhattacharya, P.; Matschullat, J.; Mukherjee, A. Section I: Regional Introduction and Overwiew. In *Natural Arsenic in Groundwaters of Latin America (Arsenic in the Environment);* Taylor and Francis, 2008.

[6] Hung, D.; Nekrassova, O.; Compton, R. Analytical Methods for Inorganic Arsenic i Water: a review. *Talanta* 2004, *64,* 269-277.

[7] Chen, H.; Brindle, I.; Le, X. Pre-reduction of arsenic(V) to arsenic(III), enhancement of the signal, and reduction of interferences by L-cysteine in the determination of arsenic by hydride generation. *Analytical Chemistry* 1992, *64* (6), 667-672.

[8] Weltz, B.; Sucmanova, M. L-cysteine as a reducing and releasing agent for the determination of antimony and arsenic using flow injection hydride generation atamoc absorption spectrometry. *Analyst* 1993, *118,* 1425.

[9]   Howard, A. (Boro)Hydride Techniques in Trace Element Speciation. *Journal of Analytical Atomic Spectrometry* 1997, *12,* 267.

[10] Naykki, T.; Peramaki, P.; Kujala, J.; Mikkonen, A. Optimization of a flow injection hydride generation atomic absorption spectrometric method for the determination of arsenic, antimony and selenium in iron chloride/sulfate-based water treatment chemical. *Anlytica Chimica Acta* 2001, *439,* 229-238.

[11] Anezaki, K.; Nukatsuka, I.; Ohzeki, K. Determination of Arsenic(III) and Total Arsenic(III,V) in Water Samples by Resin Suspension Graphite Furnace Atomic Absorption Spectrometry. *Analytical Science* 1999, *15,* 829-834.

[12] Freeney, R.; Kounaves, S. Voltammetric Measurement of Arsenic in Natural Waters. *Talanta* 2002, *58,* 23-31.

[13] Rahman, M.; Mukherjee, D.; Sengupta, M.; Chowdhury, U.; Lodh, D.; Chanda, C.; Selim, S.; Quamruzzman, Q.; Milton, A.; Shahidullah, S.; Rahman, M. D.; Chakraborti, D. Effectiveness and Reliability of Arsenic Field Testing Kits: Are the Million Dollar Screening Projects Effective of not? *Environmental Science and Technology* 2002, *36,* 5383-5394.

[14] Stetzenbach, K.; Amano, M.; Kreamer, D.; Hodge, V. Testing the limits of ICP-MS: Determination of trace elements in ground water at the part per trillion level. *Groundwater* 1994, *32,* 976-985.

[15] Sansoni, B.; Brunner, W.; Wolff, G.; Rupert, H.; Dittrich, R. Comparative instrumental multi-element analysis I: Comparison of ICP source mass spectrometry with ICP atomic emission spectrometry, ICP atomic fluorescence spectrometry and atomic absorption spectrometry for the analysis of natural waters form a granite region. *Fresenius' Journal of Analytical Chemistry* 1988, *331,* 154-169.

[16] World Health Organization. *Guidelines for Drinking-water Quality,* third edition ed.; WHO Press: Geneva Switzerland, 2008.

[17] Hossain, M.; Sengupta, M.; Ahamed, S.; Rahman, M.; Mondal, D.; Lodh, D.; Das, B.; Nayak, B.; Roy, B.; Mukherjee, A.; Chkraborti, D. Ineffectiveness and Poor Reliability of Arsenic Removal Plants in West Bengal, India. *Environmental Science and Technology* 2005, *39* (11), 4300-4306.

[18] Ngai, K.; Murcatt, S.; Shrestha, R.; Dangoi, B.; Maharjan, M. Development and dissemination of Kanchan Arsenic Filter in rural Nepal. *Water Science and Technology* 2006, *6* (3), 137-146.

[19] Khan, A.; Rasul, S.; Munir, A.; Habibuddowla, M.; Alauddin, M.; Newaz, S.; Hussam, A. Appraisal of a simple arsenic removal method for groundwater of Bangladesh. *Journal of Enviromental Science and Health* 2000, *A35* (7), 1021-1041.

[20] Cheng, A.; Green, A. V.; Jing, C.; Meng, A.; Seddique, K.; Ahmed, A. Performance of a Household-Level Arsenic Removal System during 4-month Deployments in Bangladesh. *Environmental Science and Technology* 2004, *38,* 3442-3448.

[21] Young, K.; Anzalone, A.; Pichler, T.; Picquart, M.; Alcatar, N. The Mexican Cactus as a New Environmentally Benign Material for the Removal of Contaminants in Drinking Water. *Proceedings of the Symposium JJ, Materials Research Society 2006 Spring Meeting,* 2006.

[22] D. Mohan, C. P. Arsenic removal from water/wastewater using adsorbents - A critical review. *Journal of Hazardous Materials* 2007, *142* (1-2), 1-53.

[23] Dambies, L.; Salinaro, R.; Alexandratos, S. Immobilized N-Methyl-D-glucamine as an Arsenate-Selective Resin. *Environmental Science and Technology* 2004, *38,* 6139-6146.

[24] Ramana, A.; Sengupta, A. A new class of selective sorbents for arsenic and selenium oxy-anions. *Environmental Engineering Division Journal, ASCE* 1992, *118* (5), 755-775.

[25] Sarkar, S.; Blaney, L.; Gupta, A.; Ghosh, D.; Sengupta, A. Arsenic Removal from Groundwater and Its Safe Containment in a Rural Environment: Validation of a Sustainable Approach. *Environmental Science and Technology* 2008, *42,* 4268-4273.

[26] Esparza, M. C. d. Remoción de arsénico en el agua para bebida y bioremediación de suelos. *International Congress Natural Arsenic in Gorundwaters of Latin America*, Mexico City, 2006.

[27] García, M.; D'Hiriart, J.; Giullitti, J.; Lin, H.; Custo, G.; Hidalgo, M.; Litter, M.; Blesa, M. Solar light induced removal of arsenic from contaminated groundwater: the interplay of solar energy and chemical variables. *Solar energy* 2004, *77* (5), 601-613.

[28] Solozhenkin, P.; Deliyanni, E.; Bakoyannakis, V.; Zouboilis, A.; Matis, K. Removal of As(V) Ions form Solution by Akaganeite bgr-FeO(OH) Nanocrystals. *Journal of Mining Science* 2003, *39* (3), 287-296.

[29] Lenoble, V.; Laclauture, C.; Deluchat, V.; Serpaud, B.; Bollinger, J.-C. Arsenic removal by adsorption on iorn (III) phosphate. *Journal of Hazardous Materials* 2005, *123* (1-3), 262-268.

[30] Lafferty, B.; Loeppert, R. Methyl Arsenic Adsorption and Desorption Behavior on Iron Oxides. *Environmental Science and Technology* 2005, *39* (7), 2120-2127.

[31] Raven, K.; Jain, A.; Loeppert, R. Arsenite and Arsenate Adsorption on Ferrihydrite: Kinetics, Equilibrium, and Adorption Envelopes. *Environmental Science and Techonology* 1998, *32* (3), 344-349.

[32] Lenoble, V.; Bouras, O.; Deluchat, V.; Serpaud, B.; Bollinger, J.-C. Arsenic Adsorption onto Pillared Clays and Iron Oxides. *Journal of Colloid and Interface Science* 2002, *255* (1), 52-58.

[33] Lakshmipathiraj, P.; Narasimhan, B.; Prabhakar, S.; Raju, G. Adsorption of arsenate on synthetic goethite form aqueous solutions. *Journal of Hazardous Materials* 206**,** *136* (2), 281-287.

[34] Singh, A.; Prasad, G.; Rupainwar, D. Adsorption technique for the treatment of As(V)-rich efluents. *Colloids and Surfaces A: Physicochemical and Engineering Aspects* 1996, *111* (1-2), 49-56.

[35] Sabbattini, P.; Rossi, F.; Thern, G.; Marajofsky, A.; Cortalezzi, M. F. d. Iron oxide adsorbers for arsenic removal: A low cost treatment for rural areas and mobile applications. *Desalination* 2009**,** *248,* 184-192.

[36] Zouboulis, A.; Katsoyiannis, I. Arsenic Removal Using Iron Oxide Loaded Alginate Beads. *Industrial and Engineering Chemistry Research* 2002, *42* (24), 6149-6155.

[37] Hódi, M.; Polyák, K.; Hlavay, J. Removal of pollutants from drinking water by combined ion exchange and adsorption methods. *Environment International* 1995, *21* (3), 325-331.

[38] Yoshitake, H.; Yokoi, T.; Tatsumi, T. Adsorption Behavior of Arsenate at Transition Metal Catios Captured by Amino-Functionalized Mesoporous Silicas. *Chemistry of Materials* 2003, *15* (8), 1713-1721.

[39] Jang, M.; Shin, E.; Park, J.; Choi, S. Mechanisms of Arsenate Adsorption by Highly Ordered Nano-Structured Silicate Media Impregnated with Metal Oxides. *Environmental Science and Technology* 2003, *21,* 5062-5070.

[40] Isao, Y.; Hiroshi, K.; Keihei, U. Selective adsorption of arsenic ions on silica gel impragnated with ferric hydroxide. *Analytical Letters* 1976, *9* (12), 1125-1133.

[41] Gu, Z.; Fang, J.; Deng, B. Preparation and Evaluation of GAC-Based Iron-Containing Adsorbents for Arsenic Removal. *Environmental Science and Technology* 2005, *39* (10), 3833-3843.

[42] Catalano, J.; Zhang, Z.; Park, C.; Fenter, P.; Bedzyk, M. Bridging arsenate surface complexes on the hematite (0 1 2) surface. *Geochimica et Cosmochimica Acta* 2007, *71* (8), 1883-1897.

[43] Kundu, S.; Gupta, A. Adsorptive Removal of As(III) form aqeous solution using iron oxide coated cement (IOCC): Evaluation of kinetic, equilibrium and thermodynamic models. *Separation and Purification Technology* 2006, *51* (2), 165-172.

[44] Thirunavukkarasu, O.; Viraghavan, T. Arsenic removal from drinking water using iron oxide coated sand. *Water, Air, and Soil Pollution* 2003, *142,* 95-111.

[45] Min, J.; Hering, J. Arsenate sorption by Fe(III)-doped alginate gels. *Water Research* 1998, *32* (5), 1544-1552.

[46] Shigetomi, Y.; Hori, Y.; Kojima, T. The removal of arsenate in waste water with an adsorbent prepared by binding hydrous iron(III) oxide with polyacrylamide. *Bulletin of the Chemical Society of Japan* 1980, *53,* 1475-1476.

[47] Reed, B.; Vaughan, R.; Jiang, L. As(III), As9V), Hg, and Pb Removal by Fe-Oxide Impreganted Activated Carbon. *Journal of Environmental Engineering* 2000, *126,* 189.

[48] Rau, I.; Gonxalo, A.; Valiente, M. Arsenic(V) removal from aqueous solutions by iron(III) loaded chelating resins. *Journal of Radioanalytical and Nuclear Chemistry* 2000, *246* (3), 597-600.

[49] Vaishya, R.; Gupta, S. Modelling arsenic(III) adsorption from water by sulfate modified iron-oxide coated sand (SMIOCS). *Separation Science and Technology* 2004, *39* (3), 645-666.

[50] Rose, J.; Fidalgo, M.; Moustier, S.; Magnetto, C.; Jones, C.; Barron, A.; Wiesner, M.; Bottero, J.-Y. Synthesis and Characterization of Carboxylate-FeOOH Particles (Ferroxanes) and Ferroxane-derived Ceramics. *Chemistry of Materials* 2002, *14,* 621-628.

[51] Cortalezzi, M.; Rose, J.; Wells, G.; Bottero, J.-Y.; Wiesner, M. Ceramic membranes derived from ferroxane nanoparticles: a new route for the fabrication of iron oxide ceramic membranes. *Journal of Membrane Science* 2003, *14,* 207-217.

In: Water Production and Wastewater Treatment
Editor: B. Antizar-Ladislao et al.

ISBN 978-1-61728-503-5
© 2011 Nova Science Publishers, Inc.

Chapter 14

EFFICACY OF TiO$_2$ DOPED WITH COPPER FOR WATER DISINFECTION

B. Antizar-Ladislao [a1], L. Wu [b2] and M.A. Khraisheh [c3]

[a] University of Edinburgh, Institute for Infrastructure and Environment, School of Engineering, William Rankine Building, Edinburgh EH9 3JL, UK
[b] University College London, department of Civil Engineering, Gower Street, London WC1E 6BT, UK
[c] Department of Chemical Engineering, University of Qatar, Doha, 2713, Qatar

ABSTRACT

This research was conducted to improve titanium dioxide by transition metal doping using cooper. Sol gel method was used to prepare metal doped TiO$_2$. Titanium isopropoxide and commercial TiO$_2$ P25 were employed as catalyst precursor. The role played by the varied preparation parameters such as doping level and pH of solution were discussed with respect to the final photoreactivity. Photoreactivity was carried out in a solar box with two UVA lamps. The photodisinfection of *E. coli* in aquatic solution were selected as probe to measure the photoreactivity. It is found that Cu doped TiO$_2$ exhibited enhanced results from *E. coli* photodisinfection. It was observed that the characteristic properties of catalysis like surface area can be important in predicating catalysts' photoreactivity.

[1] E-mail: B.Antizar-Ladislao@ed.ac.uk.
[2] E-mail: uceslwu@ucl.ac.uk.
[3] E-mail: m.khraisheh@qu.edu.qa.

INTRODUCTION

In early 2000, one sixth of the world's population (which equates to approximately 1.1 billion people) was without access to clean water supply (WHO, 2000). No access to good quality drinking water increases the risk of waterborne diseases such as cholera, typhoid fever and other diarrhoeal diseases. This represents a significant global problem, and a number of options available today for disinfection include chlorination, iodine treatment, UV treatment, and boiling.

The last 20 years saw the development of two of the most interesting disinfection alternatives which are solar disinfection and TiO_2 photo-disinfection under UV illumination. The combination of the two methods would result in a much greener, cheaper, more efficient and less energy consuming solution which could be produced and widely applied whilst causing no harm to human health. Considering the fact that the areas of the world that lack access to safe drinking water are also the world's poorest nations and have an abundance of sunlight irradiation, the provision of this new technique can alleviate the current burden on the global water supply and improve sanitation (World Health Organization *et al.*, 2000). TiO_2, a low cost, non toxic and inert semiconductor photocatalyst is used in many applications in foods, paints and as an antimicrobial material. Recently, it has been used in water disinfection. TiO_2 can be photoactivated by the ultraviolet irradiation (UV) spectrum of irradiation. The combination of TiO_2 and UV is a proven advanced oxidation process and the alteration of with sunlight or sunlight simulator is therefore promising.

However, the band-gap, as explained in the paragraph below, of TiO_2 is large (Eg = 3.2 eV compared to less than 2.5% of the solar photon flux has energy greater than 3.0 eV). Thus, TiO_2 is only active in the ultraviolet region (<400nm) which is < 10% of the overall solar intensity so that the light harvesting ability of TiO_2 is very limited (Linsebigler *et al.*, 1995).

Innovative strategies have thus been developed to use solar intensity in combination with TiO_2 that are here investigated. In a single free-standing atom or molecule, electrons are accommodated in their electron orbital (s, p, d etc.), which imply a discrete set of energy levels. When a great number of atoms are brought together to form a solid, the number of orbitals increases dramatically. Orbitals with similar energy levels join to form bands of energy which are separated by void regions where there are no energy levels or orbitals. The empty region is also referred to as band gap. To narrow this band gab, doping with metals is sometimes used. Doping is the process of intentionally introducing impurities into an extremely pure semiconductor to change its electrical properties, and thus, dopants could alter lattice thermal dynamics, electronic structures and furthermore photocatalytic efficiency.

EXPERIMENTAL MATERIALS AND METHODS

Undoped TiO_2 and TiO_2 doped with Cu catalysts were prepared via a sol gel method described by Ding and Liu in 1997. Titanium (IV) isopropoxide (TTIP) and alcohol (ethanol, 2(2-ethoxyethoxy) ethanol or isoproponal) were vigorously stirred in a beaker. A mixture of fixed amount of deionised water (DI water), acid (HCl or H_2SO_4) and alcohol was added drop-wise into the previous TTIP/alcohol solution and magnetically stirred. After gelation, it was dried at 60°C in an oven overnight.

Table 1. List of synthesised photocatalysts

Sample	Sol	Acid	Molar ratio			Cooper dopant	Doping level (mol%)	Calcination Temperature (°C)	BET Surface Area (m^2 g^{-1})
SGTCu43	Iso	H$_2$SO$_4$	80	14	0.06	CuCl$_2$	0.1%	600	30.91
SGTCu44	Iso	H$_2$SO$_4$	80	14	0.06	CuCl$_2$	0.5 %	600	83.16
SGTCu45	Iso	H$_2$SO$_4$	80	14	0.06	CuCl$_2$	1.0%	600	53.37
SGTCu46	Iso	H$_2$SO$_4$	80	14	0.06	CuCl$_2$	10.0 %	600	27.09

The powder was then annealed at a specific temperature for 2 h in furnace. Finally, the catalysts was pulverized through 75ìm sieves and kept in a sealed jar for further use.

For Cu doped TiO$_2$, a given amount of copper precursor (1 to 10 mol % to TiO$_2$) was mixed with DI water, acid and alcohol solution before the mixture was added into a TTIP/alcohol solution. The rest of the preparation procedure was the same as with undoped TiO$_2$. In our work, a system for naming the resultant catalyst was developed to distinguish between the vast types prepared (Table 1). Only a small number is used and are presented in this research paper. The names given depended on some synthesis variables, including preparation method, undoped or doped, difference in starting solution composition and annealing temperature. The name of a catalyst can be seen in the format of ATBC. Here "A" stands for the preparation method, it can be sol-gel method (SG) or Wet-impregnation method (IM). "T" is short for TiO$_2$ and means it is a TiO$_2$ based photocatalyst. "B" stands for a dopant which could be iron (Fe), Humic acid (HA), Manganese (Mn) but in most case, it is cooper (Cu). "C" is always a number that stands for different conditions in starting solution composition and annealing temperature, a detailed lists corresponding to that information can be found in the list of synthesised materials.

SGTCu43, for example, is a TiO$_2$ based photocatalyst which prepared from sol-gel method. In the standard sol-gel procedure, the starting solution is composed of TTIP, isopropanol, H$_2$SO$_4$ and H$_2$O at a molar ratio of 1:80:0.06:14. It is doped by Cu at a level of 0.1 mol% towards TiO$_2$ and the final annealing condition is 600°C for 2 hours. Table 2 contains the list of the catalysts synthesised and used in this paper.

Table 2. Summary of sol-gel prepared photocatalysts used in studying the influence of dopant type

Material	Sample	Treatment
Cu doped TiO2 from sol-gel method	SGTCu43	Hydrolysis and condensation of sol mixture (TTIP: Isopropanol: H2SO4: H2O: CuCl2 = 1:80:0.06:14:0.001) at room temperature and followed by drying at 600 °C for 2 h
Cu doped TiO2 from sol-gel method	SGTCu44	Hydrolysis and condensation of sol mixture (TTIP: Isopropanol: H2SO4: H2O: CuCl2 = 1:80:0.06:14:0.005) at room temperature and followed by drying at 600 °C for 2 h
Cu doped TiO2 from sol-gel method	SGTCu45	Hydrolysis and condensation of sol mixture (TTIP: Isopropanol: H2SO4: H2O: CuCl2 = 1:80:0.06:14:0.01) at room temperature and followed by drying at 600 °C for 2 h
Cu doped TiO2 from sol-gel method	SGTCu46	Hydrolysis and condensation of sol mixture (TTIP: Isopropanol: H2SO4: H2O: CuCl2 = 1:80:0.06:14:0.1) at room temperature and followed by drying at 600 °C for 2 h

Experimental Setup

The heart of photocatalytic experimental system is the design of the photoreactor. The solar box system consists of two chambers: the lamp and reactor chamber. The lamp chamber was installed on top of the reactor chamber. Two UVA lamps were located in the lamp chamber: (i) A commercial ruptile fluorescent tube lamp and (ii) A fluorescent Blacklight Blue tube lamp (18W, Silva) which transmit ultraviolet radiation peaking at 365 nm. In the reactor chamber, Pyrex glass flasks were employed as batch reactors. Water samples taken from the solar box system at a certain time interval were inoculated in petri dish before incubation for *E. coli* disinfection experiment.

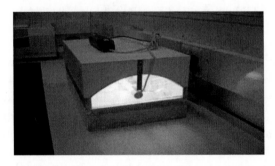

Figure 1. Schematic diagram of experimental setting ups.

Preparation of Test Solution

On the day of the experiment, certain amount of *E. coli* stock solution was transferred to centrifuge tubes and centrifuged at 3,650 rpm for 10 min. This formed a tight pellet in each tube. The broth of one centrifuge tube was poured off and the pellet was re-suspended in the same amount of DI water. In other cases, DI water was substituted by phosphate buffered saline and river water used for comparison. The samples of DI water suspension were taken every hour for 4 hours while the concentration of viable *E. coli* was enumerated using the Miles and Misra method (1938).

BET Characterizations

The surface area of the catalyst samples were obtained from nitrogen adsorption/desorption isotherms at 77K. Surface area data were calculated by applying the BET method (Sing et al., 1985).

RESULTS AND DISCUSSION

Overnight grown *E. coli* stock culture was used to investigate the effect of light exposure as well as the existence of catalysts on the *E. coli* inactivation process. TiO_2 P25 was used as undoped TiO_2 as it is commonly used standard TiO_2 in the literature.

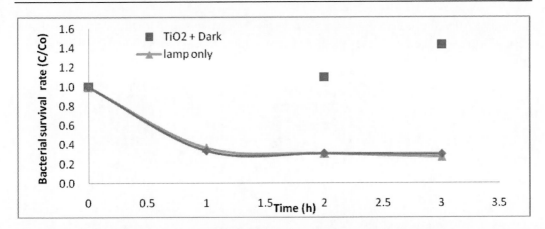

Figure 1. The decline of E. coli on TiO2 P25 in different irradiation conditions: dark (TiO2 + Dark) and solar box irradiation (TiO2 + lamp). Container size = 100ml, Catalysts dose = 1g/L, initial E. coli concentration = ~108 CFU/ml, pH = 6.3, T = 25°C. Control was used in solar box without the addition of TiO2.

As it can be seen from Figure 1, the presence of TiO_2 in dark conditions can hardly affect the viable cell number of E. coli culture in the water. A significant increase in the cell number after 2 hours indicates that TiO_2 did not exhibit any antibacterial effect in the dark. The other two tests were carried out in the solar box with weak UVA exposure. However, the difference of absence and presence of TiO_2 P25 is marginal. In both cases, there is a 60% decrease in viable E. coli cell number within the first hour and greater resistance to the UVA damage was found later and the cell number remains at a steady level at least for 2 more hours. The inefficacy of P25 to kill bacteria in the dark can be also found in open literature (Lonnen et al., 2005), but the rate of E. coli decline in the absence of P25 is much slower than the reference due to the difference of light input. The solar box system in this experiment has an irradiation range in the UVA with low intensity. Such low intensity light input may delay the production of reactive radicals for the attack of bacterial while the presence of catalyst particles in the water suspension may eliminate the penetration of light and protect the bacteria from direct exposure to harmful UV irradiation. Therefore, the use of TiO_2 P25 in water disinfection under weak UV intensity would not be necessary practical. This conclusion is comparable with that of Hu et al. (2007), who discovered that the presence of TiO_2 P25 film killed 1.8 log E. coli from an initial concentration of 6 log CFU/ml after 3 hours in weak UVA irradiation. No significant decline of E. coli can be observed in the same system without the addition of catalyst. This result reveals that TiO_2 P25 is inadequately activated under current weak irradiation conditions and modification on the photocatalysts is needed. Therefore, the following sections will be focus on Cu doped TiO_2.

TiO_2 films deposited with antibacterial metals such as copper and silver have been developed. Examining the survival rate of E. coli on Cu/TiO_2 thin film under a weak 1 uW cm^{-2} UV illumination which intensity similar to the indoor solar UV, Sunada et al. (2003) speculated the process was a combination of TiO_2 photocatalysis and Cu antibacterial properties.

As can be seen from Figure 2, the first step is postulated to be the partial decomposition of the outer membrane in the cell envelope by a photocatalytic process, followed by permeation of the Cu ions into the cytoplasmic membrane. In the second step is a disorder of the cytoplasmic membrane caused by the Cu ions, which results in a loss of the cell's integrity. After the outer membrane has been disordered and partially decomposed, the reactive species penetrate to the cytoplasmic membrane, causing the cell to die (Sunada *et al.*, 2003).

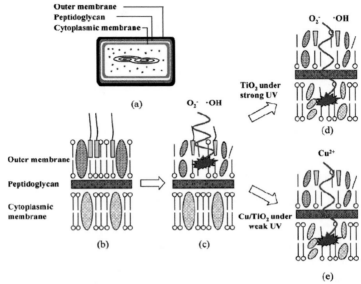

Figure 2. A schematic illustration of the bactericidal process for the copper-resistant E. coli cell on a normal TiO2 film and on a Cu/TiO2 film: (a) illustration of E. coli cell and (b) - (e) enlarged illustration of cell envelope parts (From Sunada et al., 2003).

The Influence of Doping Level

Compared with wet impregnated Cu/TiO$_2$, the doped catalyst from sol gel method may have a more homogenous distribution of dopant. The investigation into the relation between doping level and disinfection capability may give some clue in explaining its enhanced performance. The series of various Cu doped TiO$_2$ selected are shown in Table 2.

As Figure 3 illustrates, the 0.5 M% Cu doped TiO2 has apparently outperformed than other three levels of dopant 0.1 M%, 1.0 M% and 10.0 M%. Roughly, the low efficiency associated with 0.1 M% 1.0 M% and 10.0 M% is comparable with that of control without any catalysts addition which all stopped near 20% survival rate after three hours. In contrast, one hour was required for 0.5 M% Cu doped TiO2 to achieve a more than 80% bacterial disinfection. It must be noted that most photocatalytically active SGTCu44 also has the largest surface area as shown in Table 1. On one hand, low doping level catalyst SGTCu43 has a better anatase crystalline phase than 0.5 M% Cu doped TiO2. However, due to the lack of Cu ions in the catalysts, the advantage in anatase crystalline phase structure of SGTCu43 is compensated by a weaker Cu ions synthetic effect as was evident in the XRD tests (these are not included in the context of this paper). On the other hand, higher doping level catalyst SGTCu45 and SGTCu46 can provide enough Cu ions but the disadvantages in crystalline structure also lead to the degradation of catalysts activity. Hence, there seems to be a balance between doping level and TiO2 photoreactivity. The optimum doping level suggested in this experiment seems to be in the range of 0.1M% and 1.0M%. A lower level doping has not enough of Cu ions while a higher amount of Cu dopant exhibit the growth of anatase TiO2 crystalline phase.

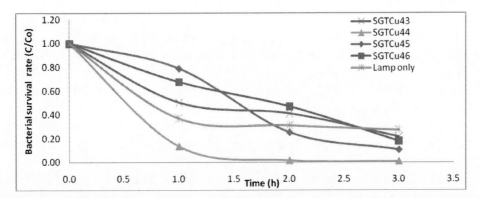

Figure 3. The decline of E. coli on irradiated Cu doped TiO2 with different doping levels: 0.1 M% (SGTCu43), 0.5 M% (SGTCu44), 1.0 M% (SGTCu45) and 10.0 M% (SGTCu46). Container size = 100ml, Catalysts dose = 1g/L, initial E. coli concentration = ~108 CFU/ml, pH = 6.3, T = 25°C. Control was used in solar box without the addition of catalyst.

Application of Cu/TiO₂ in Different pH Environment

The growth and survival of microorganisms is greatly influenced by the pH of its environment. The microorganism has the ability to grow within a specific pH range reflecting the organism's adaptation to their natural environment. A neutral or nearly neutral environment is generally advantageous to the growth of bacteria. In the present work, the pH was adjusted at the beginning of the illumination by addition of NaOH or HCl (0.1 M) to bacterial suspension. The initial pH value was set at 4, 6 and 9 according to previous report (Rincon and Pulgarin, 2004) that the TiO₂ P25 photocatalytic *E. coli* inactivation rate was independent of the initial pH between 4.0 and 9.0 because of acid tolerance response involves acid-induced proteins that protect the cells from an acid shock (pH 3.0) (Heyde and Portalier, 1990).

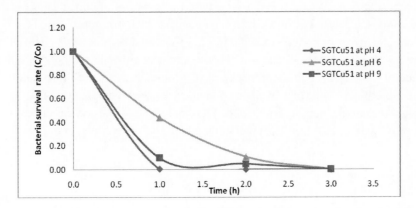

Figure 4. The decline of E. coli on irradiated Cu doped TiO2 (SGTCu51) at different water pH value (4, 6 and 9). Container size = 100ml, Catalysts dose = 1g/L, initial E. coli concentration = ~108 CFU/ml, pH = 6.3, T = 25°C.

As shown in Figure 4, in the first hour an increase in the disinfection rate was observed in both, the acidic or base compared with neutral solution. *E. coli* is a representative of the large neutrophilic bacteria groups which grows optimally between pH 6.0 and 8.0. At pH values of a unit or so beyond these limits, *E. coli* will grow slowly (Heyde and Portalier, 1990). In our experiment, a neutral environment has the least pressure on the *E. coli* viable number in the presence of Cu-doped TiO_2 because *E. coli* is more sensitive to both acid and base environment.

The acid shock on *E. coli* is the most significant, partly due to the increasing acidity pressure along with time and partly due to the fact that pH has an effect on the electrostatic charge of the TiO_2 surface, which determines the adsorption on TiO_2 of both organic substances and bacteria as well as the photocatalytic reactivity of TiO_2 (Rincon and Pulgarin, 2004).

For pH values higher than the point of zero charge of titanium (PZC, 6.5), the surface becomes negatively charged and it is the opposite for pH<PZC, according to the following equilibrium:

$$pH<PZC : TiOH+H^+ \leftrightarrow TiOH_2^+ \qquad \text{[eq 1]}$$

$$pH>PZC: TiOH+OH^- \leftrightarrow TiO^- +H_2O \qquad \text{[eq 2]}$$

In our experiment, the PZC of Cu-TiO_2 sample SGTCu51 had a PZC around 5.0, which means a positive charge at pH = 4. The positive charged surface is more advantageous for the adsorption of *E. coli* which has a net negative electrostatic charge by virtue of ionized phosphoryl and carboxylate substituents on outer cell envelope macromolecules (Wilson *et al.*, 2001).

CONCLUSIONS

Photocatalysts from sol gel method was employed for water disinfection with P25 as reference. P25 shows little sign of photocatalytic activity in *E. coli* disinfection in weak UV irradiation in solar box system. It is the same case for low level of doped TiO_2 except 0.5 M% sol gel prepared Cu/TiO2. The best performance is 10.0 M% wet impregnated Cu/TiO_2.

A synthetic effect of doped Cu and TiO_2 is discovered. In the mechanism proposed, Cu ions were involved in the production of reactive radicals either in the bulk of solution or on the surface of TiO_2 leading to the destruction of *E. coli*. A synthetic effect can occur with a certain amount of doping level as well as good anatase crystalline phase of TiO_2.

The photocatalytic activity of doped TiO_2 powder was tested in different water pH conditions. An acid or basic environment both enhanced the disinfection of *E. coli*.

REFERENCES

Ding, X. Z. and X. H. Liu, Synthesis and microstructure control of nanocrystalline titania powders via a sol-gel process, *Materials Science and Engineering A-Structural Materials Properties Microstructure and Processing, 224*(1-2), 210-215, 1997.

Heyde, M. and R. Portalier, Acid Shock Proteins of Escherichia-Coli, *Fems Microbiology Letters, 69*(1-2), 19-26, 1990.

Hu, C., J. Guo, J. H. Qu and X. X. Hu, Efficient destruction of bacteria with Ti(IV) and antibacterial ions in co-substituted hydroxyapatite films, *Applied Catalysis B-Environmental, 73*(3-4), 345-353, 2007.

Linsebigler, A. L., G. Q. Lu and J. T. Yates, Photocatalysis on TiO$_2$ Surfaces - Principles, Mechanisms, and Selected Results, *Chemical Reviews, 95*(3), 735-758, 1995.

Lonnen, J., S. Kilvington, S. C. Kehoe, F. Al Touati and K. G. McGuigan, Solar and photocatalytic disinfection of protozoan, fungal and bacterial microbes in drinking water, *Water Research, 39*(5), 877-883, 2005.

Miles, A.A. and S. S. Misra, The estimation of the bactericidal power of blood, *J. Hyg.* 38, 732–749, 1938.

Rincon, A. G. and C. Pulgarin, Field solar *E. coli* inactivation in the absence and presence of TiO$_2$: is UV solar dose an appropriate parameter for standardization of water solar disinfection?, *Solar Energy, 77*(5), 635-648, 2004.

Sing, K.S.W., D.H. Everett, R.A.W. Haul, L. Moscou, R.A. Pierotti, J. Rouquerol and T. Siemieniewska, Reporting physisorption data for gas/solid systems with special reference to the determination of surface area and porosity, *Pure Appl. Chem.* 57, 603–619, 1985.

Sunada, K., T. Watanabe and K. Hashimoto, Bactericidal activity of copper-deposited TiO$_2$ thin film under weak UV light illumination, *Environmental Science and Technology, 37*(20), 4785-4789, 2003.

World Health Organization., UNICEF., Global water supply and sanitation assessment 2000 report, Geneva, Switzerland : New York : World Health Organization ; United Nations Children's Fund, 2000.

In: Water Production and Wastewater Treatment
Editor: B. Antizar-Ladislao et al.

ISBN 978-1-61728-503-5
© 2011 Nova Science Publishers, Inc.

Chapter 15

ASSESSING REVERSE OSMOSIS AND ION-EXCHANGE FOR CONDENSATES RECYCLING IN FERMENTATION

Claire Fargues[a], Marjorie Gavach[a], Marielle Bouix[b], and Marie-Laure Lameloise[a]

[a]AgroParisTech, UMR 1145 Ingénierie Procédés Aliments,
1 avenue des Olympiades, F-91300 Massy, France
[b]AgroParisTech, UMR 782 Laboratoire de Génie et Microbiologie des Procédés Alimentaires, avenue L. Brétignières, F-78850 Thiverval Grignon, France

ABSTRACT

In fermentation industries and beet distilleries in particular, recycling the stillage condensates to dilute worts in the fermentation step would represent an effective way to decrease wastewater production and ground water consumption. However, condensates contain many fermentation inhibiting solutes, such as volatile acids, alcohols and aromatic compounds. The purification process should match the industrial scale, be robust, environmental friendly and cost-effective. Previous work has assessed the interest of reverse osmosis (RO) and ion-exchange (IE) for the removal of acidic and neutral inhibitors. Convenient membranes and resins were selected and optimized operating conditions were determined. In this chapter, impact of RO and IE treatments on the growth kinetics and physiological state of *Saccharomyces cerevisiae* was investigated in order to help for the choice of an adequate detoxification process.

INTRODUCTION

Industries including fermentation processes use important volumes of ground water to dilute their worts. In beet distilleries, this water is recovered as condensates during stillage concentration. Due to their organic content (COD from 5 to 10 g $O_2.L^{-1}$), these condensates cannot be discarded without a treatment. They are generally sent to wastewater treatment plant or stabilization ponds before being spread on land.

Table 1. Characteristics and concentration of the inhibitory solutes of the industrial condensates studied

Inhibitory Solutes	*MW* g.mol^{-1}	*pKa*	Formula	Concentration (meq.L^{-1})
Formic acid (f.a.)	46.03	3.8		1 - 1.5
Acetic acid (a.a.)	60.05	4.8		10 - 20
Propanoic acid (p.a.)	74.08			1 - 2
Butanoic acid (b.a.)	88.10	4.8		1 - 2
Valeric acid (v.a.)	102.15			0 - 0.5
Hexanoic acid (h.a.)	116.2	4.90		Traces
Furfural (f)	96.08			0.02 - 0.2
2-phenylethanol (phol)	122.17			0.1 - 0.2

With the increase in ethanol production, better management of water resource is needed. Recycling the stillage condensates to dilute worts in the fermentation step would represent an effective way to decrease wastewater production and spare ground water. However, as was already observed by technologists and assessed by Morin Couallier (2006a), condensates contain many fermentation inhibiting solutes, such as volatile acids, alcohols and aromatic compounds, released from the raw material or formed during alcohol production process.

Eight molecules were proved to be especially problematic because of their concentration and/or their inhibitory effect and were chosen as targets for further investigations: formic (f.a.), acetic (a.a.), propanoic (p.a.), butanoic (b.a.), valeric (v.a.) and hexanoic (h.a.) acids, furfural (f) and 2-phenylethanol (phol) (Table 1). The purification process should match the industrial scale, be robust, environmental friendly and cost-effective. Moreover, only physico-chemical treatments could be considered here, as restrictive rules in EU limit the reuse of biologically treated water for food contact. Reverse osmosis is widely used for sea-water desalination and most existing membranes are characterized according to this major application (retention of NaCl). However, the interest of reverse osmosis for treating and reusing industrial effluents and especially containing organic molecules is more and more stressed; it was shown to be a suitable process in fields as various as textile (Fabiani et al. 1996), metal plating (Qin et al. 2002), paintings (Converti et al. 2000) or agro-chemistry (Karabela et al. 2001, Noworyta et al. 2003). Many studies underline the interest of RO for re-use applications in agro-industries. Morin-Couallier et al. (2006b) showed the usefulness of RO for condensates detoxification with Dow Filmtec FT 30 membrane. Less tighty membranes (brackish water grade) were further selected by Sagne et al. (2008a): Dow Filmtec BW30, Hydranautics ESPA2 and CPA2. Based on batch experiments at pilot scale with Hydranautics ESPA2 membrane, a 10-15 bar transmembrane pressure (*TMP*), a low Volume Reduction Factor (*VRF*) and a pH increased until 6 appeared as a good compromise between permeate flux and inhibitory compounds rejection rate.

Ion-exchange (IE) can also be considered for the removal of acidic compounds. Detoxification of hemicellulosic hydrolysates containing similar compounds through IE was related in literature. Working with industrial condensates, Morin-Couallier et al. (2008) showed the interest of a weak anionic resin (Amberlyst A21 Rohm and Haas) to retain the best the acidic compounds. In the following, impact of RO and IE treatments on the growth kinetics and physiological state of *Saccharomyces cerevisiae* was investigated in order to help for the choice of an adequate detoxification technology.

ANALYTICAL MEANS

For evaluating the efficiency of the treatments, the target inhibitory compounds have to be quantified. An HPLC method was developed at AgroParisTech (Massy, France) and used to determine f.a., a.a., p.a., b.a., v.a., h.a., f and phol concentrations. The chromatographic separation was performed on a high density C18 column Thermo-Electron Corporation BetaMax Neutral heated at 50°C. The mobile phase flow rate was 1 mL.min^{-1}. The mobile phase was a gradient of (A) H_2SO_4 5.10^{-4} mol.L^{-1} aqueous solution and (B) acetonitrile. The gradient program went from 5 to 40% of acetonitrile in 10 min and returned to 5% after a 5 min plateau. After each run, the column was equilibrated under the starting conditions for 10 min.

Fermentation tests have been implemented to evaluate the detoxification of the treated condensates and their ability for recycling:

Strain and growth medium. The yeast strain was 46 EDV *Saccharomyces cerevisiae* (Martin Vialatte Oenologie). The growth medium was prepared so as to get a saccharose concentration of 180 g.L^{-1}. It was composed of syrup 236 g.L^{-1}, molasses 59 g.L^{-1}, yeast extract 0.5 g.L^{-1}, peptone 2 g.L^{-1}, (NH$_4$)$_2$SO$_4$ 2 g.L^{-1}, H$_3$PO$_4$ 0.3 g.L^{-1}, MgSO$_4$ 0.1 g.L^{-1}, and qsp 1L with a) tap water, b) raw condensate, c) RO permeate at natural pH, d) RO permeate at pH 6, e) IE treated condensate. The pH was adjusted to 3.6 with H$_2$SO$_4$.

Yeast growth was studied by monitoring the cell multiplication over time with a Bioscreen C device (Labsystems). Wells of a microplate were filled with 200 µL of each of the growth media (20 replicates) and inoculated with *Saccharomyces cerevisiae* at 10^5 cells per mL. For each well, the optical density (OD) reflected the yeast development.

Yeast physiology was assessed during continuous fermentation in a 1.75 L chemostate where ethanol concentration was stabilized at 50±3 g.L^{-1}. Four chemostates were successively carried out with a), b), c), e) media. The specific growth rate of yeast µ (h^{-1}) was calculated as the ratio between feed flow and chemostate volume. Ethanol productivity (g.L^{-1}.h^{-1}) was deduced given the concentration. Samples from the chemostate were collected twice a day for viability staining. A double staining was applied: about 10^6 cells were suspended in 1 mL Mc Ilvaine buffer (citric acid 100mM and disodium hydrogen phosphate 200mM) set to pH 4; 1µL of 1mg.mL^{-1} propidium iodide was added and the suspension was incubated 20 min at 40°C; then 2µL of carboxyfluorescein diacetate (Chemchrome, Chemunex) were added and the suspension was incubated again 10 min before performing flow cytometer analysis with a Partec flow cytometer.

CONDENSATE TREATMENT BY REVERSE OSMOSIS

Theory

Extrapolation of pilot-scale studies as well as generalizing the results to other applications requires the development of models and the calculation of transfer parameters. One of the simplest models to represent the solute permeation through reverse osmosis membranes is the Solution-diffusion (SD) model (Londsdale, 1965). In this model, solute transport through the membrane is initiated by a partition between solution and membrane, quantified by the coefficient $K_{\ell,i}$. The sorbed solute then diffuses through the membrane as a result of its concentration gradient from one side to the other of the membrane and the following expression of permeate flux (J_P m s^{-1}) arises, assuming a steady-state regime in the membrane:

$$J_P = A(TMP - \Delta\Pi) \tag{1}$$

where A (m.s^{-1}.Pa^{-1}) is the water permeability, *TMP* the transmembrane pressure (Pa), $\Delta\Pi$ the osmotic pressure difference between retentate and permeate (Pa), (*TMP*-$\Delta\Pi$) also being called the effective pressure.

Concerning the solute i flux, it leads to:

$$J_i = -D_i \frac{dC_{m,i}(x)}{dx} = \frac{D_i}{\delta}\left(C_{mR,i} - C_{mP,i}\right) \tag{2a}$$

$$= \frac{D_i K_{\ell,i}}{\delta} \left(C_{R,i} - C_{P,i} \right) = B_i \left(C_{R,i} - C_{P,i} \right) \qquad (2b)$$

where x is the spatial coordinate through the membrane ($x = 0$ on the retentate membrane side and $x = \delta$ on the permeate membrane side), D_i the solute diffusivity ($m^2.s^{-1}$), $K_{\ell,i}$ its partition coefficient between the solution and the membrane, B_i the solute permeability ($m.s^{-1}$), $C_{m,i}(x)$ the concentration in the membrane at x ($mol.m^{-3}$), $C_{mR,i}$ and $C_{mP,i}$ the concentration in the membrane on the retentate and permeate sides respectively ($mol.m^{-3}$), $C_{R,i}$ and $C_{P,i}$ the concentration in retentate and permeate solutions respectively ($mol.m^{-3}$) and δ the membrane thickness (m).

For given conditions of *TMP* and solutes concentrations, the global permeability parameters *A* and *B* can be calculated and further used for extrapolation or generalization of studied cases.

Material and Methods

The treatment experiments of the beet distillery condensates were run on a 2540 spiral-wound RO pilot (2.6 m^2 of membrane surface area) from Polymem (Figure 1). In order to avoid artifact sorption, most of the different parts of the pilot are of stainless steel. Before each experiment a cleaning step was performed (30 min at 20 °C with KOH at 0.4 g L^{-1} followed by rinsing with filtrated de-ionized water). Each solution to treat was previously filtered through 10 μm and 3 μm cartridges to lower turbidity under 1 NTU as recommended by membranes' manufacturers. Retentate flow rate was set at 400 L.h^{-1} and temperature was maintained at 20°C with a thermostated water bath.

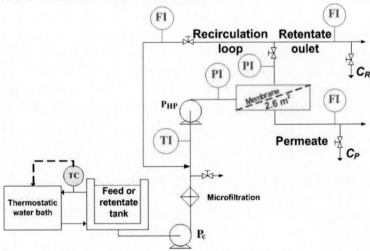

Figure 1. Scheme of the reverse osmosis pilot.

RO experiments were carried out in continuous feed-and-bleed mode. A recirculation loop allowed a fraction of the retentate to be recycled in the module; the remaining was extracted continuously. In feed-and-bleed mode, *VRF* was calculated as follows:

$$VRF = 1 + \frac{Q_P}{Q_R} \qquad\qquad (3)$$

where Q_P is the extracted permeate flow $(m^3.h^{-1})$ and Q_R the extracted retentate flow $(m^3.h^{-1})$.

Experiments were run with an industrial condensate from a French beet distillery. The influence of pH was evaluated at $TMP = 10$ bar and $VRF = 2$ for two values of pH: condensates natural pH (pH = 3.4) and pH = 6 (adjusted by addition of 16.7 mmol of NaOH 1N per litre of condensate). Feed, retentate and permeate were sampled for both experiments.

Efficiency of RO was evaluated through its influence on the yeast physiology and growth and on the inhibitory compounds rejection rate, calculated for the overall system as follows:

$$R_S = \left(1 - \frac{C_p}{C_R}\right) * 100 \qquad\qquad (4)$$

where C_P is the solute concentration in permeate $(meq.L^{-1})$ and C_R the solute concentration in retentate at the outlet of the membrane $(meq.L^{-1})$.

Due to the good rejection results obtained by Sagne (2008a) for the inhibitory solutes in a previous study on a plate and frame equipment, the Hydranautics ESPA2 membrane was chosen here (NaCl rejection rate = 99.6% with TMP of 10.5 bar and 1500 ppm NaCl). This membrane is a "brackish water" type with active layer of cross-linked aromatic polyamide obtained via interfacial polymerization of m-phenylenediamine and trimesoyl chloride. This layer was characterized through surface streaming potential measurements using a ZETACAD zeta-meter (CAD Inst., France) and following a procedure described by Fievet et al. (2004). ζ-potentials versus pH data measurements achieved at 20°C with KCl 10^{-3} M showed that it exhibits an isoelectric point at pH = 5.1 (Figure 2), with a positive net charge at acidic pH due to a great number of amine groups. When the pH increases, the surface of the membrane becomes negative because of the neutralization of the $-NH_3^+$ groups and the dissociation of the carboxylic groups -COOH into -COO$^-$. This net charge and its fluctuation can be responsible for some of the rejections observed and the pH influence on them, as well as for adsorption phenomena.

Reverse Osmosis Treatment: Efficiency Results

Water permeability A for the ESPA2 membrane is around 2.3 $L.h^{-1}.m^{-2}.bar^{-1}$ which is in the usual range for this kind of membrane for industrial effluents: between 1 and 5 $L.h^{-1}.m^{-2}.bar^{-1}$ (Qin et al. 2002, Bodalo-Santoyo et al. 2003, Suthanthararajan et al. 2004).

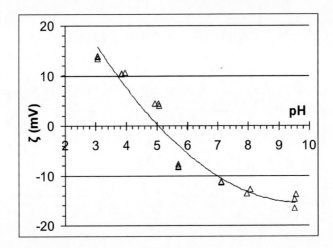

Figure 2. ζ-potential measurements for the ESPA2 membrane performed at 10^{-3} M KCl (Sagne, 2008b).

Concerning the inhibitory solutes, for the studied conditions of *TMP* and flow-rate, the permeability *B* is zero for valeric acid and 2-phenylethanol as those solutes do not permeate through the ESPA2 membrane. Permeability increases when the molecular weight of the acid compound increases, with *B* about $0.5 \ 10^{-6}$ m.s^{-1} for butanoic acid, $2 \ 10^{-6}$ m.s^{-1} for propanoic acid, $8 \ 10^{-6}$ m.s^{-1} for acetic acid for example, showing that for this family of solutes sieving is the dominant transfer mechanism. This membrane exhibits for furfural permeability similar to that of butanoic acid: around 10^{-6} m.s^{-1} (Sagne, 2008b).

The acids rejection rates increase with the pH, especially for the low molecular weight formic and acetic acids (Table 2). For pH < 5, a classical polyamide surface exhibits a positive charge due to free amine groups, attracting the carboxylate form of the acids: the smallest ones then cross the membrane in a certain extent (Bellona et al. 2004, Ozaki et al. 2002). At pH = 6, all acids show a rejection rate higher than 90% explained by electrostatic repulsions between the ionized form of the acids, predominant for pH above 5, and the negative net charge of the membrane surface at that pH value (Gerard et al. 1998, Sagne 2008b). This repulsion is as more important as the acid is small, due to its higher charge density. For acids and regardless of pH conditions, the higher the molecular weight, the better the rejection rate, in agreement with literature observations. Regarding neutral compounds, furfural was always absent from the condensates studied. 2-phenylethanol was the best retained solute, with no effect of pH.

Table 2. Permeate composition and rejection rates with pH
(*VRF* = 2 and *TMP* = 10 bar)

		f.a.	a.a.	p.a.	b.a.	phol
Natural pH	C_P (meq.L^{-1})	2.94	7.98	0.49	0.28	0.02
	R_S (%)	0.0%	48.5%	64.0%	91.2%	93.1%
pH 6	C_P (meq.L^{-1})	0.16	1.44	<0.10	<0.08	0.02
	R_S (%)	92.0%	93.9%	>92.4%	>95.9%	93.6%

Eventually, condensate treatment at natural pH does not seem to lead to a sufficient detoxification level, with a rejection of only 50% for the acetic acid corresponding to a concentration of about 0.5 g.L^{-1} still in the permeate. Fermentation tests are necessary to confirm if a complementary treatment would be essential to this effluent recycling.

As permeate obtained at pH 6 contains less inhibitory target compounds than the natural pH permeate, it is expected to be much less inhibitory.

ION EXCHANGE TREATMENT

Choice of the Resin

A weak-base (anion-) exchanger resin was chosen for the retention of most of the acidic compounds contained in the beet distillery condensate. Indeed, weak ion-exchange resins are known to exhibit higher exchange capacities as compared to strong ones (Dorfner 1991). Moreover, they regenerate better, by changing the pH which results in the neutralisation of the exchanger groups. Eventually, other works have assessed their potentiality for the carboxylic acids retention (Morin-Couallier et al., 2008) or in the related context of hemicellulosic hydrolyzates detoxification (De Mancilha et al. 2003, De Carvalho et al. 2004).

On these supports, the ion-exchange mechanism for weak acidic compounds approximates that of an ion pairing between the carboxylic acids and the resin amine groups, both undissociated (Figure 3) (Bhandari et al. 1992), in addition to nonionic sorption as noticed by Helfferich (1962).

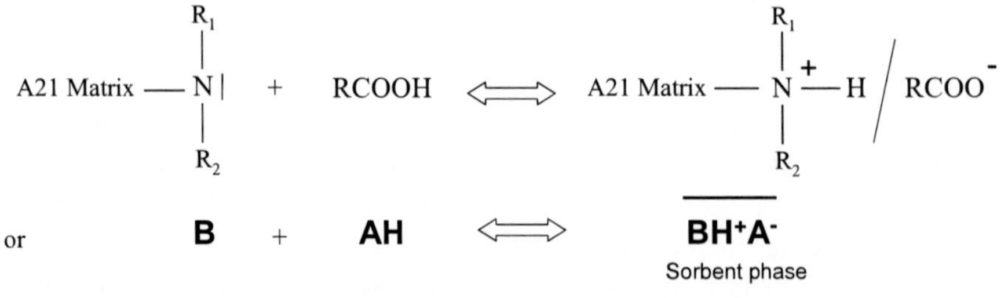

Figure 3. Acid sorption on weak-base resin: protonation of the free ionogenic sites, followed by electrostatic interaction.

Material and Methods

As "food grade" resins are preferable for this application, Amberlite FPA 51 showing characteristics identical to Amberlyst A21 used by Morin-Couallier et al. (2008) was selected.

Isotherm Measurements

In order to assess and quantify the ability of the FPA51 to retain the inhibitory molecules, experiments were performed with synthetic solutions containing only one target solute at different initial concentrations. Therefore, batch experiments were carried out in 250 cm³ glass flasks, where $V = 50$ cm³ of single solute i solution of a known concentration C_{0i} (meq.L^{-1}) was added to 1 g to 10 g of wet support depending on the batch. The flasks were then covered and placed in an agitator at room temperature (25°C) for 24h to achieve equilibrium. Supernatant samples were then analysed to obtain the equilibrium concentration of solute i, C_i^* (meq.L^{-1}) and the resin sample of each flask filtered under vacuum and let to dry at 105 °C until constant dry weight m (g). The solid-phase concentration q_i^* (meq.g^{-1}) in equilibrium with C_i^* was further calculated by mass balance in the batch according to:

$$q_i^* = \frac{(C_{0i} - C_i^*)V}{m}$$ (5)

where m is corrected for the mass of molecule adsorbed.

For modelling of the adsorption isotherms thus obtained on the FPA51 resin, the commonly used Langmuir equation was tested:

$$q_i^* = \frac{q_{si} K_i C_i^*}{1 + K_i C_i^*}$$ (6)

where q_{si} is the maximum sorption capacity for the solute i (meq.g^{-1}) and K_i the equilibrium constant for its sorption (L.meq^{-1}). This constant represents the affinity of the support for the solute.

Ion Exchange Treatment in Column

For the treatment in column, the equipment shown in Figure 4 was used. All experiments were run at room temperature, using a 25 cm x 1 cm ID glass column (Omnifit, Bioblock). The height of the bed was adjusted by means of a piston, delimiting a given resin Bed Volume BV. The column was fed until saturation at a flow rate of 10 BV.h^{-1} with industrial condensate, of initial concentration $C_{init\,i}$ (meq.L^{-1}) in each solute. The pH of the effluent was continually recorded and fractions collected for HPLC analyses and breakthrough curves plotting.

Breakthrough curves are then analysed for solute i which leads the experimental stoichiometric breakthrough volume V_{Si} (or mean breakthrough volume, L) to be calculated:

$$V_{Si} = \frac{\displaystyle\int_0^{C_{init\,i}} V \mathrm{d}C_i}{C_{init\,i}}$$ (7)

This volume corresponds to the maximum condensate volume that can be treated with the resin under concern, before outlet of the corresponding solute.

The corresponding capacity q_i (meq.g^{-1}) can be deduced through an overall mass balance on the column:

$$q_i = \frac{(V_{Si} - V_P)C_{init\ i}}{m_C} \tag{8}$$

where V_p (L) is the void volume deduced from a previous RTD study and m_C (g) the dry mass of resin in the column, obtained after the experiment.

This capacity is to be compared to the predicted one, obtained according to the Langmuir model previously calculated. As column experiments are run with real condensates containing at least five solutes, competitive effects are likely to take place. The extended Langmuir model based on the mechanism of direct competition of solutes for the adsorption sites can be tested to account for these effects. Resin capacity for solute i in a mixture of n solutes can be evaluated by:

$$q^*_{i,n} = \frac{q_{si}K_iC^*_i}{1+\sum\limits_{j=1}^{n}K_jC^*_j} \tag{9}$$

where q_{si} and K_i are the model parameters obtained for each of the n solutes separately by Langmuir modelling (equation 6) and C_i^* taken as their concentration in the feed.

Inhibition effect and yeast physiology influence were tested on a detoxified fraction taken at the column outlet.

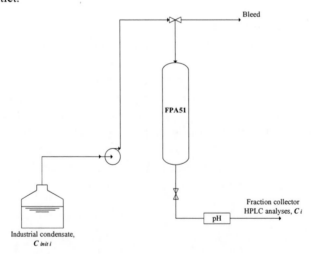

Figure 4. Treatment of the industrial condensate by anion-exchange resin.

Ion Exchange Treatment: Efficiency Results

Ion-Exchange Isotherms

Figure 5 shows the ion-exchange isotherms obtained for the four carboxylic acids on FPA51 resin. These curves are well represented by the Langmuir model which parameters were calculated (Table 3).

Table 3. Langmuir modelling of the adsorption on FPA51 resin of the major carboxylic acids contained in the condensates

	Formic acid	Acetic acid	Propanoic acid	Butanoic acid
q_{si} (meq.g-1)	9.08	7.00	6.11	5.66
K_i (L.meq-1)	0.832	0.140	0.256	0.426

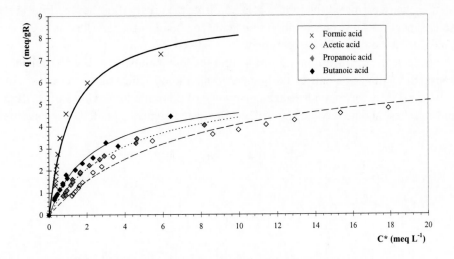

Figure 5. Adsorption isotherms of the acid solutes on FPA51 resin - Experimental points and Langmuir modelling (lines).

Except for formic acid, ion-exchange curves for acetic, butanoic and propanoic acids are quite superimposed, with a maximum sorption capacity about 6 meq L^{-1}, which can be explained by their similar pKa values (about 4.8). On the contrary, FPA51 resin presents for formic acid a much higher capacity and affinity (K_i parameter), due to its more acidic character. With a pKa of 3.75, it interacts much stronger with the weak-base exchanger sites.

Further results show that 2-phenylethanol quite does not adsorb on the FPA51 resin. Therefore, its isotherm curve is not shown here.

Condensate Treatment in Column

The breakthrough curves are plotted for acetic, propanoic and butanoic acids, as well as 2-phenylethanol (Figure 6). With a stoichiometric volume of 3.8 BV, 2-phenylethanol is very weakly retained, as could be expected from its equilibrium isotherm on a similar anionic resin (Morin-Couallier et al., 2008). Its retention is due to adsorption on the styrenic matrix because of π−π interaction with phenyl groups rather than exchange of alcoholate ion with functional groups. Its breakthrough presents a peak of excess concentration, sign of a displacement effect. This phenomenon is observed in multi component adsorption (Huang et al. 1995). The 2-phenylethanol concentration drop occurs simultaneously with the acidic compounds breakthrough. According to theses curves, acidic compounds break through after the elution of 40 BV of condensate.

Table 4 confirms the good retentions for the acid solutes, increasing with molecular weight. Calculation of the predicted capacity was made for each solute according to the Langmuir models (equations 6 and 9). 2-phenylethanol was not taken into account in the extended Langmuir model because of its negligible adsorption. Results show that the mono-component modelling ($q_{i\ Langmuir}$) greatly overestimates the retention capacity for all the solutes. A competition for the exchange sites does occur between the acids, decreasing by a factor until eight the efficiency of the resin. The extended model ($q_{i\ extended\ Langmuir}$) gives a good fit for acetic acid, the major inhibitory compound. For propanoic and butanoic acids, breakthrough is overestimated even when competition is taken into account. The high retention capacity predicted for formic acid confirms the great affinity of the FPA51 resin for this solute, even at low concentration and with competing effects. Thus, it could not have appeared during the time of the experiment.

As expected, pH evolution at the outlet of the column is directly related to the breakthrough of the acids and could be chosen as a good indicator for process monitoring. Actually, a pH of 5 corresponds to the emergence of the inhibitory acids in the effluent. The treatment process should then be stopped and the resin regenerated before a second feed cycle takes place.

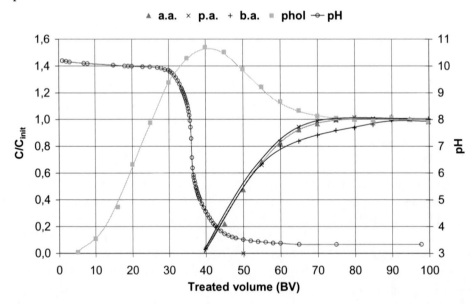

Figure 6. Breakthrough curves of inhibitory compounds in industrial condensate on Amberlite FPA 51.

Table 4. Experimental stoichiometric breakthrough volume and capacity for the inhibitory compounds

	f.a.	a.a.	p.a.	b.a.	phol
$C_{init\ i}$ (meq.L^{-1})	1.2	15.6	1.43	1.99	0.14
$V_{S\ i}$ (BV)	> 100	51.8	51.9	49	3.80
q_i (meq.g^{-1})	> 0.42	2.86	0.26	0.34	0.003
$q_{i\ Langmuir}$ (meq.g^{-1})	4.53	4.79	1.64	2.6	-
$q_{i\ extended\ Langmuir}$ (meq.g^{-1})	1.68	2.83	0.41	0.89	-

Eventually, the 40 BV fraction recovered at the column outlet is totally free of acids, but not of neutral compounds as 2-phenylethanol which could affect to a certain extend the fermentation activity. A complementary treatment should then be necessary.

IMPACT OF REVERSE OSMOSIS AND ION-EXCHANGE TREATMENTS ON THE GROWTH KINETICS AND THE PHYSIOLOGY OF YEAST

Tested treated condensates. Table 5 sums up the composition in inhibitory target compounds of the condensate before and after the different treatments.

Influence on yeast growth. Figure 7 confirms that the raw condensate inhibits strongly the yeast growth. The lag phase lasts near 24h instead of a few hours for the other media. Compared to other media, the specific growth rate (represented by the slope of the OD during the growth phase) and the maximal OD are lower for the raw condensate. Maximal OD reached for all condensates treated are similar each other and close to the blank. IE treated condensate and natural pH RO permeate present results equivalent to the blank during the first 60 hours. pH 6 RO permeate shows a slightly lower specific growth rate, which was unexpected considering its lower concentration in inhibitory compounds. Such a result can be explained considering that this permeate showed a higher pH and overall a higher mineral level due to the addition of soda. A proportionally higher quantity of H_2SO_4 had hence to be added when preparing the growth medium (d) (cf. 2.4). The increased osmotic pressure resulting may impact on the fermentability, by stressing the yeast (Bai et al. 2008) and disrupting yeast growth (Leveau et al. 1993). Due to this preliminary result, pH 6 RO permeate was not included in the further experiments on continuous fermentation (chemostate).

Influence on yeast physiology. Continuous fermentation was investigated on a chemostate stabilized at 50 g.L^{-1} ethanol. The proportion of viable, dead and stressed yeast cells as given by the flow cytometry analyses are presented table 6. Unstained cells (i.e. ghosts) correspond to lysed cells that can no more be strained. The harmful influence of raw condensate on yeast activity is confirmed. Compared to the blank, both IE and RO treated condensates present similar specific growth rates. However, a slight difference with the blank on physiological state is noticeable. Moreover, ethanol productivity seems a little lower in the case of IE permeate than for RO permeate. If these differences are significant (due to remaining inhibitors, i.e. acidic compounds for RO permeate and neutral compounds for IE treated condensate), carrying out fermentation at higher ethanol concentrations will dramatically emphasize the lethal effect on yeast physiology.

Table 5. Concentration of inhibitory compounds (in meq.L^{-1}) in raw and treated condensates used for fermentation tests

	f.a.	a.a.	p.a.	b.a.	phol
Raw condensate	1.19	15.60	1.43	1.99	0.14
IE treated condensate	<0.08	<0.09	<0.096	<0.08	0.09
RO permeate – natural pH	2.94	7.98	0.49	0.28	0.02
RO permeate – pH 6	0.16	1.44	<0.10	<0.08	0.02

Table 6. Mean values of viable, stressed, dead and unstained cells, specific growth rate and ethanol productivity during fermentation with IE or RO treated and raw condensates

	% Viable	% Dead	% Stressed	% Unstained	μ (h^{-1})	Ethanol productivity (g.L^{-1}.h^{-1})
Blank	56.6	18.3	17.3	7.8	0.04	2.06
IE treated condensate	48.0	24.4	17.1	10.5	0.038	1.89
Natural pH RO permeate	51.5	23.0	16.0	9.5	0.04	2.06
Raw condensate	19.2	17.4	44.3	19.1	0.017	0.86

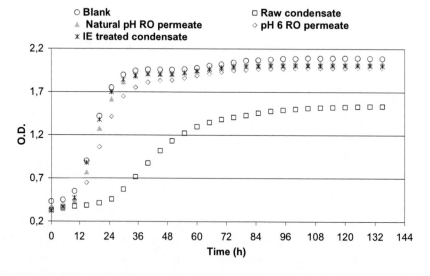

Figure 7. Optical density obtained with treated and raw condensates versus fermentation time.

Further fermentation experiments at concentrations >100 g.L^{-1} are therefore needed to definitely assess a convenient purification process. Three or four chemostates in series will have to be implemented for reaching such high ethanol levels.

CONCLUSION

Condensates treated either by reverse osmosis (RO) on a Hydranautics ESPA 2 membrane (*TMP*=10 bars, *VRF*=2 and natural pH) or by anion-exchange (IE) on a Rohm and Haas Amberlite FPA 51 weak resin displayed fermentation activities almost equivalent to tap water chosen as the blank. The remaining inhibitory compounds (mainly acids for RO and neutral for IE) did not seem to hinder significantly yeast growth or yeast physiology. Regarding reverse osmosis (RO), although acidic inhibitory compounds were better rejected when operating at pH $\geq$ 6 than at the natural pH of the condensates, the permeate obtained in the former conditions proved a little less fermentable perhaps because of an increased osmotic pressure due to the addition of soda.

Continuous fermentability experiments were carried out at ethanol concentrations twice lower than in industrial conditions. Further experiments at concentrations >100 g.L^{-1} are therefore needed to definitely assess the convenient purification process.

REFERENCES

Bai, F. W.; Anderson, W. A.; Moo-Yung, M. *Biotech. Adv.* 2008, *26*, 89-105.

Bellona, C.; Drewes, J. E.; Xu, P.; Amy, G. *Water Res.* 2004, *38*, 2795-2809.

Bhandari, V. M.; Juvekar, V. A.; Patwardhan, S. R. *Ind. Eng. Chem. Res.* 1992, *31*, 1073-1080.

Bodalo-Santoyo, A.; Gomez-Carrasco, J. L.; Gomez-Gomez, E.; Maximo-Martin, F.; Hidalgo-Montesinos, A. M. *Desalination* 2003, *155*, 101-108.

Converti, A.; Dominguez, J. M.; Perego, P.; da Silva, S. S.; Zilli, M. *Chem. Eng. Technol.* 2000, *23 (11)*, 1013-1020.

De Carvalho, W.; Canilha, L.; Mussatto, S. I.; Dragone, G.; Morales, M. L.; Solenzal, A. I. N. *J. Chem. Technol. Biotechnol.* 2004, *79*, 863-868.

De Mancilha, I. M.; Karim, M. N. *Biotechnol. Prog.* 2003, *19 (6)*, 1837-1841.

Dorfner, K. *Ion Exchangers*; Walter de Gruyter: Berlin - New York, 1991; p 1495.

Fabiani, C.; Pizzichini, M.; Spadoni, M.; Zeddita, G. *Desalination* 1996, *105*, 1-9.

Fievet, P.; Szymczyck, A.; Sbaï, M.; Magnenet, C.; Fatin-Rouge, N. In *Recent developments in colloids and interface research*, Transworld research network: 2004; Vol. 2, pp 1-27.

Gerard, R.; Hachisuka, H.; Hirose, M. *Desalination* 1998, *119*, 47-55.

Helfferich, F. G., *Ion exchange*. McGraw-Hill Book Company, Inc.: New-York, 1962.

Huang, R. T.; Chen, T. L.; Weng, H. S. *Sep. Sci. Technol.* 1995, *30 (13)*, 2731-2746.

Karabelas, A. J.; Yiantsios, S. G.; Metaxiotou, Z.; Andritsos, N.; Akiskalos, A.; Vlachopoulos, G.; Stavroulias, S. *Desalination* 2001, *138*, 93-102.

Leveau, J.-Y.; Bouix, M. In *Microbiologie industrielle*; Leveau, J.-Y., Bouix, M., Eds.; Lavoisier: Paris, 1993.

Londsdale, H.; Merten, U.; Riley, R. *J. Appl. Polym. Sci.* 1965, *9*, 1341.

Morin-Couallier, E.; Payot, T.; Pastore Bertin, A.; Lameloise, M.-L. *Appl. Biochem. Biotechnol.* 2006a, *133 (3)*, 217-238.

Morin-Couallier, E.; Salgado Ruiz, B.; Lameloise, M.-L.; Decloux, M. *Desalination* 2006b, *196*, 306-317.

Morin-Couallier, E.; Fargues, C.; Lewandowski, R.; Decloux, M.; Lameloise, M.-L. *J. Cleaner Prod.* 2008, *16*, 655-663.

Noworyta, A.; Koziol, T.; Trusek-Holownia, A. *Desalination* 2003, *156*, 397-402.

Ozaki, H.; Li, H. *Water Res.* 2002, *36*, 123-130.

Qin, J. J.; Wai, M. N.; Oo, M. H.; Wong, F. S. *J. Membr. Sci.* 2002, *208 (1-2)*, 213-221.

Sagne, C.; Fargues, C.; Lewandowski, R.; Lameloise, M.-L.; Decloux, M. *Desalination* 2008a, *219*, 335-347.

Sagne, C. Etude des mécanismes de transfert de molécules organiques en osmose inverse - Application au recyclage des condensats issus de la concentration de vinasses de distilleries. Thesis AgroParisTech, Massy, France, 2008b.

Suthanthararajan, R.; Ravindranath, E.; Chitra, K.; Umamaheswari, B.; Ramesh, T.; Rajamani, S. *Desalination* 2004, *164*, 151-156.

In: Water Production and Wastewater Treatment
Editor: B. Antizar-Ladislao et al.

ISBN 978-1-61728-503-5
© 2011 Nova Science Publishers, Inc.

Chapter 16

APPLICATION OF THEORETICAL SCALING POTENTIAL INDEX TO PREDICT ONSET OF COMPOSITE CALCIUM CARBONATE AND CALCIUM SULFATE FOULING AND CRYSTAL TYPES AND PHASES IN SEAWATER REVERSE OSMOSIS TREATMENT

R. Sheikholeslami[1], Y. Wang and H. Yu
School of Engineering University of Edinburgh
Edinburgh, UK, EH9 3JL

ABSTRACT

Desalination of saline water by reverse osmosis (RO) is used both for production of potable water and treatment of waste water. However, membrane fouling (or usually referred as scaling) caused by sparingly soluble inorganic salts, such as calcium sulfate and calcium carbonate is often encountered as the feed water is being concentrated in the RO module. Once the solubilities of these salts are exceeded, they will precipitate and accumulate on the membrane surface and as such will reduce the production capacity and will increase the need for cleaning which also reduces the membrane life. The strong adhesion of these scales on the membranes complicates the cleaning procedure and they are not amenable to physical processes and require chemical agents to dissolve and remove them. These salts have been mostly investigated in isolation while in actual practice they coexist; the interactive and synergistic effects when they co-exist further complicate and adversely impact the operation. Morphology and adhesive strength of scales from mixed precipitation will be different from that obtained in single salt precipitation. However, due to the complexity of process, not much attention has been paid on these effects and specifically in a dynamic set-up. The aim of this work is to investigate the co-precipitation of calcium sulfate and calcium carbonate at seawater salinity range, different recovery levels, various SO_4^{2-}/HCO_3^- molar ratios in seawater RO

---

[1] Roya.sheikholeslami@ed.ac.uk.

systems, and to apply Sheikholeslami's [1, 2] theoretical Scaling Potential Index (SPI) which is based on fundamental thermodynamic principles and incorporation of Gibbs free energy of reaction to predict the onset of scale formation and the specific polymorph formed. In the theoretical assessments ion interactive effects are incorporated using Pitzer relationship [3] and concentration polarization effect is incorporated to assess the concentrations seen by the membrane surface. Results showed that the presence of carbonate species in the feed solution influenced the induction period of calcium sulfate at the same supersaturation levels. Precipitation kinetics and morphology and mineralogy of scales were found to be strongly affected by SO_4^{2-}/HCO_3^- molar ratios in feed water of the same calcium ion content and salinity. The theoretical predictions by Sheikholeslami's SPI for gypsum, calcite, and aragonite were in good agreements with experimental results.

1. INTRODUCTION

Fresh water shortage and availability of saline water sources bring about a great market for membrane reverse osmosis (RO) desalination which has grown exponentially in the last 10-15 years. However, the high potential of fouling of membranes seriously impacts the operation and cannot be avoided easily. In saline water RO desalination systems, some sparingly soluble salts, such as calcium sulfate and calcium carbonate have tendency to deposit on the membrane surface. This accumulation of undesired deposits results in a continuous decline in water production and hence reduces the overall efficiency, leads to more frequent membrane cleaning and replacement, and increases the operation and maintenance costs. The precipitation of individual salts has been mostly investigated in isolation for many years both in thermal desalination plants and RO membrane systems. Also, the co-precipitation of calcium sulfate and calcium carbonate has been studied in batch tests at various salinities and temperatures [3-8]. Composite fouling and thermodynamics and kinetics of mixed salts precipitation have been discussed elsewhere [9-11]. The thermodynamic and kinetic data for pure salt precipitation cannot be extended to co-precipitation. In fact, these two salts usually co-precipitate on the membrane surface due to the co-existence in natural waters. Furthermore, the morphology of mixed precipitate is different from single salt precipitation; it also varies with changes in SO_4^{2-}/HCO_3- molar ratios. In addition, the solubility varies with the level of salinity. The interactive effects complicate the operation and cleaning procedure. However, due to the complexity of fouling process in dynamic RO systems, few studies have been conducted in this field. Little information is available in the literature regarding the co-precipitation of $CaSO_4$ and $CaCO_3$ in a complex seawater RO system. The situation is complicated because the kinetics of crystallization will differ for a stable batch experiment compared with dynamic condition where crystals grow concomitantly with the passage of water and retention of ions by RO membrane and progressive concentration in the feed channel.

The complexity of fouling analysis in a dynamic RO unit arises from the decrease of flux which is not only resulted from scale formation but also from increase in the osmotic pressure due to concentration as the feed passes through the module. Therefore, it is necessary to exclude the effects of osmotic pressure in analysis so that effects of scaling can be isolated and investigated. Furthermore, the deposition occurs on the membrane surface on which the concentration of the salts is higher than that in the bulk solution. So the effects of concentration polarization must be incorporated in evaluating the supersaturation levels of co-precipitating salts on the membrane surface.

The aim of this work is to investigate the co-precipitation of calcium sulfate and calcium carbonate in dynamic RO systems, particularly the effects of calcium carbonate on the precipitation kinetics, the effect of SO_4^{2-}/HCO_3^- molar ratio on the co-precipitation of $CaSO_4$ and $CaCO_3$ in a dynamic seawater RO, and to identify the differences in deposit morphology for single salt precipitation, co-precipitation and for varying SO_4^{2-}/HCO_3^- ratios on composite fouling. Sheikholeslami's [1, 2] theoretical Scaling Potential Index (SPI) was used to predict onset of gypsum, calcite and aragonite formation and the predictions were validated by the experimental results for flux decline and analytical results.

2. EXPERIMENTAL

2.1. Operation System

The experiments were carried out in a partial recycling RO unit which is illustrated in Figure1. It consists of a closed-loop circulation system which includes a 33 cm x 33 cm x 44 cm PVC feed solution storage tank, a Hydra-Cell positive displacement industrial pressure pump, manufactured by Warner Engineering, a cooling water system, a membrane cell, and a series of pressure, temperature and flow measuring and control devices. The membrane cell is a plate-and-frame module with the membrane active area 294cm^2 (49cm in length and 6 cm in width). The test cell was connected to the test loop through two union joints for quick connection and removal from the system. The RO seawater membranes were made of composite polyamide and provided by Hydranautics (Catalogue designation: SWC2).

The system was designed to operate on both full recycling and partial recycling modes. For these experiments the system operated at partial recycling mode where there was withdrawal of the product flow constantly during the operation resulting in concentration of feed solution with time. The partial recycling mode emulates the concentration of water along the feed channel and, once the osmotic pressure effect is corrected, it is a convenient method for investigating the permeate flux decline resulted from the onset of fouling at increasing feed water recovery levels.

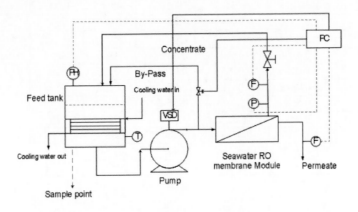

Figure 1. Schematic diagram of operation system.

The experiments were conducted at constant flow velocity 2-2.1m/s and feed pump pressure 40 bar (580 psi). The corresponding concentration polarization modulus (CP) is about 1.25~1.26. The temperature of the feed solution was controlled at $25\pm1°C$ by a cooling water system. The data acquisition and control system (Genie, American Advantach Co.) was used to control the feed pressure, concentrate flowrate at set values and to monitor and record permeate flux and solution pH. The results were constantly displayed on the computer screen and recorded into the computer's hard disk at given time intervals.

2.2. Experimental Conditions and Procedures

Synthetic seawater was prepared by dissolving analytical grade $CaCl_2$, $MgCl_2 \cdot 6H_2O$, Na_2SO_4 and $NaHCO_3$ in 15 L NaCl solution of predetermined concentration resulting in constant Na^+, Ca^{2+}, Mg^{2+}, and Cl^- but varying SO_4^{2-} and HCO_3^- concentrations to compare single salt with composite fouling and also the effect of SO_4^{2-}/HCO_3^- molar ratios on composite fouling. The water used was distilled and filtered with 0.22-μ m Millipore filter. The initial pH value of feed solution was adjusted to 7.3±0.2 with HCl or NaOH. The operating conditions and feed composition of each test are listed in Table 1 and detailed elsewhere [12, 13]. The data logging program was initiated as the test solution was transferred to the feed storage tank. In order to mix the bulk solution completely and stabilize the system, the system was operated at full recycling mode for 10 minutes. After that, the permeate flow was withdrawn from the system for partial recycling mode to mimic the condition at increasing water recovery levels. The operating pressure and brine velocity were controlled at set values throughout the run. In order to identify the difference between single salt precipitation and co-precipitation of two salts with a common ion Ca^{2+}, feed solution in the absence of sulfate ion or carbonate species was also tested.

Table 1. Operating and feed conditions of different tests

Test No.	A	B	C	1	2	3	4
Feed pump pressure, psi	580.90±7.80	580.18±11.44	580.17±5.67	580 ±4	580. ±11	580 ±6	582 ±18
Conc. flow velocity, m/s	2.05 ±0.02	2.02 ±0.04	2.12 ±0.05	2.01 ±0.07	2.02 ±0.04	2.05 ±0.07	2.10 ±0.10
CP	1.26	1.26	1.24	1.26	1.26	1.26	1.25
Temperature, °C	26	26	25	25	26	25	26
Na^+, Mole/L	0.4859	0.4859	0.4859	0.4859	0.4859	0.4859	0.4859
Ca^{2+}, Mole/L	0.0105	0.0105	0.0105	0.0105	0.0105	0.0105	0.0105
Mg^{2+}, Mole/L	0.0542	0.0542	0.0542	0.0542	0.0542	0.0542	0.0542
Cl^-, Mole/L	0.5545	0.5545	0.5545	0.5545	0.5545	0.5545	0.5545
SO_4^{2-}, Mole/L	0.03	0.03	-	0.0482	0.029	0.029	0.0202
HCO_3^-, Mole/L	-	0.00241	0.00241	0.0024	0.0024	0.0057	0.0202
Initial pH	7.0	7.5	7.4	7.5	7.5	7.09	7.0
SO_4^{2-}/HCO_3^-, R	∞	12	0	20	12	5	1

In most seas around the world, the molar ratio of SO_4^{2-}/HCO_3^- is between 10 and 20 [14]. For example, this ratio in the Persian Gulf water is about 11 while in the Red Sea water is about 14. This ratio can be higher than 20 or lower than 5 in some circumstances - in the Mediterranean Sea water it is 3.5 [15] while for groundwater of Red Sea, unlike its surface water, is higher than 20.

Typically each experiment ran for a period of about 24 hours. During this period, about 40-50% of product flow was withdrawn from the system which was to mimic recovery levels in seawater RO desalination. The concentration of Ca^{2+} and SO_4^{2-} in the feed tank were measured periodically by Inductively Coupled Plasma – Atomic Emission Spectroscopy (ICP-AES). Total alkalinity was determined by titration according to the standard methods for water examination [16].

After each run, the scale deposits on a small representative piece of membrane was analysed by Scanning Electron Microscopy (SEM), Energy Dispersion X-ray Spectroscopy (EDS) and X-ray Diffraction (XRD) to assess and determine morphology, chemical compositions, and crystal phases of the deposits.

3. RESULTS AND DISCUSSION

Osmotic Pressure Effects

Permeate flux decline may be resulted from either an increase in the osmotic pressure under non-scaling condition or from both scale formation on membrane and the increase in osmotic pressure due to concentration effects. In order to isolate these two contributing factors and investigate the effects of scaling, an experiment was carried out using pure NaCl solution to assess flux decline due to osmotic pressure increase as a result of increases in solution concentration under non-fouling conditions. The system was initially operated by a total recycling mode for 1 hour for permeate flux to stabilize. Then the system was switched to partial recycling mode by withdrawing the product flow for 1 hour so as to increase the water recovery to a higher level. The system was returned to total recycling mode for another 1 hour to get the stabilized permeate flux at this higher water recovery level; the process was repeated and the change in permeate flux as a function of water recovery levels is presented in Figure2 for both fouling and non-fouling tests.

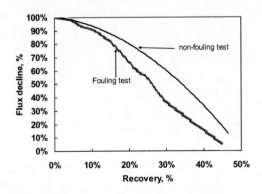

Figure 2. Comparison of permeate flux decline between fouling and non-fouling test.

Scaling Potential Index

Sheikholeslami's theoretical Scaling Potential Index (SPI) using Gibbs Free Energy [1, 2] was utilized to assess the scaling tendency for sparingly soluble salts in RO systems. The effect of ion interaction was incorporated through use of Pitzer model [3]. Since concentrations at the membrane surface are important to assess the scaling propensity, the effect of concentration polarization was incorporated in the SPI assessments and the SPI was evaluated for conditions prevailing on the membrane surface. The determination of the concentration polarization modulus CP requires the measurement of mass transfer coefficient which is based on the evaluation of the permeate flux decline induced by addition of NaCl solution to an initially salt –free water[17].

$$CP = \exp\left(\frac{Jv}{k}\right) \tag{1}$$

where Jv is the permeate flux, k is the mass transfer coefficient.

For calcium sulfate:

$$SPI = \log\left(\frac{\{Ca^{2+}\}_w \cdot \{SO_4^{2-}\}_w}{K_{sp}(CaSO_4)}\right) = \log\left(\frac{\gamma_\pm^2 \cdot (CP \cdot [Ca^{2+}]) \cdot (CP \cdot [SO_4^{2-}])}{K_{sp}(CaSO_4)}\right) \tag{2}$$

where $\{Ca^{2+}\}_w$ and $\{SO_4^{2-}\}_w$ are the activities of calcium and sulfate on the wall, respectively, $K_{sp}(CaSO_4)$ is the solubility product of calcium sulfate (gypsum) which is a function of the standard molar Gibbs free energy of reaction, $\gamma_\pm$ is the mean ionic coefficient [18], CP is the concentration polarization modulus, and $[Ca^{2+}]$ and $[SO_4^{2-}]$ are the bulk concentration of calcium and sulfate, respectively.

For calcium carbonate, the equation of SPI is similar to that of calcium sulfate (Equation 2) using the bulk concentration of carbonate $[CO_3^{2-}]$ instead of $[SO_4^{2-}]$. $[CO_3^{2-}]$ was calculated by Equation 3 [1] in this work.

$$[CO_3^{2-}] = \frac{[T.A.] + [H^+] - [OH^-]}{2\left(1 + [H^+]\gamma_{H^+}\gamma_{CO_3^{2-}} / \left(2\gamma_{HCO_3^-}K_2\right)\right)} \tag{3}$$

where $[T.A.]$ is the total alkalinity; γ is the activity coefficient; and K_2 is the second dissociation constant for carbonic acid.

Gypsum (CaSO$_4$·2H$_2$O) is the most stable crystal phase of calcium sulfate while two common forms of calcium carbonate formed at high salinities are calcite and aragonite. Therefore, the solubility products of calcium sulfate and calcium carbonate are calculated from the standard Gibbs free energies of reaction for gypsum, calcite and aragonite to give a more accurate estimation of the thermodynamic solubility products of these salts. Therefore, the SPI for gypsum, calcite and aragonite was calculated from the Gibbs free energy of reactions for these salts are obtained from the standard Gibbs free energies of formation [19].

Comparison of Mixed Precipitate with Single Salt Precipitates

The normalized permeate flux for each test was plotted against water recovery levels (Figure3). SPI values of calcium sulfate and calcium carbonate as a function of water recovery were also plotted in the same chart.

Flux – SPI Charts

Test A (SO_4^{2-}=0.02856mole/L, HCO_3^-=0) (see Figure 3a) – The decrease of permeate flux was not significant up to 37% of water recovery. The permeate flux dropped dramatically as SPI of gypsum became positive at 37% of water recovery. XRD result showed that gypsum ($CaSO_4 \cdot 2H_2O$) was the crystal structure of precipitate.

Test B (SO_4^{2-}=0.02856mole/L, HCO_3^-=0.00241mole/L) (see Figure 3b) - This run used the standard seawater compositions[20] except that potassium ion was replaced by sodium and bromide was substituted by chloride. In the presence of carbonate species, permeate flux began to drop at 12% of water recovery level at which the SPI of $CaCO_3$ (calcite) became positive. SPI also indicated that aragonite became supersaturated at 22% of water recovery level. XRD illustrated that calcium sulfate precipitated as gypsum phase while calcium carbonate precipitates consisted of both calcite and aragonite.

Test C (SO_4^{2-}=0, HCO_3^-=0.00241mole/L) – The scaling phenomenon happened at 8% of water recovery at which SPI of $CaCO_3$ (calcite) became positive. pH varied from 7.2 to 8.1 and increased dramatically from 7.4 at 5% of water recovery to 7.9 at 11% of water recovery. This verifies that $CaCO_3$ is highly pH dependent. Aragonite probably begun to form at 11% of water recovery. XRD measurements identified that both calcite and aragonite built up the precipitate.

Results Comparison –

In the absence of calcium carbonate, an almost non-fouling phenomenon could be detected up to 37% of water recovery. By contrast, the deposition of calcium carbonate induced an abrupt decline of permeate flux after 8% water recovery. This showed that $CaCO_3$ had a high SPI and no induction period and so precipitated quickly. On the other hand, the presence of sulfate ion had suppressed the crystallization of $CaCO_3$. Thus, the permeate flux dropped at a higher recovery level in combined sulfate and carbonate solution than that in sulfate free solution. The effect of sulfate ion on the crystallization of $CaCO_3$ might be due to either the buffering effect of the solution pH or the increasing solubility of $CaCO_3$[21, 22]. The changing pH level of Test B and Test C are shown in Figure 4. With the presence of sulfate ion, pH increased continuously while without sulfate ion, pH increased dramatically from 7.4 at 5% of water recovery to 7.9 at 11% of water recovery. However, this does not mean the co-existence of sulfate and carbonate may mitigate the fouling tendency.

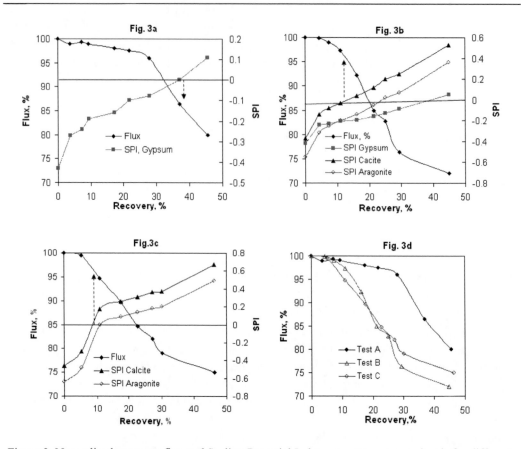

Figure 3. Normalized permeate flux and Scaling Potential Index vs. water recovery levels for different feed waters. a: carbonate free solution, b: sulfate and carbonate mixed solution, c: sulfate free solution, d: comparison of the above three tests.

When the water recovery level was up to 37% in Test B, CaSO$_4$ became supersaturated and began to precipitate. The co-precipitation of CaSO$_4$ and CaCO$_3$ further adversely impact the water production so that the overall decline of permeate flux was 5% more in Test B than that in Test C, and 10% more than that in Test A (see Figure 3d).

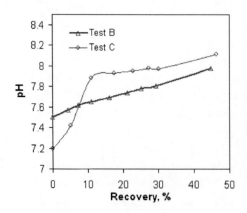

Figure 4. The comparison of pH changes in Test B and Test C.

SEM Micrographs –

Figure 5 shows the morphology of the precipitates formed at different feed conditions. The pure $CaSO_4$ (Figure 5a) which was obtained from Test A has a long needle shape. The scales were not very adhesive. The pure $CaCO_3$ obtained from Test C has a hexagonal (the structure of calcite) or orthorhombic structure (the structure of aragonite) (Figure 5c). This scale was found to adhere to the surface of the stainless membrane module strongly and could not be flushed away by water. From the images of the mixed precipitates obtained from Test B (Figure 5b), it can be seen that the needle shape gypsum grows on the hexagonal crystals and becomes smaller and shorter. These scales were not as tenacious as the pure calcium carbonate but more adhesive and stronger than pure calcium sulfate crystals. These results are in good agreement with the previous data in batch tests [7]. Therefore, the co-precipitates are harder and more adhesive than pure calcium sulfate scales which will complicate the cleaning procedure in practice.

a   b   c

Figure 5. SEM images of different deposits.

Effect of Varying SO_4^{2-}/HCO_3^- Molar Ratio on Composite Scale Formation

Runs 1 to 4 listed in Table 1 were used to assess the effect of varying SO_4^{2-}/HCO_3^- molar ratio.

Flux-SPI-Recovery Chart -

The normalized permeate flux (the effect of salinity on flux decline has been excluded) for each test was plotted against water recovery levels. SPI values of gypsum, calcite and aragonite as a function of water recovery level were also plotted in the same chart (Fig 6(a)-(d)). The difference in flux decrease with water recovery increase was observed for feed waters SO_4^{2-}/HCO_3^- values of 20, 12, 5 and 1.

In Run 1 (R=20, Fig 6(a)) permeate flux began to drop at 20% water recovery which was resulted from the precipitation of gypsum. SPI indicated calcite became supersaturated at 26% water recovery. This was because the precipitation of $CaSO_4$ reduced supersaturation level of $CaCO_3$. Aragonite had a potential to precipitate as the water recovery increased to 40% but only a very low peak of aragonite was detected from XRD results.

Run 2 tested the circumstance of R=12 (see Fig 6(b)) which is the molar ratio of SO_4^{2-}/HCO_3^- in the standard seawater [20]. Permeate flux began to drop at 12% water recovery level at which the SPI of $CaCO_3$ (calcite) became positive. SPI also indicated that another forms of $CaCO_3$ crystal-aragonite precipitated at 22% of water recovery level. XRD illustrated that $CaSO_4$ precipitated as gypsum which happened as the water recovery became greater than 37%. XRD patterns also exhibited the deposits consisted of both calcite and aragonite.

The increasing ratio of HCO_3^- resulted in quick precipitation of $CaCO_3$ and flux decline at only 3% of water recovery in Run 3 (R=5, Figure 6(c)). $CaCO_3$ was the dominant scale and XRD exhibited the scales contained calcite as well as aragonite. Although SPI predicted no gypsum would precipitate, a little amount of gypsum was detected by XRD which was also illustrated by the detection of sulfur in EDS. This is probably due to $CaSO_4$ solution being trapped in the interfacial spaces and evaporated and so formed the deposit after the run. Moreover, SPI is currently evaluated by the Gibbs free energy of formation for pure compounds which probably resulted in this deviation.

The decline of permeate flux in Run 4 (R=1, Figure 6(d)) was similar with that in Run 3. SPI indicated gypsum was under saturated throughout the test. Only aragonite was detected in XRD patterns. This is because rapid precipitation, high concentration of reactants and the presence of divalent cations increase the possibilities to produce aragonite [23]. In addition, the flux declined to a lowest level as water recovery was between 20~30%. This is probably because the membrane was blocked completely and the scales became thicker and thicker and not much water could be produced. This can be confirmed by visual examination. It was found that the white and compact scales covered the whole membrane. Therefore, the water recovery level was only 34% after 24 hours of operation.

In Run 3 (R=5) and Run 4 (R=1), due to the increasing of contents of HCO_3^-, more significant decrease of initial permeate flux were observed for both cases than that of Run 1 (R=20) and Run 2 (R=12) (see Figure 7). Also, due to a large amounts of $CaCO_3$ deposited and the scales were very tenacious (see Figure 8(c) and 8(d)) which blocked the membrane, the permeate flux declined to 40% for the case of R=1 and to 55% for the case of R=5 at the end of tests. Both impacted the water production more seriously than Run 1 and Run 2.

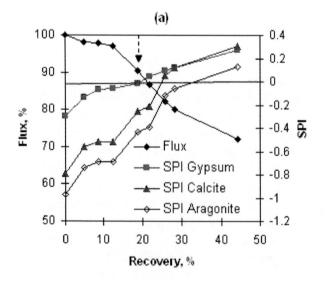

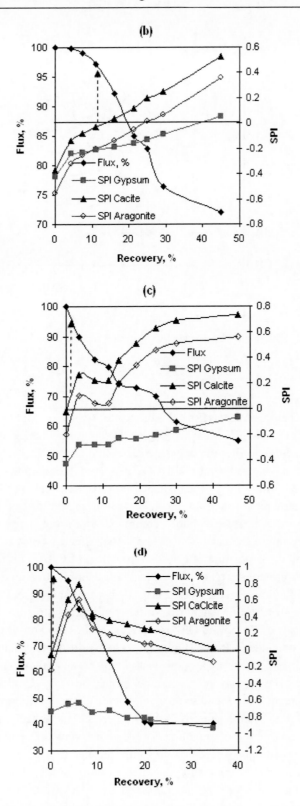

Figure 6. Normalized permeate flux and SPI vs. water recovery levels for varying SO_4^{2-}/HCO_3^- molar ratio (R) of feed waters. a: R=20, b: R=12, c: R=5, d: R=1.

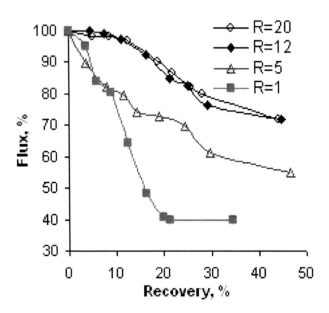

Figure 7. Comparison of normalized permeate flux vs. water recovery level for SO42-/HCO3- various values.

SEM-EDS Analysis

The physico-chemical properties of composite scales of $CaSO_4$ and $CaCO_3$ were characterized using SEM-EDS analysis. Figure 8 shows the image micrographs and the corresponding elemental profiles of composite scales at different SO_4^{2-}/HCO_3^- (R) values.

It can be observed that as the ratio of HCO_3^- increased, the morphological structure of the precipitates changed. Many long needle shaped crystals were obtained in Run 1 (Fig 8(a)). This is the typical structure of gypsum. It can be seen these needle shaped crystals were loose and attached over some hexagonal shaped combined with some short stick shaped crystals. The hexagonal crystals were calcite. The short stick shaped crystals were thought to be gypsum affected by the deposition of $CaCO_3$. The effect of $CaCO_3$ on the scale morphology of $CaSO_4$ has been previously reported by Sheikholeslami[3]. In Run 2 (Fig 8(b)), with the increasing HCO_3^-, the long needle shaped crystals became shorter and smaller and grew on the hexagonal (the structure of calcite) or orthorhombic (the structure of aragonite) scales. Moreover, high peaks of Ca, S, and O were detected by EDS in both Run1 and Run 2. It can be seen the scales obtained in Run 3 (Figure 8(c)) had a different structure with the previous precipitates, which had either a hexagonal structure or an orthorhombic structure. These scales were found to adhere to the membrane surface strongly. Compared to the previous runs, the sulfur contents were found to be much lower. When the carbonate increased and the ratio decreased to 1 in Run 4 (Figure 8(d)), the deposits exhibited orthorhombic structure which is the typical structure of aragonite. These scales were very tenacious and adhered to the membrane more strongly. There was no sulfur detected by EDS in this case and no stick like scale was found. All of these morphological features and chemical compositions were accordance with the crystalline phases observed by XRD which have been presented in Section 3.4.1.

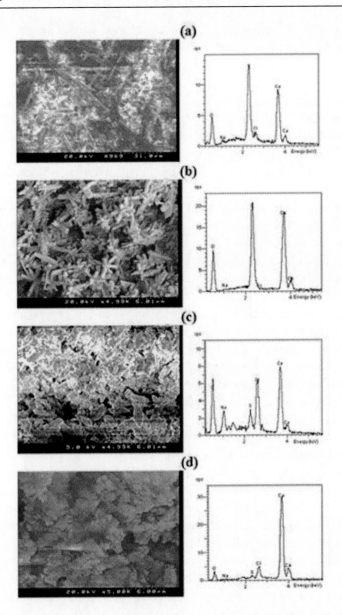

Figure 8. SEM images and EDS profiles of different tests. a: R=20, b: R=12, c: R=5, d: R=1.

4. CONCLUSION

The objective of this work was three-fold: (1) to investigate the difference between single calcium sulfate or calcium carbonate precipitation and co-precipitation of these two salts in a dynamic seawater RO desalination system; (2) to assess the effect of varying SO_4^{2-}/HCO_3^- (at 20, 12, 5, and 1) on the composite fouling of $CaSO_4$ and $CaCO_3$; and (3) to apply Sheikholeslami's theoretical Scaling Potential Index (SPI) [1, 2] to predict onset of scale formation for different crystal phases of calcium carbonate and calcium sulfate and compare the predictions with experimental results.

It was found that the precipitation kinetics as well as the deposit morphology and mineralogy were significantly affected by the presence of carbonate species in feed solution. Calcium carbonate had high scaling potential and precipitated quickly which resulted in an abrupt decrease of permeate flux. Also, $CaCO_3$ precipitated as two forms of crystals: calcite and aragonite and both forms of the scales were observed to be hard and tenacious. In contrast, calcium sulfate had a relatively lower scaling potential and precipitated only as gypsum. Thus the decline of permeate flux occurred at relatively higher water recovery level. Moreover, gypsum scale was not as adhesive. However, once $CaCO_3$ and $CaSO_4$ co-precipitated on the membrane surface, the membrane was seriously blocked and water could not be produced.

It was found with the increasing of HCO_3^- ratio, the precipitation kinetics, morphology and crystalline phases of the scales were different. $CaCO_3$ had high scaling potential and precipitated very fast which resulted in an abrupt drop of permeate flux at a very low water recovery level. It precipitated as two crystalline phases: calcite and aragonite. Both forms of crystals were observed to be hard and tenacious. $CaSO_4$ had a relatively lower scaling potential in seawater systems and precipitated as gypsum. At high SO_4^{2-}/HCO_3^- ratio, gypsum exhibited a long needle like structure and was loose. When $CaCO_3$ precipitated with $CaSO_4$, $CaSO_4$ scale became shorter and smaller and more adherent. $CaCO_3$ scales enhanced the tenacity of the co-precipitates. The formation of $CaCO_3$ is highly pH dependent and pH control is regarded as an effective approach to mitigate $CaCO_3$ fouling while pH has no effect on $CaSO_4$ deposition. Therefore, composite fouling of $CaSO_4$ and $CaCO_3$ complicates the fouling mitigation operation and so effective methods of fouling control must be developed.

In dynamic seawater RO desalination systems, many factors affect the fouling process and they must be taken into account. These factors include the effects of osmotic pressure and concentration polarization, and the effects of salinity and ion interactive forces on the solubility of these sparingly soluble salts. The theoretical SPI was used to assess the onset and type of scale formed at different recoveries. The ion interactive effects and the effect of concentration polarization were incorporated in SPI calculations. A positive SPI denotes that the salt has a potential to form scale. It was seen that the decline of permeate flux took place about when SPI of these sparingly soluble salts became positive – the minor deviation is expected to be due to some unpredictable factors in the complex dynamic system, such as the effects of impurities or inherent system fluctuations. The predictable water recovery levels at which scale had a potential to form exhibited good agreements with the recovery levels at which permeate flux declined, using as the indicator of the onset of fouling. The SPI calculations could also predict the crystal phase deposited at different recoveries. Theoretical predictions by SPI have shown good agreements with the experimental results of flux decline as well as analytical results by SEM, EDS and XRD assessments. The theoretical SPI can be a powerful tool to assess the scaling potential and the type of deposited scale in RO desalination systems.

ACKNOWLEDGMENTS

The authors gratefully acknowledge Hydranautics for providing the membranes and MEDRC for the financial support.

REFERENCES

[1] Sheikholeslami, R., *Scaling Potential Index (SPI) for Calcium Carbonate Based on Gibbs Free Energies*. AIChE, 2005. 51(6): p. 1782-1789.

[2] Sheikholeslami, R., *Assessment of the scaling potential for sparingly soluble salts in RO and NF units*. Desalination, 2004(167): p. 247-256.

[3] Sheikholeslami, R. and H.W.K. Ong, *Kinetics and Thermodynamics of Calcium Carbonate and Calcium Sulfate at Salinities up to 1.5m*. Desalination, 2003. 157: p. 217-234.

[4] Sheikholeslami, R., T.H. Chong, and M. Ng. *Calcium Carbonate and Calcium Sulfate Coprecipitation - Thermodynamics and Kinetics*. in *Chemeca'99*. 1999. Newcastle, Australia: Institution of Engineers Australia.

[5] Sheikholeslami, R. *Strategies and Future Directions for Systematic Characterization of Feed Water and Determination of Scaling Limits and Rates for Process Assessment and Optimization*. in *International Desalination Association*. 2001. Bahrain.

[6] Sheikholeslami, R. and M. Ng, *Calcium Sulfate Precipitation in Presence of Non-dominant Calcium Carbonate: Thermodynamics and Kinetics*. Ind. Eng. Chem. Research, 2001. 40(16): p. 3570-3578.

[7] Sudmalis, M. and R. Sheikholeslami, *Coprecipitation of $CaCO_3$ and $CaSO_4$. The Canadian Journal of Chemical Engineering*, 2000. 78(1): p. 21-31.

[8] Dydo, P., M. Turek, and J. Ciba, *Scaling analysis of nanofilatration systems fed with saturated calcium sulfate solutions in the presence of carbonate ions*. Desalination, 2003. 159: p. 245-251.

[9] Sheikholeslami, R., *Fouling in Membranes and Thermal Units - Unified Approach to Its Principles, Assessment, Control and Mitigation*. 2007, Desalinations Publications L'Aquila, Italy. p. 242.

[10] Sheikholeslami, R., *Nucleation and Kinetics of Mixed Salts in Scaling*. AIChE, 2003. 49(1): p. 194-202.

[11] Sheikholeslami, R., *Mixed Salts - Scaling Limits and Propensity*. Desalination, 2003. 154(2): p. 117-127.

[12] Wang, Y. and R. Sheikholeslami. *The Effects of SO42-/HCO3- Molar Ratio on the Composite Fouling of Calcium Sulfate and Calcium Carbonate in a Seawater RO Desalination Unit*. in *Chemeca2005*. 2005. Brisbane: Institute of Engineers Australia.

[13] Wang, Y. and R. Sheikholeslami. *Co-Precipitation of Calcium Sulfate and Calcium Carbonate in a Seawater RO System*. in *IDA World Congress on Desalination and Water Reuse*. 2005. Singapore: International Desalination Association.

[14] Pankratz, T., Tonner, J., *Desalination.com an environmental primer*. 2004, Houston: Lone Oak Publishing.

[15] El-Manharawy, S., Hafez, A., *Water type and guidelines for RO system design*. Desalination, 2001. 139: p. 97-113.

[16] A.P.H.A, *Standard methods for the examination of water and wastewater*. 20th ed. 1998: Washington, D. C. American Public Health Association: APHA-AWWA-WEF.

[17] Sutzkover, I., Hsson, D., Semiat, R, *Simple technique for measuring the concentration polarization level in a reverse osmosis system*. Desalination, 2000. 131: p. 117-127.

[18] Meijer, J.A.M., Van Rosmalen, G. M., *Solubility and supersaturations of calcium sulfate and its hydrates in seawater.* Desalination, 1984. 51: p. 255-305.

[19] Benjamin, M.M., *Water Chemistry.* 2002: McGraw Hill.

[20] Marshall, W.L., Slusher, R., *Solubility to 200C of calcium sulfate and its hydrates in sea water and saline water concentrates, and temperature-concentration limits. Journal of Chemical and Engineering Data.* 1968. 13(1): p. 83-93.

[21] Chong, T.H., Sheikholeslami, R., *Thermodynamics and Kinetics for Mixed Calcium Carbonate and Calcium Sulfate Precipitation. Chemical Engineering Science.* 2001. 56: p. 5391-5400.

[22] Mucci, A., Canuel, R., Zhong, S., *The solubility of calcite and aragonite in sulfate-free sea water and the seeded growth kinetics and composition of the precipitates at 25C.* Chemical Geology, 1989. 74(3-4): p. 309-320.

[23] Othmer, K., *Encyclopedia of Chemical Technology.* 4th Ed. ed. 1992, New York: John Wiley and Sons.

INDEX

D

E

N

O

P